Theory of Partial Coherence

PRENTICE-HALL, INC.

PRENTICE-HALL
INTERNATIONAL, INC.,
United Kingdom and Eire

PRENTICE-HALL
OF CANADA, LTD.,
Canada

PRENTICE-HALL INTERNATIONAL SERIES IN PHYSICS

Mark J. Beran

Associate Professor of Mechanical Engineering
Towne School, University of Pennsylvania

George B. Parrent, Jr.

Technical Operations, Inc.
Burlington, Massachusetts

Theory of Partial Coherence

PRENTICE-HALL, INC., ENGLEWOOD CLIFFS, N.J.

PRENTICE-HALL INTERNATIONAL, INC., *London*
PRENTICE-HALL OF AUSTRALIA, LTD., *Sydney*
PRENTICE-HALL OF CANADA, LTD., *Toronto*
PRENTICE-HALL OF INDIA (PRIVATE) LTD., *New Delhi*
PRENTICE-HALL OF JAPAN, INC., *Tokyo*
PRENTICE-HALL DE MEXICO, S.A., *Mexico City*

Printed in the United States of America
Library of Congress Catalog Card Number: 64-10741

C-91461

Dedicated to our wives:

Barbara Beran and Marilyn Parrent

Preface

The purpose of this book is to consider classical electromagnetic fields that may be described from a statistical point of view. The theory of partial coherence was developed principally in the field of optics, and this book will show this bias. The concepts developed, however, apply to the whole spectrum of radiation for which a classical theory is appropriate.

This book is intended as a research monograph. It sets forth most of the concepts used in the field, but the treatment is certainly not exhaustive. The reader is expected to have a knowledge of mathematics equivalent to that of, perhaps, a second-year graduate student in physics or engineering and to have familiarity with ordinary electromagnetic theory. An excellent introduction to this book is Chapter 10 of Born and Wolf's *Principles of Optics* (New York: Pergamon, 1959). We also recommend O'Neill's *Introduction to Statistical Optics* (Reading, Mass.: Addison-Wesley, 1963) for a fuller discussion of the material developed in Chapters 7 and 8 and for a treatment of matrix methods.

The statistical formulation given in this book is not as rigorous as the structure one would develop if the Fourier-Stieltjes integral were used. We felt, however, that it is more intuitive to use limiting forms of truncated functions when considering functions whose Fourier integral does not exist. The final measurable results are, of course, the same in both formulations.

In the past year, there has been considerable discussion of the proper quantum mechanical formulation of coherence theory. We mention this approach only briefly at the conclusion of Chapter 11 and then in connection with black-body radiation. We refer the reader interested in these developments to the references at the conclusion of an article by Mandel on this subject in *Physics Letters* (Vol. 7, p. 117). He will note that much of the work was still in press in November, 1963, and, therefore, we feel that it is premature to give a summary of such work at this time.

The latter chapters of the book include a certain amount of formalism that to date is without application. This work was included for its own intrinsic interest and in the expectation that these developments will provide a basis for future work along the lines presented.

We wish to express our debt to Professor Wolf, who introduced us to this field, and with whom we have had many stimulating discussions over the past years.

We wish to thank Prof. O'Neill and Prof. Gamo for their careful reading of our manuscripts and their many helpful suggestions. We also wish to thank Messrs. P. Corson, J. Devalis, T. Ho, and J. Molyneux for reading our book in its various stages of development. Our thanks are also extended to Dr. B. Thompson for useful suggestions as well as for supplying informative figures.

We wish to take this opportunity to thank Mr. Zucker and other members of the Air Force Cambridge Research Center for their encouragement of our work in the area of partial coherence when we were serving in the Air Force.

One of the authors (M. B.) is particularly indebted to the Army Research Office, Durham, N. C., for a research grant on "Studies in the Theory of Partial Coherence" that he received in the summer of 1962. While this grant was not used to support the writing of this book, the studies that were carried out under this grant helped to illuminate many subjects covered in the text. The research by Messrs. Ho and Molyneux reported in this book was supported by this grant.

We wish to thank our publisher Prentice-Hall and, in particular, Messrs. T. Aloisi, N. Stanton, and J. Walsh for the excellent cooperation they have given to us. Lastly, we wish to thank Mrs. W. Rice, Miss P. Taglieri, and Mrs. C. York for typing this manuscript in its many forms.

MARK J. BERAN GEORGE B. PARRENT, JR. MARCH, 1964

Contents

10

PARTIAL POLARIZATION 138

11

VECTOR FORMULATION 146

12

INTENSITY INTERFEROMETRY 159

chapter 1

Introduction

It is customary to describe interference and diffraction of electromagnetic waves in terms of either strictly coherent or strictly incoherent vibrations, ignoring completely the possibility of the intermediate partially coherent states. In principle it is, of course, clear that there are intermediate states, and in fact that strictly coherent or strictly incoherent vibrations are only a mathematical idealization. The practical utility of considering these states, however, has not been made clear until recently.

This is perhaps surprising since an example of the inadequacy of the concepts of complete coherence and complete incoherence for the description of a physically interesting phenomenon was known as early as about

1869. At that time, Verdet (1869) demonstrated that the light from two pinholes in a screen illuminated by the sun will interfere in Young's interference experiment if the separation of the pinholes is less than about $\frac{1}{20}$ mm. Since interference is customarily viewed as a property of coherent oscillators and sunlight is customarily viewed as incoherent, this result would suggest the need for considering intermediate states.

Nevertheless, from the middle of the nineteenth century until the last two decades, states of partial coherence received but little attention. The few papers that did appear on the subject were more or less disconnected, since each investigator introduced his own apparently different formulation of the theory. The lack of interest in the subject during that period may be attributed to the fact that applications in which the theory is important were either unknown or involved measurements which were not refined enough to take account of variations with the degree of coherence.

More recently, however, the concept of partial coherence has become important in almost every branch of physics which involves electromagnetic radiation regardless of the frequencies considered. In visible optics, for example, coherence theory is tantamount to the understanding of such topics as image formation, the effect of illumination on the resolution in a microscopic image, and atmospheric effects on resolution. In spectroscopy, the influence of the slit width on the degree of coherence of the illumination, can produce measurable effects. In radio astronomy, source diameters are measured by interferometric techniques, which effectively involve the measurement of the degree of coherence of the radiation. Similar problems arise in those applications of radar where questions of resolution and mapping are of central importance. Most recently, the development of optical masers or lasers has brought the concepts of coherence and incoherence under close scrutiny by a large number of investigators.

1.1 DISCUSSION OF THE MUTUAL COHERENCE FUNCTION $\Gamma_{12}(\tau)$

It should be made clear immediately that discussions of coherence or incoherence or partial coherence need never enter a treatise on classical electromagnetic theory. In the classical electromagnetic theory governed by Maxwell's equations, one assumes that the electric field **E** and the magnetic field **H** are measurable functions of position and time. In principle, one can, if one chooses, follow in detail the instantaneous variations of the electric or magnetic field, no matter how intricate the boundary conditions.

In many cases, however, this procedure is extremely difficult and may, in fact, mask important physical effects. For example, in determining the diffraction pattern of a large number of independent radiators, a detailed rigorous solution is difficult and would be applicable only to the particular collection of radiators for which it was calculated. Clearly, an averaging procedure is desired (as the term *independent* implies) which will yield results that are applicable to all such collections of radiators that have similar properties in some average sense. The situation is analogous to the one arising in classical statistical mechanics. Although in principle it is possible to follow in detail the dynamics of a system, it often proves much more useful to provide a statistical description.

In its primary emphasis, the theory of partial coherence may be described as the theory treating with the statistical aspects of electromagnetic theory. As such, it describes the behavior of average values of appropriate functions of the electromagnetic field. For example, statements about the linear addition of power (associated with incoherent states) make sense only in terms of some averaging procedure. As just stated, this averaging may be taken in a physical process (assuming a classical theory), simply for convenience. It also, however, may be taken because no instruments are available to measure the instantaneous values of **E** and **H**. In any case, some averaging procedure is necessary before the concept of coherence is defined.

Thus, the theory of partial coherence which we shall study in this book is the theory of an average quantity of the electromagnetic field. There are, of course, many averaged quantities that could be studied, but it was most convenient to choose the second-order moment, $\Gamma_{12}(\tau)$, termed the *mutual coherence function.* $\Gamma_{12}(\tau)$ is a natural generalization of earlier coherence functions defined in connection with studies of coherence and incoherence in optics and, following Wolf (1955), is defined as

$$\Gamma_{12}(\tau) = \langle V_1(t + \tau) V_2^*(t) \rangle \tag{1–1}$$

where $V_1(t)$ and $V_2(t)$ are the complex field disturbances at two points P_1 and P_2, the sharp brackets denote a time average, and τ is a time delay. Its normalized form $\gamma_{12}(\tau)$ is defined as

$$\gamma_{12}(\tau) = \frac{\Gamma_{12}(\tau)}{\sqrt{\Gamma_{11}(0)\Gamma_{22}(0)}} \tag{1–2}$$

and is termed the *complex degree of coherence.*

$V_1(t)$ is formulated as a complex quantity only for convenience (we shall carefully define it in the next chapter) and most often the real part of $V_1(t)$ will be one cartesian component of the electric field.

The study of the function $\Gamma_{12}(\tau)$, and its natural generalizations to allow for spatial and ensemble averaging and for the vector nature of the electromagnetic field, is essentially what we consider to be the theory of partial coherence. Recent work considering higher-order coherence functions will be considered only briefly in the latter part of this book, except in Chapter 12, where we present a discussion of intensity interferometry.

As we have implied, we wish to consider here principally the classical electromagnetic field; we do not wish to treat the quantum aspects of the electromagnetic field in any detail. Further, in this book, we shall not consider the elementary processes giving rise to a partially coherent field, except briefly in Chapter 4. Rather, we shall principally be concerned with how $\Gamma_{12}(\tau)$ propagates once it is specified over some surface.

To illustrate the utility of $\Gamma_{12}(\tau)$, it is useful to discuss how it may be measured in Young's interference-type experiments. Before proceeding to such a discussion, however, we give a brief historical survey of basic work done in coherence theory.

1.2 SURVEY OF PREVIOUS RESEARCHES

Early research on partial coherence is associated with the names of Verdet (1869), von Laue (1907), Berek (1926, a, b, c, d), van Cittert (1934, 1939) and Zernike (1938). The later basic investigations of this subject are found primarily in the work of Hopkins (1951, 1957), Blanc-Lapierre and Dumontet (1955), and Wolf (1955).

After the work of Verdet (1869), mentioned earlier, a paper by von Laue (1907) gave a quantitative measure for partial coherence. This paper discussed the thermodynamical aspects of diffraction, and in it the quantity, γ_L, proportional to the square of the time-averaged product of the disturbances at two points in the field, proved to be of central importance. Although this quantity was sufficient to characterize the optical field for the problems discussed by von Laue, the formulation is too restrictive for general application. We may mention, however, that the interesting experiment of Hanbury-Brown and Twiss (1956 a, b) (see Chapter 12) measured precisely the quantity γ_L.

It may be shown that, under certain conditions,

$$\gamma_L = |\gamma_{12}(0)|^2 \tag{1–3}$$

The next theoretical treatment of the subject appeared some twenty years later in the work of Berek (1926) in which the so-called degree of consonance was introduced as a measure of coherence. Berek's formulation was applied to some problems in the theory of image formation in the microscope. Some of his results, however, were contradicted by the experiments of Lakeman and Groosmuller (1928).

After another decade, the subject was again reformulated. Van Cittert (1936) showed that, in a plane illuminated by an incoherent, nearly monochromatic source, the optical disturbance is normally distributed. Three theorems concerning his *komplex Korrelation* were also given in this paper. The best-known of these theorems expresses the correlation in the illuminated plane in terms of the intensity distribution across the source plane. The analysis of this paper is in terms of ensemble averages, but by invoking the ergodic hypothesis,† it can be shown that when the treatment is applicable (incoherent, quasi-monochromatic sources‡) the correlation function introduced by van Cittert is equal to the zero ordinate of the complex degree of coherence,

$$\gamma_C = \gamma_{12}(0) \tag{1-4}$$

A significant augmentation of the theory of partial coherence was given by Zernike (1938). In this paper, the treatment of the subject is tightly bound to the interpretation of Young's interference experiment in terms of Michelson's visibility (a quantity introduced by Michelson (1890) to measure the quality of interference fringes). In fact, the degree of coherence between the disturbances at two points is defined in that paper as the visibility of the fringes obtained by allowing the light from these points to interfere in a suitable experiment (i. e., short path differences and equal intensities at the two points). So valuable has this experimental definition proved in understanding the physical aspects of partial coherence, that many later authors overlook the fact that Zernike formulated the subject analytically.

Zernike's formulation is applicable to quasi-monochromatic fields produced by any source (coherent, partially coherent, or incoherent) and, in this sense, is the most general treatment before the work of Blanc-Lapierre and Dumontet (1955) and, independently, by Wolf (1955) to be discussed later. The fundamental quantity in Zernike's analysis is the *mutual intensity function*, defined as the time-averaged product of the disturbance at one point with the complex conjugate of the disturbance at the second point. The degree of coherence is the mutual intensity function suitably normalized. Zernike's degree of coherence, γ_Z, may be shown to be equal to the zero ordinate of the complex degree of coherence used here,

$$\gamma_Z = \gamma_{12}(0) \tag{1-5}$$

In the same paper, an approximate law for the propagation of the mutual intensity was also presented; and as a consequence of this law, a theorem relating to the mutual intensity on a plane illuminated by an incoherent plane source was determined. By virtue of the ergodic hypothesis, this theorem is the same as the theorem of van Cittert's mentioned earlier and is now termed *the van Cittert-Zernike theorem* (cf. Born, M. and Wolf, E., 1959, p. 507).

In 1951, H. H. Hopkins (1951) reformulated the theory of partial coherence. In this treatment, the complex degree of coherence is defined in

---

†See Skinner (1961a).

‡*Quasi-monochromatic sources* are sources emitting radiation with very narrow though finite spectral width. The application of this approximation is physically meaningful only if the radiation path differences involved are suitably small.

terms of an integral over the primary source of the radiation, assumed always to be incoherent. The arguments of this paper have been the subject of considerable discussion [cf. Wolf (1954, 1958), Hopkins (1956), Zuker (1957)], but the techniques introduced have proved very powerful for many practical optical problems. When the formualtion of this paper is applicable (i. e., incoherent quasi-monochromatic sources), it is equivalent to that of Zernike. Hence,

$$\gamma_H = \gamma_{12}(0) \tag{1–6}$$

where γ_H is the degree of coherence as defined by H. H. Hopkins.

In spite of the usefulness of the results presented in the papers just described, we must point out three unsatisfactory aspects of their formulations: (1) the formulations are applicable only to quasi-monochromatic fields; (2) apart from Zernike's work, the analyses are applicable only when the source is incoherent; (3) apart from that of von Laue, each of the preceding formulations is in terms of complex functions whose significance is obscure.

The first of these considerations is perhaps the most important; for the restriction to incoherent sources is removed by Zernike's formulation, and the ambiguity as to complex representation may be removed either by dealing exclusively with real functions or by carefully defining the complex representation. The restriction to quasi-monochromatic light, however, is not simply removable. In fact, the theory of partial coherence could be extended to fields of arbitrary spectral width only after the introduction of the cross-correlation function.

These shortcomings were eliminated in the formulation of the subject by Wolf (1955) and that of Blanc-Lapierre and Dumontet (1955). Both of these formulations are rigorously applicable to polychromatic fields created by any type of source (coherent, partially coherent, or incoherent), and both define the degree of coherence in terms of the cross-correlation of the disturbance at two points in the field. The essential difference between these two formulations is that Wolf treats the subject in terms of carefully defined complex functions, whereas Blanc-Lapierre and Dumontet deal, in the main, with real functions.

These two treatments are rigorous and general, but the several advantages of the complex representation—discussed by Born and Wolf (1959) and Parrent (1959)—make it more suitable for an analysis in which the usual optical theorems for natural light are to be regarded as limiting forms. The degree of coherence as defined in the real function treatment, γ_B, is simply the real part of the complex degree of coherence, that is,

$$\gamma_B(\tau) = \operatorname{Re}[\gamma_{12}(\tau)] \tag{1–7}$$

For the reasons referred to, this book uses, almost exclusively, the formulation of coherence theory due to Wolf. We shall deviate from this formulation only in discussing problems requiring the generality of a different averaging procedure and in our discussion of higher-order moments. The physical significance of these definitions will be made clear in the next section.

1.3 YOUNG'S INTERFERENCE EXPERIMENT

By considering in some detail the simplest phenomenon in which the considerations of coherence theory are important, i. e., Young's interference experiment, we can illustrate the significance of $\Gamma_{12}(\tau)$ and demonstrate its measurability. This latter point is conceptually very important and, in fact, provides the impetus for research in this field. For clarity, we shall here demonstrate the measurability of $|\gamma_{12}(\tau)|$ for radiation of narrow spectral width and reserve until Chapter 2 consideration of radiation of finite spectral width for the function $\Gamma_{12}(\tau)$. We refer the reader to the papers of Arnulf, Dupuy and Flamant (1953), Thompson and Wolf (1957), Markovic (1957), and Thompson (1958) for a discussion of experiments.

In Fig. 1–1 let Σ represent an incoherent† source of radiation of finite spatial extent and finite but narrow spectral width. P_1 and P_2 are two pinholes in the screen A a distance of l_1 from the source. Interference fringes are observed in the intenisty pattern on the screen B a distance l_2 from the screen

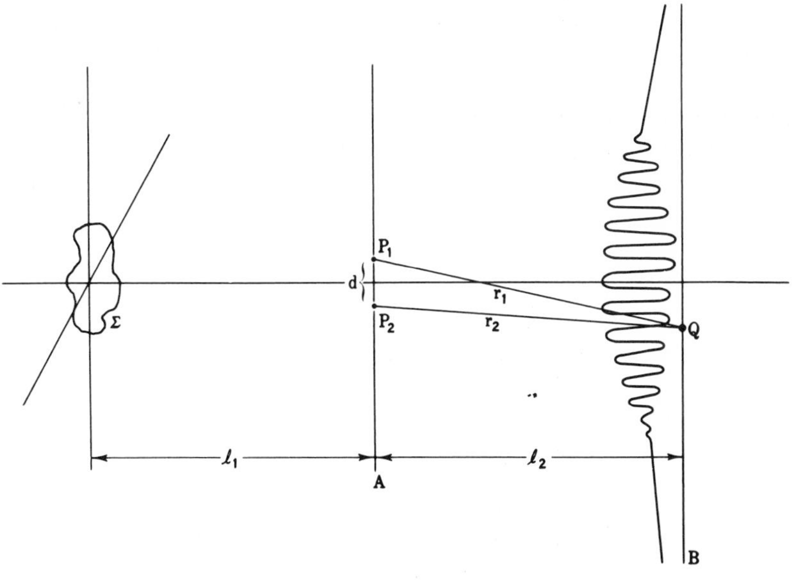

Figure 1-1. Young's interference experiment.

†This term is precisely defined in Chapter 4. Here one may think of a luminous source like a filtered mercury arc lamp.

A. The distances from P_1 and P_2 to a representative point Q on the screen B are r_1 and r_2 respectively. The pinholes are separated by a distance d. We will observe the intensity pattern on B along a line formed from the intersection of the plane containing the pinholes and the normal to B, and the plane B.

We may imagine a series of experiments performed in which the "quality" of the fringes observed on the screen B is measured as we vary the other parameters in the experiment. As a measure of this "quality," Michelson (1890) introduced the term *visibility* which may be defined as follows: let I_{max} be the maximum intensity and I_{min} be an adjacent minimum; then the visibility of the fringes, $\mathcal{V}$ is

$$\mathcal{V} = \frac{I_{max} - I_{min}}{I_{max} + I_{min}} \tag{1–8}$$

Note that, under adverse experimental conditions, e. g., too broad a spectrum, too large path differences, etc., this measure may not be defined, since the height of the maximums or depth of the minimums may vary too rapidly to permit the unambiguous identifications of a maximum and minimum. As we shall see, the complex degree of coherence is always defined. For the present, however, we shall consider our experiment idealized to the point where the visibility can be determined.

We begin our series of experiments by allowing the size of $\sum$ to vary while keeping the other paramecters fixed, and note that, in a general way, the visibility of the fringes is increased by decreasing the size of the primary source. Furthermore, for a fixed source size, the visibility of the fringes is varied by changing the separation of the pinholes. Thus as we separate the pinholes farther, the quality of the fringes diminishes until we reach a separa-

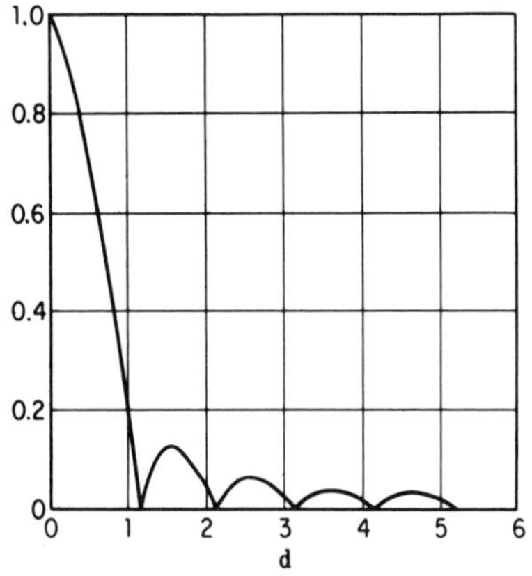

Figure 1-2. Visibility *vs* separation.

tion for which there are no fringes. Separating the pinholes still farther, however, results in a reappearance of the fringes shifted in space by an amount equal to the width of half a fringe. Further separation of the pinholes results in increasing, then decreasing visibility. Thus for a circular source Σ a plot of $\mathcal{V}$ versus d would appear as in Fig. 1–2. Conversely varying the source size while holding the pinhole separation constant produces the same effect. These results are a direct demonstration of the van Cittert-Zernike theorem and will be discussed in detail in a later chapter. This variation in visibility with pinhole separation is often referred to as an *effect of spatial coherence* (see Chapter 2).

Varying the lengths l_1 and l_2 results simply in a change in scale of the results just discussed, provided that both l_1 and l_2 are large compared to d and the maximum dimension in Σ. Examining the quality of the fringes as we move away from the center of the interference pattern, we note that the visibility diminishes with the increasing path difference, $r_1 - r_2$, eventually vanishing completely. By varying the spectral width of the illumination, $\Delta\nu$, we note that the path differences, Δr, for which the fringes exist, satisfy the inequality,

$$\Delta r \ll \frac{c}{\Delta\nu} \tag{1–9}$$

where c is the velocity of the light. The decrease in fringe visibility with increasing path difference is often referred to as an illustration of imperfect time coherence (again see Chapter 2).

From these considerations, it is clear that the notion that "coherent light interferes and incoherent does not" is inadequate to describe even the simplest physical situation and that we need a measure to describe the intermediate states of partial coherence.

To put the preceding discussion on a slightly firmer foundation, it will prove useful to develop in a rather formal way an expression for the visibility of fringes in a Young's experiment with illumination of finite but narrow spectral width. To this end let $V_1(t)$ and $V_2(t)$ be suitably chosen complex representations of the disturbances at P_1 and P_2, respectively, in Fig. 1–1. Then, assuming, for example, we are dealing with a cartesian component of the electric vector, V is propagated in free space by the wave equation

$$\nabla^2 V = \frac{1}{c^2}\frac{\partial^2 V}{\partial t^2} \tag{1–10}$$

Since Eq. (1–10) is a linear equation, we may represent the disturbance at Q as a superposition of the contributions from P_1 and P_2, thus;

$$V_Q(t) = k_1 V_1\left(t - \frac{r_1}{c}\right) + k_2 V_2\left(t - \frac{r_2}{c}\right) \tag{1–11}$$

where k_1 and k_2 are propagators independent of time.† The intensity at Q, I'_Q, will be proportional to the time average of $V_Q V_Q^*$. Denoting by I'_s ‡ the intensity at the screen due to hole s and sharp brackets, $\langle\ \rangle$, the time average,§ we may write

$$I'_Q = I'_1 + I'_2 + 2\mathrm{Re}\left[\left\langle k_1 V_1\left(t - \frac{r_1}{c}\right) k_2^* V_2^*\left(t - \frac{r_2}{c}\right)\right\rangle\right] \tag{1–12}$$

where Re denotes the real part. However, k_1 and k_2 are independent of time; thus, if we set $t_s = r_s/c$ $(s = 1, 2)$ we may rewrite Eq. (1–12) as

$$I'_Q = I'_1 + I'_2 + 2k_1k_2^* \mathrm{Re}\,[\langle V_1(t - t_1)\, V_2^*(t - t_2)\rangle] \tag{1–13}$$

The term inside the brackets in Eq. (1–13) is simply the complex cross-correlation of the two disturbances. The correlation is a function of the time difference $\tau = t_1 - t_2$ only and we may rewrite Eq. (1–13) as

$$\begin{aligned} I'_Q &= I'_1 + I'_2 + 2k_1k_2^* \mathrm{Re}\,[\langle V_1(t + \tau)\, V_2^*(t)\rangle] \\ &= I'_1 + I'_2 + 2k_1k_2^* \mathrm{Re}\,\Gamma_{12}(\tau)\text{§§} \end{aligned} \tag{1–14}$$

Before considering Eq. (1–14) further, we note that

$$\Gamma_{ss}(0) = [\langle V_s(t)\, V_s^*(t)\rangle]$$

is simply the intensity at the point P_s $(s = 1, 2)$. This theorem will be demonstrated in Chapter 2. With this in mind, however, we may normalize $\Gamma_{12}(\tau)$ in Eq. (1–14) and noting that

$$k_1k_2^*\sqrt{\Gamma_{11}(0)\,\Gamma_{22}(0)} = \sqrt{|k_1|^2\,\Gamma_{11}(0)\,|k_2|^2\,\Gamma_{22}(0)} \tag{1–15}$$

we may rewrite Eq. (1–14) as

$$I'_Q = I'_1 + I'_2 + 2\sqrt{I'_1 I'_2}\,\mathrm{Re}\,[\gamma_{12}(\tau)] \tag{1–16}$$

Here we have used the definition of $\gamma_{12}(\tau)$ as given by Eq. (1–2).

If we imagine the experiment in Fig. 1–1 to be set up with what Zernike refers to as the *best conditions*, that is, $I'_1 = I'_2 = I'$ with the path differences small, and if we write $\gamma_{12}(\tau)$ in the form

$$\gamma_{12}(\tau) = |\gamma_{12}(\tau)|\, e^{i\Phi_{12}(\tau)} \tag{1–17}$$

we may rewrite Eq. (1–16) as

---

†The k's are pure imaginary numbers which depend on r, the size of the pinhole, the angle to Q, and the mean frequency $\bar{\nu}$. It is noted that, for a broad spectrum, V_Q cannot be written in this simple form; $\Gamma_{12}(\tau)$ will still be measurable but, as shown in Chapter 2, the measurement procedure is more complex. The propagators defined in this section differ by exponential factors from the propagators defined in Chapter 2.

‡I'_s is denoted the *intensity* for convenience. Because of the introduction of the complex notation, I'_s is twice the measurable intensity I_s.

§The exact form of the time average will be discussed in Chapter 2.

§§It should be pointed out again here that, for this equation to hold, we must have $\tau\,\Delta\nu \ll 1$ (where $\Delta\nu$ is the spectral width of the radiation). The point will be clearly shown in Chapter 4.

(1–18) $$I'_Q = 2I'\,[1 + |\gamma_{12}(\tau)| \cos \Phi_{12}(\tau)]$$

From Eq. (1–18), we can compute the visibility of the fringes as

(1–19) $$\mathcal{V} = \frac{2I'[(1 + |\gamma_{12}(\tau)|) - (1 - |\gamma_{12}(\tau)|)]}{2I'[(1 + |\gamma_{12}(\tau)|) + (1 - |\gamma_{12}(\tau)|)]} = |\gamma_{12}(\tau)|$$

Thus in those cases where the visibility is defined, the modulus of the degree of coherence is equal to the visibility and thus is simply measurable. (As previously stated, a general measurement procedure will be given in Chapter 2.)

chapter

2

Definitions and Mathematical Preliminaries

In this chapter, we lay the mathematical framework necessary for the development of the theory of partial coherence and present the definitions and basic formulations of the theory in a precise fashion. Although for the most part, we deal with the theory as introduced by Wolf, from time to time, we shall need a more general formulation in terms of ensemble averages. Consequently, we also present a definition of mutual coherence in terms of ensemble averages. The theory presented in this chapter will be a scalar theory. The vector nature of the radiation is considered in Chapters 10 and 11. We shall conclude this chapter with a discussion of the measurability of the mutual coherence function $\Gamma_{12}(\tau)$.

Sections 2.1, 2.2, and 2.3 give considerable mathematical detail about the complex analytic signal. This is done principally for the use of specialists in the field. Since coherence theory can be formulated in terms of real quantities, the use of a complex notation is only a convenience (albeit a considerable one, we feel). We caution the reader against overemphasizing these three sections unless he intends to do detailed work in coherence theory.

2.1 THE ANALYTIC SIGNAL

As mentioned in the introduction, coherence theory as introduced by Wolf does not deal directly with the real field quantity, but rather with the analytic signal associated with this quantity. This representation was introduced by Gabor (1946) to treat problems arising in communication theory. Its advantages for coherence problems stem from the following considerations: it involves only positive frequencies; it is a convenient generalization of the method of associating an exponential with a cosine as is done for strictly periodic radiation; it provides an extremely convenient framework for extracting the quasi-monochromatic approximations which form the basis for most practical problems involving coherence theory; its modulus is the envelope of the real function with which it is associated. Further advantages of the analytic signal representation of a purely mathematical nature are as follows: there is a particularly simple relation between real and imaginary parts; the function regarded as a function of a complex variable is analytic in half the complex plane; and finally, the analytic signal can be represented as a linear transform of the real function with which it is associated.

There are two essentially equivalent methods of associating an analytic signal with a given real function. The first method we shall consider has the advantage of stressing the physical significance of the representation; the second method is more convenient for further mathematical developments. Since our purpose is to provide a reference for physicists and engineers, little attempt at mathematical rigor will be made in this or later chapters except where absolutely necessary.

Let $V^r(t)$ be a real function of the real variable t such that it possesses a Fourier transform,† that is,

---

†The necessary and sufficient conditions for the existence of the Fourier transform are, of course, not known. A sufficient condition is that $V^r(t)$ be square integrable, and for the most part, we shall deal with functions of this type. In considering the limiting forms of $\Gamma_{12}(\tau)$, however, we shall have to admit a larger class of functions. In those cases, we simply assume that the transform exists and that the inversion theorems apply. We shall, for example, not hesitate to use the Dirac delta function, with a constant as its Fourier transform.

(2–1)
$$V^r(t) = \int_{-\infty}^{\infty} \hat{V}^r(\nu)\, e^{-2\pi i\nu t}\, d\nu$$

The inversion theorem gives

(2–2)
$$\hat{V}^r(\nu) = \int_{-\infty}^{\infty} V^r(t)\, e^{2\pi i\nu t}\, dt$$

Throughout the book, the hooked notation $\hat{V}^r(\nu)$ will be used to denote Fourier transforms on the time variable. In Eq. (2–1), we may break the integral into two parts giving:

(2–3)
$$V^r(t) = \int_{-\infty}^{0} \hat{V}^r(\nu)\, e^{-2\pi i\nu t}\, d\nu + \int_{0}^{\infty} \hat{V}^r(\nu)\, e^{-2\pi i\nu t}\, d\nu$$

If we set $\nu = -\nu$ and change the order of integration in the first integral in Eq. (2–3), we can, after noting from Eq. (2–1) that

(2–4)
$$[\hat{V}^r(\nu)]^* = \hat{V}^r(-\nu)$$

rewrite Eq. (2–3) as

(2–5)
$$V^r(t) = 2\mathrm{Re}\left[\int_{0}^{\infty} \hat{V}^r(\nu)\, e^{-2\pi i\nu t}\, d\nu\right]$$

If we set

(2–6)
$$\hat{V}^r(\nu) = a(\nu)\, e^{i\Phi(\nu)}$$

where $a(\nu)$ and $\Phi(\nu)$ are real functions

(2–7)
$$V^r(t) = \int_{0}^{\infty} 2a(\nu) \cos\left[-2\pi\nu t + \Phi(\nu)\right] d\nu$$

Thus any real function which possesses a Fourier integral can be represented as a Fourier cosine integral. The physical implication of this result is simply that all the information (in the popular usage of the term information) about a real function is contained in the positive (or negative) frequencies only.

We now introduce another real function $V^i(t)$ obtained by changing the phase of each spectral component of $V^r(t)$ by $\pi/2$, that is,

(2–8)
$$V^i(t) = \int_{0}^{\infty} 2a(\nu) \sin\left[-2\pi\nu t + \Phi(\nu)\right] d\nu$$

In terms of this function, the analytic signal $V(t)$ associated with the real function $V^r(t)$ may be defined as

(2–9)
$$V(t) = V^r(t) + iV^i(t)$$

Or, in the frequency domain,

(2–10)
$$V(t) = \int_{0}^{\infty} 2a(\nu)\, e^{-i(2\pi\nu t - \Phi(\nu))}\, d\nu = \int_{0}^{\infty} \hat{V}(\nu)\, e^{-2\pi i\nu t}\, d\nu$$

where $\hat{V}(\nu) = 2\hat{V}^r(\nu)$.

From Eq. (2–10), it is clear that the analytic signal representation is simply a generalization to polychromatic fields of the technique of replacing a cosine by an exponential for simply periodic functions. Note also that the analytic signal contains only positive frequencies which is an important property for a representation of a real disturbance. Thus the inversion theorem for analytic signals becomes

$$\hat{V}(\nu) = \int_{-\infty}^{\infty} V(t)\, e^{2\pi i\nu t}\, dt \qquad \nu > 0$$
$$= 0 \qquad \nu < 0 \tag{2–11}$$

Although the foregoing definition of the analytic signal is useful to give insight into the physical significance, two alternate but equivalent forms are more useful for subsequent mathematical developments. Accordingly, we shall digress briefly and discuss them at this point. We denote by $V^r(t)$ a real function such that its Hilbert transform exists.† Its Hilbert transform, $V^i(t)$, is expressed as

$$V^i(t) = \frac{1}{\pi} ⨍_{-\infty}^{\infty} \frac{V^r(t')\, dt'}{t' - t} \tag{2–12}$$

Here the symbol $⨍_{-\infty}^{\infty}$ denotes Cauchy's principal value. Thus,

$$V^i(t) = \frac{1}{\pi} \lim_{\varepsilon \to 0} \left[\int_{-\infty}^{t-\varepsilon} \frac{V^r(t')\, dt'}{t' - t} + \int_{t+\varepsilon}^{\infty} \frac{V^r(t')\, dt'}{t' - t} \right] \tag{2–13}$$

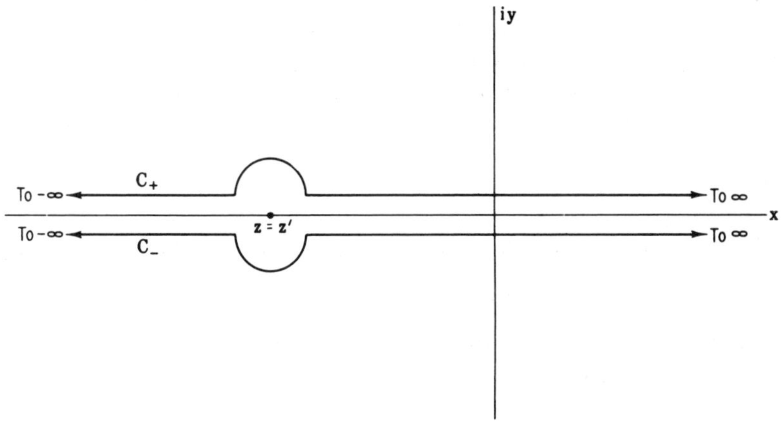

Figure 2-1. Contours for complex representation of Hilbert transform.

†The conditions for the existence of the Hilbert transform, like those for the existence of the Fourier transform, are not known. It may, however, be shown [see, for example, Titchmarsh (1948)] that a sufficient condition for the existence of the Hilbert transform is that $V^r(t)$ be square integrable. As before, when we deal with nonsquare-integrable functions, we introduce the separate assumption that the Hilbert transform exists and the inversion theorem holds.

In terms of the Hilbert transforms, denoted symbolically by $\mathrm{H}[V^r(t)]$, we may define the analytic signal $V(t)$ by the relation:

$$V(t) = V^r(t) + i\mathrm{H}\,[V^r(t)] \tag{2–14}$$

The equivalence of the two definitions may be readily demonstrated by substituting one of the forms directly into the other. The integrations are more readily performed, however, in the complex plane. Furthermore, in almost every instance, it will prove easier to obtain the principal value in the complex domain. Accordingly, we shall consider the principal value integral in the complex plane. To this end, we replace t by $z = x + iy$ and assume that the function $V^r(t)$ is continuous in some neighborhood of $z = z'$. Then the principal value may be defined by

$$⨍_{-\infty}^{\infty} \frac{V^r(z')\,dz'}{z' - z} = \frac{1}{2}\left[\int_{C_+} \frac{V^r(z')\,dz'}{z' - z} + \int_{C_-} \frac{V^r(z')\,dz'}{z' - z}\right] \tag{2–15}$$

Here the integrals on the right are along the open curves C_+ and C_-. The C_+ and C_- extend along the real axis from left to right, curving respectively above and below the point $z = z'$ in semicircular arcs. The geometry is illustrated in Fig. 2–1.

The values of the line integrals in Eq. (2–15) are, of course, independent of the actual path of the curved part of C_+ and C_- as long as they do not include singularities. The line integrals, therefore, remain unchanged in the limit of vanishing radius for the semicircular arcs. The continuity of $V^r(z')$ in the neighborhood of $z' = z$ assures that in the limit the contributions from the upper and lower arcs will cancel each other; thus the equivalence of the two definitions of principal value is demonstrated.†

The integrals in Eq. (2–15) are line integrals; the paths by which C_+ and C_- are closed will, of course, depend on the form of $V^r(z')$ in any given problem.

As we stated above in terms of the Hilbert transform, the analytic signal may be defined as follows: let $V^r(t)$ be a real function of t such that its Hilbert transform $V^i(t)$, exists. The analytic signal may then be defined as

$$V(t) = V^r(t) + iV^i(t) \tag{2–16}$$

The equivalence of this and the previous definition Eqs. (2–7)–(2–10), may now be demonstrated as follows: express $V^r(t)$ as the Fourier integral,

$$V^r(t) = \int_0^{\infty} 2a(\nu)\cos\,[\Phi(\nu) - 2\pi\nu t]\,d\nu \tag{2–17}$$

Take the Hilbert transform of both sides of Eq. (2–17) after setting $t = z$ and expressing the cosine in terms of complex exponentials. Thus,

---

†Actually Eq. (2–15) is a more general definition including Eq. (2–13) as a special case; for Eq. (2–13) will not exist if $V^r(z')$ has a pole at $z' = z$, whereas the definition given in Eq. (2–15) will always exist unless $V^r(z')$ has an essential singularity at $z' = z$.

$$V^i(z) = \frac{1}{2\pi}\int_0^\infty 2a(\nu) \int_{-\infty}^{\infty} \frac{e^{i(\Phi(\nu)-2\pi\nu z')}}{(z'-z)}\,dz'\,d\nu + \frac{1}{2\pi}\int_0^\infty 2a(\nu) \int_{-\infty}^{\infty} \frac{e^{-i(\Phi(\nu)-2\pi\nu z')}}{(z'-z)}\,dz'\,d\nu \tag{2-18}$$

The order of integration has been interchanged and the inner integrals are interpreted as the line integrals in Fig. 2–1. The contour is closed at infinity below the axis in the first integral and at infinity above the axis in the second integral. Since there are no poles within the contour in either integrand except at $z' = z$, we obtain, by the residue theorem,

$$V^i(t) = \int_0^\infty 2a(\nu)\sin(\Phi(\nu) - 2\pi\nu t)\,d\nu \tag{2-19}$$

where we have replaced z by t after performing the integration. Comparison of Eq. (2–19) and Eq.(2–8) establishes the equivalence of the two definitions.

A third and often useful form for the analytic signal can be obtained in terms of the improper functions $\delta_+(t'-t)$ and $\delta_-(t'-t)$. These may be defined by the relationships

$$\delta_+(t'-t) = \int_0^\infty e^{-2\pi i\nu(t'-t)}\,d\nu = \frac{1}{2}\left(\delta(t'-t) - \frac{i}{\pi}\frac{P}{t'-t}\right) \tag{2-20}$$

and

$$\delta_-(t'-t) = \int_0^\infty e^{+2\pi i\nu(t'-t)}\,d\nu = \frac{1}{2}\left(\delta(t'-t) + \frac{i}{\pi}\frac{P}{t'-t}\right) \tag{2-21}$$

The terms δ_+ and δ_- are to be regarded as functionals or integral operators and the P in the second term denotes that the Cauchy principal value is to be taken in integrals involving this term. Using these operators, the analytic signal may be expressed as a linear transform of the real function with which it is associated. Thus

$$V(t) = 2\int_{-\infty}^{\infty} \delta_-(t'-t)\,V^r(t')\,dt' \tag{2-22}$$

and

$$V^*(t) = 2\int_{-\infty}^{\infty} \delta_+(t'-t)\,V^r(t')\,dt' \tag{2-23}$$

This representation often proves useful for formal developments.

2.2 HILBERT TRANSFORMS AND CONVOLUTION THEOREMS FOR ANALYTIC SIGNALS

Hilbert transforms

As must be clear from the preceding section, Hilbert transforms play a rather central role in the mathematics of coherence theory. Since surprisingly little material which discusses this transform is available, we shall devote this section to collecting the theorems which are closely related to the developments of the book. [For a more rigorous though less extensive discussion, see Titchmarsh (1948).]

A table of well-known theorems concerning the Hilbert transform may be found in the Bateman Project, Tables of Integral Transforms, Vol. 2 (1953), and has been reproduced here slightly condensed as Table 2–1 in our notation.

TABLE 2–1

Theorem	$f(t)$	$\frac{1}{\pi}\int_{-\infty}^{+\infty}\frac{f(t')\,dt'}{t'-t}$
	$V^r(t)$	$V^i(t)$
I	$V^i(t)$	$-V^r(t)$
II	$V^r(t+a)$	$V^i(t+a)$
III	$V^r(\pm at)$	$\pm V^i(\pm at)$
IV	$(t+a)V^r(t)$	$(t+a)V^i(t)+\frac{1}{\pi}\int_{-\infty}^{\infty}V^r(t)\,dt$
V	$\frac{d}{dt}V^r(t)$	$\frac{d}{dt}V^i(t)$

The first of these theorems is the inversion theorem. The other theorems in the table may be demonstrated directly from the definition.

Convolution theorems for analytic signals

We shall require several theorems concerning the cross-correlation of analytic signals. Since these theorems do not seem to appear explicitly elsewhere in the literature, we shall give a detailed derivation of them at this point. Because of the complication introduced by the time average in the cross-correlation function, we shall first demonstrate these theorems in terms of convolution integrals and in Section 2.3 derive the correlation theorems from them. We define the convolution† of two functions $f_1(t)$ and $f_2(t)$ as

$$\int_{-\infty}^{\infty} f_1(t)f_2(t+\tau)\,dt$$

The common definition of the cross-correlation of $f_1(t)$ and $f_2(t)$ is

$$\lim_{T\to\infty}\frac{1}{2T}\int_{-T}^{T} f_1(t)f_2(t+\tau)\,dt$$

†Actually this expression is not a convolution as usually defined, but its properties are similar to a convolution type integral defined as

$$\int_{-\infty}^{\infty} f_1(\tau-t)f_2(t)\,dt$$

Theorem VI: The convolution of two real functions $f_1(t)$ and $f_2(t)$ is equal to the convolution of their Hilbert transforms, $g_1(t)$ and $g_2(t)$, (in the same order), that is,

$$\int_{-\infty}^{\infty} f_1(t) f_2(t+\tau)\,dt = \int_{-\infty}^{\infty} g_1(t)\, g_2(t+\tau)\,dt \tag{2–24}$$

The proof of this theorem can be obtained with the help of Theorems I and II of Table 2–1. Let

$$F(\tau) = \int_{-\infty}^{\infty} f_1(t) f_2(t+\tau)\,dt \tag{2–25}$$

Applying the inversion theorem (Theorem I, Table 2–1) twice to both sides of Eq. (2–25), we obtain

$$\pi^2 F(\tau'') = -\,⨍_{-\infty}^{\infty} \frac{1}{\tau' - \tau''} ⨍_{-\infty}^{\infty} \frac{1}{\tau - \tau'} \int_{\infty} f_1(t) f_2(t+\tau)\,dt\,d\tau\,d\tau' \tag{2–26}$$

Using Theorem II of Table 2–1 after inverting the order of integration, we find

$$\pi F(\tau'') = -\,⨍_{-\infty}^{\infty} \frac{1}{\tau' - \tau''} \int_{-\infty}^{\infty} f_1(t)\, g_2(t+\tau')\,dt\,d\tau' \tag{2–27}$$

Introducing a new variable $\tau = t + \tau'$, and interpreting the integral over t as a principal value integral, we obtain

$$\pi F(\tau'') = \int_{-\infty}^{\infty} ⨍_{-\infty}^{\infty} \frac{f_1(t)\, g_2(\tau)\,dt\,d\tau}{t - (\tau - \tau'')} \tag{2–28}$$

Using the definition of the Hilbert transform again, we finally have the result that

$$F(\tau'') = \int_{-\infty}^{\infty} g_1(\tau - \tau'')\, g_2(\tau)\,d\tau \tag{2–29}$$

On setting $\tau - \tau'' = t$, Eq. (2–29) reduces to Eq. (2–24) and the theorem is demonstrated.

Two special cases of theorem Eq. (2–24) are of particular interest. The first case, $f_s(t) = V_s^r(t)$ $(s = 1, 2,)$ leads to

$$\int_{-\infty}^{\infty} V_1^r(t)\, V_2^r(t+\tau)\,dt = \int_{-\infty}^{\infty} V_1^i(t)\, V_2^i(t+\tau)\,dt \tag{2–30}$$

The second case, $f_1(t) = V_1^r(t)$ and $f_2(t) = V_2^i(t)$, leads to

$$\int_{-\infty}^{\infty} V_1^r(t)\, V_2^i(t+\tau)\,dt = -\int_{-\infty}^{\infty} V_1^i(t)\, V_2^r(t+\tau)\,dt \tag{2–31}$$

Using Eqs. (2–30) and (2–31), we may obtain the convolution theorems for analytic signals from which some of the advantages of this complex formulation will be clear. Consider the integral

$$\int_{-\infty}^{\infty} V_1(t)\, V_2^*(t+\tau)\,dt \tag{2–32}$$

where $V_s(t)$ $(s = 1, 2)$ is of the form of Eq. (2–9). Substituting from Eq. (2–9) into Eq. (2–32) and using Eqs. (2–30) and (2–31), we obtain

$$\begin{aligned}\int_{-\infty}^{\infty} V_1(t)\, V_2^*(t+\tau)\, dt &= 2\int_{-\infty}^{\infty} V_1^r(t)\, V_2^r(t+\tau)\, dt \\ &\quad - 2i\int_{-\infty}^{\infty} V_1^r(t)\, V_2^i(t+\tau)\, dt\end{aligned} \tag{2–33}$$

Equation (2–33) expresses the useful result that the real part of the convolution of two analytic signals is, apart from a factor of two, the convolution of the real functions with which they are associated. Another useful property of the analytic signals is seen by putting $V_1(t)$ equal to $V_2(t)$ in Eq. (2–33) and then setting $\tau = 0$. Thus

$$\begin{aligned}\frac{1}{2}\int_{-\infty}^{\infty} V_1(t)\, V_1^*(t+\tau)\, dt &= \int_{-\infty}^{\infty} V_1^r(t)\, V_1^r(t+\tau)\, dt \\ &\quad - i\int_{-\infty}^{\infty} V_1^r(t)\, V_1^i(t+\tau)\, dt\end{aligned} \tag{2–34}$$

Evaluating the second integral on the right using Eq. (2–31), we find

$$\int_{-\infty}^{\infty} V_1^r(t)\, V_1^i(t+\tau)\, dt = -\int_{-\infty}^{\infty} V_1^i(t)\, V_1^r(t+\tau)\, dt \tag{2–35}$$

and evaluating Eq. (2–35) at $\tau = 0$ gives

$$\int_{-\infty}^{\infty} V_1^r(t)\, V_1^i(t)\, dt = 0 \tag{2–36}$$

that is, $V_1^r(t)$ and $V_1^i(t)$ are orthogonal. Evaluating Eq. (2–34) at $\tau = 0$ and using Eq. (2–36), we obtain finally

$$\int_{-\infty}^{\infty} V_1(t)\, V_1^*(t)\, dt = 2\int_{-\infty}^{\infty} V_1^r(t)\, V_1^r(t)\, dt \tag{2–37}$$

Equation (2–37) expresses a second important property of the analytic signals; namely, the integral over all time of the squared modulus of an analytic signal is, apart from a factor of two, the integral over all time of the square of the real function with which it is associated.

An additional theorem on the convolution of analytic signals, which will prove important in the next section, is

Theorem VII

$$\operatorname{Im}(F(\tau)) = -\frac{1}{\pi}\int_{-\infty}^{\infty} \frac{\operatorname{Re}(F(\tau'))}{\tau' - \tau}\, d\tau' \tag{2–38}$$

where

$$F(\tau) = \int_{-\infty}^{\infty} V_1(t)\, V_2^*(t+\tau)\, dt$$

Using Eqs. (2–30) and (2–31), $F(\tau)$ can be rewritten as

$$F(\tau) = \int_{-\infty}^{\infty} V_1^r(t)\, V_2^r(t + \tau)\, dt + \int_{-\infty}^{\infty} V_1^i(t)\, V_2^i(t + \tau)\, dt$$

(2–39)

$$- i\left\{\int_{-\infty}^{\infty} V_1^r(t)\, V_2^i(t + \tau)\, dt - \int_{-\infty}^{\infty} V_1^i(t)\, V_2^r(t + \tau)\, dt\right\}$$

Denoting by Re and Im the real and imaginary parts respectively and taking the Hilbert transform of the real part of $F(\tau)$, we obtain

(2–40)
$$\frac{1}{\pi} \fint_{-\infty}^{\infty} \frac{\mathrm{Re}[F(\tau')]}{\tau' - \tau}\, d\tau' = -\mathrm{Im}[F(\tau)]$$

and Theorem VII is demonstrated.

The results established in this section are, of course, applicable only to convolutions and the definitions introduced in Chapter 1 are in terms of correlations. We shall show in the next section that these theorems are also valid for the cross-correlation of analytic signals if the time average is suitably defined

2.3 THE CROSS-CORRELATION OF ANALYTIC SIGNALS

The complex cross-correlation function may be defined in several ways. The customary definition is [cf. Davenport and Root (1958), p. 70]

(2–41)
$$\Psi_{12}(\tau) = \lim_{T\to\infty} \frac{1}{2T} \int_{-T}^{T} f_1^*(t) f_2(t + \tau)\, dt$$

For our present purposes, however, the function† $\Gamma_{12}(\tau)$, is defined as

(2–42)
$$\Gamma_{12}(\tau) = \lim_{T\to\infty} \frac{1}{2T} \int_{-\infty}^{\infty} V_1(T, t + \tau)\, V_2^*(T, t)\, dt$$

where

(2–43)
$$V(T, t) = V^r(T/t) + i\, {}_TV^i(t)$$

and

(2–44)
$$V^r(T/t) = \begin{cases} V^r(t), & |t| < T \\ 0 \quad , & |t| > T \end{cases}$$

and

(2–45)
$${}_TV^i(t) = \frac{1}{\pi} \fint_{-\infty}^{\infty} \frac{V^r(T/t')\, dt'}{t' - t}$$

---

†The general definition of $\Gamma_{12}(\tau)$ is given in Section 2.5. In order to preserve the continuity of our mathematical developments, we are working in this section with the extremely important special case of stationary random time processes. For periodic processes, the definition Eq. (2–41) is more appropriate. As we stated in the introduction, our primary emphasis is on the statistical aspects of the electromagnetic field but, for completeness, and with limiting cases in mind, we also consider periodic processes (see Section 2.4).

The different notation, $V^r(T/t)$ and ${}_TV^i(t)$, is used since, although $V^r(T/t)$ vanishes for $|t| > T$, its Hilbert transform ${}_TV^i(t)$ will not in general vanish in this range. Since $V^r(t)$ is assumed to be everywhere finite, the function $V^r(T/t)$ is square integrable; its Hilbert transform ${}_TV^i(t)$, is therefore also square integrable [cf. Titchmarsh (1948)]. Consequently, all the required Hilbert transforms exist. The equivalence of the two definitions of an average, of the type Eqs. (2–41) and (2–42) is discussed by Born and Wolf (1959). For our purposes, it is more convenient to employ the definition Eq. (2–42), and accordingly the sharp brackets are defined as

$$\langle V_1(t+\tau)\, V_2^*(t)\rangle = \lim_{T\to\infty} \frac{1}{2T}\int_{-\infty}^{\infty} V_1(T, t+\tau)\, V_2^*(T, t)\, dt$$

The presence of the parameter T, in $V(T, t)$ in no way affects the arguments of the previous section; and the operation $\lim_{T\to\infty}$ will commute with the integrations involved, (provided they exist) since T and t are independent variables. The theorems estabilshed in Section 2.2 may, therefore, be taken over *mutatis mutandis* for the cross-correlation function $\Gamma_{12}(\tau)$. Thus, if we adopt the notation

$$\Gamma_{12}^{rr}(\tau) = \langle V_1^r(t+\tau)\, V_2^r(t)\rangle \tag{2–46}$$

and

$$\Gamma_{12}^{ri}(\tau) = \langle V_1^r(t+\tau)\, V_2^i(t)\rangle \tag{2–47}$$

We may summarize the principal theorems as follows:

$$\Gamma_{12}(\tau) = 2[\Gamma_{12}^{rr}(\tau) - i\Gamma_{12}^{ri}(\tau)] \tag{2–48}$$

$$\Gamma_{11}^{ri}(0) = 0 \tag{2–49}$$

Setting $V_1(t)$ equal to $V_2(t)$ and $\tau = 0$ in Eq. (2–48) and using Eq. (2–49), we obtain the result anticipated in Chapter 1, namely,

$$\Gamma_{11}(0) = 2\Gamma_{11}^{rr}(0) = 2I(P_1) \tag{2–50}$$

where $I(P_1)$ is the intensity at P_1. Further, it follows from Eq. (2–38) and the arguments of this section that

$$\Gamma_{12}^{ri}(\tau) = -\Gamma_{12}^{ir}(\tau) = \frac{1}{\pi}\int_{-\infty}^{\infty} \frac{\Gamma_{12}^{rr}(\tau')}{\tau' - \tau}\, d\tau' \tag{2–51}$$

Thus the mutual coherence function is an analytic signal.

For the sake of continuity in later arguments, we include at this point two lemmas concerning complex cross-correlation functions for stationary processes. Both of these lemmas are well known and follow immediately from the definition of $\Gamma_{12}(\tau)$ and the stationarity condition; they are, therefore, given here without proof:

(2–52)

Lemma I $\Gamma_{21}(-\tau) = \Gamma_{12}^*(\tau)$

Lemma II $\hat{\Gamma}_{21}(\nu) = \hat{\Gamma}_{12}^*(\nu)$

The hooked notation is used to denote temporal Fourier transforms, that is,

$$\hat{\Gamma}_{12}(\nu) = \int_{-\infty}^{\infty} \Gamma_{12}(\tau)\, e^{2\pi i\nu\tau}\, d\tau \qquad \nu > 0$$
(2–53)
$$= 0 \qquad \nu < 0$$

The spectrum of $\Gamma_{12}(\tau)$ is zero for half the frequency range, since the mutual coherence function is an analytic signal.

The function $\hat{\Gamma}_{12}(\nu)$ is related to the function $\hat{V}(T, \nu)$ where

(2–54)
$$V_1(T, t) = \int_0^{\infty} \hat{V}_1(T, \nu)\, e^{-2\pi i\nu t}\, d\nu$$

To see this write the definition of $\Gamma_{12}(\tau)$ and substitute for $V_1(T, t + \tau)$ and $V_2^*(T, t)$. We find

(2–55)
$$\Gamma_{12}(\tau) = \lim_{T\to\infty} \frac{1}{2T} \int_{-T}^{T} dt \int_0^{\infty} \int_0^{\infty} d\nu\, d\nu'\, \hat{V}_1(T, \nu)\, \hat{V}_2^*(T, \nu')\, e^{-2\pi i\nu(t+\tau)}\, e^{2\pi i\nu' t}$$

Interchanging limits and remembering that

(2–56)
$$\lim_{T\to\infty} \int_{-T}^{T} e^{2\pi it(\nu'-\nu)}\, dt = \delta(\nu' - \nu)$$

we find

(2–57)
$$\Gamma_{12}(\tau) = \int_0^{\infty} d\nu \lim_{T\to\infty} \frac{\hat{V}_1(T, \nu)\, \hat{V}_2^*(T, \nu)}{2T}$$

Thus we have finally, assuming the existence of the limit,

(2–58)
$$\hat{\Gamma}_{12}(\nu) = \lim_{T\to\infty} \frac{\hat{V}_1(T, \nu)\, \hat{V}_2^*(T, \nu)}{2T}$$

(2–59)
$$\Gamma_{12}(\tau) = \int_0^{\infty} \hat{\Gamma}_{12}(\nu)\, e^{-2\pi i\nu\tau}\, d\nu$$

Strictly speaking, the limit in Eq. (2–58) does not exist, in general, for stationary processes. Properly to form the limit, one must have recourse to the ensemble theory given in the next sections and define the limit as

(2–60)
$$\hat{\Gamma}_{12}(\nu) = \lim_{T\to\infty} \left\{ \frac{\hat{V}_1(T, \nu)\, \hat{V}_2^*(T, \nu)}{2T} \right\}$$

where the brackets indicate an ensemble average. Middleton (1960) discusses this point at length for autocorrelation and spectral density functions.

The difficulty may be circumvented, however, by assuming that, in our formulation of $\hat{\Gamma}_{12}(\nu)$, we are using detectors that smooth each frequency component ν over an interval $\nu + \Delta\nu_0$. Then if in a real problem we choose $\Delta\nu_0 T \gg 1$ and assume an ergodic hypothesis (see "Stationary Systems" in Chapter 2), the limit in Eq. (2–60) exists in this smoothed sense. For T large enough, $\Delta\nu_0$ may be taken quite small (we take the limit $\Delta\nu_0 T$, $T \to \infty$, $\Delta\nu_0 \to 0$, such that $\Delta\nu_0 T \gg 1$) and thus this procedure introduces no real restriction on any of the formulations used in this book. We shall assume the limit in Eq. (2–58) always exists in this sense if necessary.

2.4 REPRESENTATIONS OF THE SOURCE RADIATION

In this book, we shall be principally concerned with sources whose radiation may be considered to be representable in time as either a stationary random time series or the sum of a finite number of periodic components. Together, these representations encompass most of the processes for which long time averaging is a useful procedure. We shall find as we proceed that this covers a wide class of physical processes involving radiation. These representations do, however, exclude some important problems where time averaging is inappropriate. Hence, in this chapter, we shall give an ensemble definition of mutual coherence in addition to the time-averaged form $\Gamma_{12}(\tau)$. Moreover, to define properly a random stationary time series, it is appropriate to define an ensemble average first and then invoke an ergodic type hypothesis. Thus, we discuss in this section some aspects of both ensemble and time averaging. As was just mentioned, the theory to be developed in this chapter will be a scalar theory, but similar analysis applies to a full vector theory.

Ensemble of systems

To define a random process, we consider, as in statistical mechanics, an ensemble of systems with identical macroscopic properties. For reasons of ignorance or convenience, we do not consider the microscopic processes in each system. As a consequence, in such an ensemble only the average properties of the system are considered predictable. Applied to radiation problems, this means that, in many cases, the instantaneous temporal variation of the radiation (and this has meaning for a classical field) varies from system to system, although the macroscopic properties are constant from system to system. If this occurs, it is often appropriate to specify the radiation in a statistical sense and consider the process random.

The radiation in a random process must then be described by functions of the form:†

$$P_s\{V_1(\mathbf{x}_1, t_1), V_2(\mathbf{x}_2, t_2), V_3(\mathbf{x}_3, t_3) \ldots V_s(\mathbf{x}_s, t_s)\} \\ dV_1(\mathbf{x}_1, t_1) \ldots dV_s(\mathbf{x}_s, t_s) \tag{2–61}$$

defined as the probability that a given system's radiation will have a value

†In "Ensemble of Systems" and "Stationary Systems" of Chapter 2, we consider V to be a real function. We omit the r superscript to avoid confusing notation. The analytic signal is here considered only in connection with time averages.

between $V_1(\mathbf{x}_1, t_1)$ and $V_1(\mathbf{x}_1, t_1) + dV_1(\mathbf{x}_1, t)$ at position $\mathbf{x}_1$ and time $t_1 \ldots$ and a value between $V_s(\mathbf{x}_s, t_s)$ and $V_s(\mathbf{x}_s, t_s) + dV_s(\mathbf{x}_s, t_s)$ at position $\mathbf{x}_s$ and time t_s.

From P_s, we can calculate moments of the form:

$$M(V_1^{n_1} \ldots V_s^{n_s}) = \underbrace{\int \ldots \int}_{s\text{-fold integral}} V_1^{n_1} V_2^{n_2} \ldots V_s^{n_s} \, P_s(V_1, V_2 \ldots V_s)\, dV_1 \ldots dV_s \tag{2-62}$$

Alternately, these moments may be calculated directly from measurements as

$$\lim_{N \to \infty} \frac{1}{N} \sum_{i=1}^{N} V_{1i}^{n_1} V_{2i}^{n_2} \ldots V_{si}^{n_s} \tag{2-63}$$ †

where i denotes which system in the ensemble is being considered.

We note that, if all moments of P_s are known, P_s itself may be calculated, if it is suitably regular.

Stationary systems

The moments

$$M\{[V_1(\mathbf{x}_1, t_1)]^{n_1} \ldots [V_s(\mathbf{x}_s, t_s)]^{n_s}\}$$

are, in general, functions of time. However, if all P_s and hence all moments, are independent of absolute time, the process is called a *stationary random process*.

When the random process is stationary, one often assumes an ergodic type hypothesis and equates the infinite time average of any stystem i and the ensemble average. That is, one assumes

$$\lim_{N \to \infty} \frac{1}{N} \sum_{i=1}^{N} V_{1i}^{n_1} \ldots V_{si}^{n_s} = \langle V_{1i}^{n_1} \ldots V_{si}^{n_s} \rangle \Big|_{i \text{ is fixed}} \tag{2-64}$$

We shall assume this equivalence to be true in all the stationary processes we consider. In such cases, the temporal variation of V for any system is termed a *stationary random series*. It should be noted that

$$\Gamma_{12}^{rr}(\tau) = \langle V_1^r(t + \tau)\, V_2^r(t) \rangle$$

is of course simply a second-order moment.

Periodic radiation

When the radiation is composed of a finite number of periodic components, averaging over an ensemble is inappropriate unless one allows the phase or amplitude to vary with the ensemble system. Time averaging, however, is a useful procedure for conditions of fixed phase and amplitude.

---

†Sometimes V_{1i} will be denoted ${}^iV_1$ in later chapters, if another subscript is needed.

Thus, for example, the moment $\Gamma_{12}(\tau) = \langle V_1(t+\tau)\, V_2^*(t)\rangle$ has meaning for either a random stationary time series or a time variation made up of periodic components. The Fourier transform of $\Gamma_{12}(\tau)$, however, yields a series of Dirac delta functions when $\Gamma_{12}(\tau)$ is formed from periodic components. Although not rigorous, these delta functions cause no difficulties and may be handled consistently in the theory. In considering periodic functions though, one should use a definition of form Eq. (2–41) rather than Eq. (2–42) which is introduced to allow for a more careful definition of the Fourier transform of $\Gamma_{12}(\tau)$ in random processes.

In the subsequent development then, $\Gamma_{12}(\tau)$ will be used to describe both stationary random processes and processes containing only periodic components. As we have stated, our principal interest will be in random processes.

Higher moments of V

In principle there is no reason to assume that in random processes the second moment $\Gamma_{12}(\tau)$ characterizes all physical processes of interest. Indeed, P_s which includes all moments of V as $s \to \infty$ is needed to characterize completely a physical process. The assumption is often made, however, that the random processes may be described by gaussian statistics, and in this case, all higher moments are determined from $\Gamma_{12}(\tau)$.

Some recent work—Beran and Parrent (1961)—described in Chapter 13 has appeared considering the fourth-order moments for cases of nongaussian statistics, and these moments can be shown to be important in certain physical problems involving turbulence. Further, Beran (1960) and Glauber (1963a) have defined higher order moments. Beran defined the higher order moments in an ensemble sense and derived governing differential equations. Glauber has defined the higher order moments using a quantum formalism and stressed the need for these moments in considering the radiation emitted by a laser. He also gives a definition of coherence in terms of all moments. As a result of the complexity of higher order moment analysis, however, and perhaps the comparative newness of the formulation of $\Gamma_{12}(\tau)$ itself, there is little other work on higher order moments for nongaussian statistics known to the authors.

Intensity interferometry, which measures a contracted fourth-order moment, will be described in Chapter 12. To date most of this work assumes gaussian statistics, and the fourth-order moment is measured not to provide information not in $\Gamma_{12}(\tau)$ but only as a more convenient method to determine $\Gamma_{12}(\tau)$.

Validity of scalar theory

We shall assume in this book, until Chapter 10, that a scalar theory is applicable for the description of the full electromagnetic field. This is to avoid the considerable calculational difficulties introduced by the vector nature of the field. However, all the basic ideas introduced in these chapters may be readily generalized to a full vector theory and some generalization is carried out in Chapters 10 and 11.

The validity of a scalar theory is difficult to justify, and it is not our purpose here to state when such a theory is applicable. We note only that it has been very successfully used in many electromagnetic problems as any book on optics will indicate. When we use it in practical problems in this book, we assume that we are considering radiation with small angular spread and that the scalar quantity we consider is one cartesian component of the electromagnetic field. However, scalar theory is almost certainly of more generality than this.

It is of some interest to remark that much of this book is applicable to the study of random acoustical waves where a scalar theory is appropriate.

2.5 DEFINITIONS

We are now in a position to give consideration to the general definitions which form the foundations of coherence theory. As we stated in the previous section we shall first give an ensemble definition of the coherence function and then a time-averaged definition.

Definition of the mutual coherence function in terms of an ensemble

We define the mutual coherence function $\Gamma_E(\mathbf{x}_1, t_1; \mathbf{x}_2, t_2)$ as follows:

$$\Gamma_E(\mathbf{x}_1, t_1; \mathbf{x}_2, t_2) = \underset{N\to\infty}{\frac{1}{N}} \sum_{i=1}^{N} V_{1i}^r(\mathbf{x}_1, t_1)\, V_{2i}^r(\mathbf{x}_2, t_2) \tag{2-65}$$

where the summation i is over an ensemble of systems. We consider here $V^r(\mathbf{x}, t)$ to be a real function satisfying the wave equation.

This definition is appropriate if the statistics are either stationary or non-stationary. If the statistics are stationary $\Gamma_E(\mathbf{x}_1, t_1; \mathbf{x}_2, t_2) = \Gamma_E(\mathbf{x}_1, \mathbf{x}_2, \tau)$ where $\tau = t_1 - t_2$. Then

$$\Gamma_E(\mathbf{x}_1, \mathbf{x}_2, \tau) = \underset{N\to\infty}{\frac{1}{N}} \sum_{i=1}^{N} V_{1i}^r(\mathbf{x}_1, t_2 + \tau)\, V_{2i}^r(\mathbf{x}_2, t_2) \tag{2-66}$$

where t_2 may have any value.

As stated in the previous section, we shall always assume in this book that, when the statistics are stationary, we may equate time and ensemble averages. Thus, we assume

(2–67) $$\Gamma_E(\mathbf{x}_1, \mathbf{x}_2, \tau) = \Gamma_{12}^{rr}(\tau) = \langle V_1^r(\mathbf{x}_1, t + \tau)\, V_2^r(\mathbf{x}_2, t)\rangle$$

Definition of the mutual coherence function in terms of time averages

If the statistics are stationary, we see it is appropriate to define the mutual coherence function as a time average. Similarly, if the radiation is periodic, this is an appropriate representation. When performing time averaging, however, it is much more convenient to use a complex representation in terms of the analytic signal. Thus, we define the time-averaged mutual coherence function $\Gamma_{12}(\tau)$ as

(2–68) $$\Gamma_{12}(\tau) = \langle V(\mathbf{x}_1, t + \tau)\, V^*(\mathbf{x}_2, t)\rangle\dagger$$

The complex degree of coherence $\gamma_{12}(\tau)$ [the normalized form of $\Gamma_{12}(\tau)$] is defined as

(2–69) $$\gamma_{12}(\tau) = \frac{\Gamma_{12}(\tau)}{\sqrt{\Gamma_{11}(0)\,\Gamma_{22}(0)}}$$

From Eq. (2–69) and the Schwarz inequality, it follows immediately that the modulus of $\gamma_{12}(\tau)$ is bounded by 0 and 1. These extremes characterize respectively incoherence and coherence. The disturbances at $\mathbf{x}_1$ and $\mathbf{x}_2$ are considered to be coherent if $|\gamma_{12}(\tau)| = 1$, and they are incoherent if $|\gamma_{12}(\tau)| = 0$. Of course, $|\gamma_{12}(\tau)|$ is not a constant even for two fixed points, but rather varies as a function of τ. There is, therefore, some ambiguity in the foregoing definitions, since a given pair of disturbances may be coherent for some τ, say τ_1, and incoherent for another value of τ, say τ_2. In Chapter 4, where the implications of the definitions are examined in detail, this point is again considered and the ambiguity is removed. For our present purpose, however, the definitions just given will suffice.

Several functions which are easily derivable from $\Gamma_{12}(\tau)$ are of sufficient importance in the theory of partial coherence to have received special terminology. These will be introduced at this point. The self-coherence function is the complex autocorrelation of the field at a typical point $\mathbf{x}$, that is,

(2–70) $$\Gamma_{11}(\tau) = \langle V_1(\mathbf{x}_1, t + \tau)\, V_1^*(\mathbf{x}_1, t)\rangle$$

This function plays a key role in the description of the Michelson two-beam interferometer and will be discussed in some detail at a later point. It is clear that the zero ordinate of the self-coherence function is twice the intensity at the point $\mathbf{x}$.

The zero ordinate of the mutual coherence function $\Gamma_{12}(0)$ is termed the *mutual intensity function* and plays a central role in the description of the

†In this book, $\Gamma_{12}(\tau)$ will often be denoted as $\Gamma(P_1, P_2, \tau)$ or $\Gamma(\mathbf{x}_1, \mathbf{x}_2, \tau)$ if it is clearer explicitly to display the space variables. Similarly, the function $V(\mathbf{x}, t)$ will have a variety of notation.

stellar interferometer.

The Fourier transform of $\Gamma_{12}(\tau)$, $\hat{\Gamma}_{12}(\nu)$, with respect to τ is termed the *mutual power spectrum*, that is,

$$\begin{aligned} \hat{\Gamma}_{12}(\nu) &= \int_{-\infty}^{\infty} \Gamma_{12}(\tau)\, e^{2\pi i\nu\tau}\, d\tau \qquad \nu > 0 \\ &= 0 \qquad\qquad\qquad\qquad\qquad\quad \nu < 0 \end{aligned} \tag{2-71}$$

That $\Gamma_{12}(\nu)$ is zero for $\nu < 0$ follows from the fact that $\Gamma_{12}(\nu)$ is an analytic signal. The power spectrum of the radiation is, of course, the Fourier transform of the self-coherence function; that is,

$$\begin{aligned} \hat{\Gamma}_{11}(\nu) &= \int_{-\infty}^{\infty} \Gamma_{11}(\tau)\, e^{2\pi i\nu\tau}\, d\tau \qquad \nu > 0 \\ &= 0 \qquad\qquad\qquad\qquad\qquad\quad \nu < 0 \end{aligned} \tag{2-72}$$

Space and time coherence

Recently, the concepts of space and time coherence have been used in the literature. We conclude this section with a brief discussion of these terms.

Although, as we shall see, all the information concerning the coherence of the field is contained in the mutual coherence function, in many cases it proves helpful to separate as much as possible those coherence effects which arise from the finite spatial extent of the primary source of the radiation from those which arise from the finite spectral width of the radiation. A complete separation of these effects is, of course, not possible, but a partial separation which is useful for many problems is possible. The terminology arises from the following considerations. Strictly monochromatic radiation is always coherent whereas radiation of finite spectral width can never be

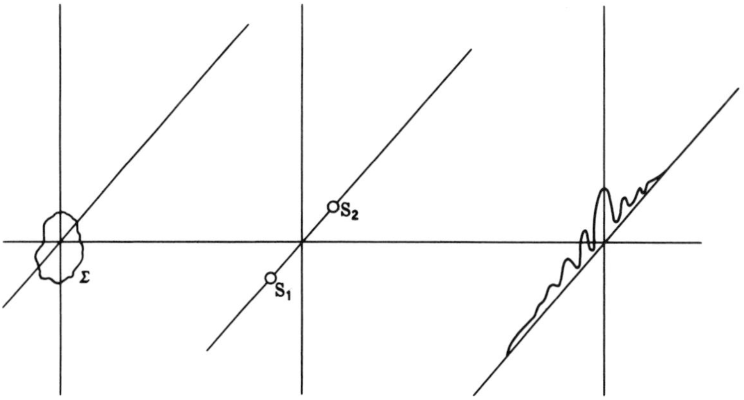

Figure 2-2. Interference experiment.

strictly coherent. (This point is discussed at length in Chapter 4.) Partial coherence effects arising primarily from the finiteness of the spectral width are termed *temporal coherence effects*. On the other hand, light emanating from a point source is always very nearly coherent for small path differences at least, whereas light emanating from a large self-luminous source tends to give very poor quality interference effects. The term *space coherence* has been used to describe effects directly related to source size.

These two concepts may be easily demonstrated by considering a simple interference experiment as illustrated in Fig. 2–2. Let $\sum$ be a self-luminous source of light placed on the perpendicular bisector of the line between the two holes S_1 and S_2. Consider the limit where $\sum$ becomes a point source of finite spectral width. Under these conditions, the disturbances at S_1 and S_2 are identical. Thus the mutual coherence between the oscillation at S_1 and S_2 is essentially the self-coherence of the source; that is,

$$\begin{aligned} \Gamma(S_1, S_2, \tau) &= \langle V(S_1, t+\tau)\, V^*(S_2, t)\rangle \\ &= \Gamma_{11}(\tau) \end{aligned} \tag{2–73}$$

By measuring $\Gamma_{11}(\tau)$, we obtain the autocorrelation of the source disturbance. Its Fourier transform $\hat{\Gamma}_{11}(\nu)$ is the power spectrum of the source. This is the principle of the Michelson two-beam interferometric technique for determining the spectral distribution of a source. That the fringes in this experiment tend to vanish for increasing path differences is attributed to the time coherence of the light illuminating the two pinholes. In short, $\Gamma_{11}(\tau)$ measures the time coherence.

If in the preceding experiment, we fix the spectral width of the source to some small value and increase the size of the source $\sum$, we find that the visibility of the central fringes decreases with increasing size of $\sum$ (as discussed in Chapter 1). In this case, clearly the disturbances at S_1 and S_2 are no longer identical and the measurements yield the mutual coherence function, $\Gamma_{12}(\tau)$. By restricting our attention to the fringes in the center of the pattern, we measure $\Gamma_{12}(0)$. This decrease in fringe visibility with source size is termed an *effect of spatial coherence* and plays a central role in the description of the Michelson stellar interferometer. Thus, $\Gamma_{12}(0)$, the mutual intensity, describes in this case, the space coherence of the light.

2.6 MEASUREMENT

Conditions for measurability

The measurability of $\Gamma_{12}(\tau)$ is of central importance in the theory of partial coherence. It is the purpose of much of the theory to show that in many important physical processes $\Gamma_{12}(\tau)$ alone need be considered to explain the process, and it is paramount that $\Gamma_{12}(\tau)$ be measurable. The measurement of $\Gamma_{12}(\tau)$ is subject to many restrictions, however, and we shall present them here. There is a wide class of problems that meet these restrictions, however, and it is for these cases that the theory of partial coherence was primarily developed.

We shall consider the measurement of $\Gamma_{12}(\tau)$ only in connection with a radiation field. The mathematical formulation of the theory to be developed will not make this distinction, but as a practical matter we shall be concerned with measuring only the coherence of the radiation field.

$\Gamma_{12}(\tau)$ is defined in terms of scalar quantities and our discussion of the measurement of $\Gamma_{12}(\tau)$ is confined to those conditions under which a scalar theory is applicable. For our purposes here, this means radiation fields with small angular spread.

As we mentioned in Chapter 1, we will measure $\Gamma_{12}(\tau)$ by interference type experiments, that is, by letting the radiation from two pinholes interfere. In optics, for reasons of convenience, the pinholes are usually many wavelengths large. In any electromagnetic field we consider here, however, even if the pinholes could be made smaller than a wavelength and two pinholes could be put within a wavelength, we should not do so. Variations in $\Gamma_{12}(\tau)$ in distances of the order of a wavelength occur only if a plane wave decomposition of $V(t)$ shows that the plane waves have a large angular spread. The applicability of scalar theory, however, demands that the angular spread of the plane waves be very small.

This condition of small angular spread is apparently violated only in the case of incoherent sources (see Chapter 4) in which the source emits radiation over a wide angular region and the coherence changes in the order of a wavelength. In most problems using incoherent radiation, however, we shall be looking at only a small angular region of the total angular spectrum that is emitted, and hence we are permitted to use scalar theory.

The problem of the nature of $\Gamma_{12}(\tau)$ on the surface of an incoherent source does arise even though we consider only a portion of the angular spectrum emitted. To bring out the nature of an incoherent source, we consider incoherence in Chapter 4 from a purely scalar point of view, though of course strictly speaking this is incorrect. In Chapter 4 we derive reasonable forms for $\Gamma_{12}(\tau)$ on the surface of an incoherent radiator. From a theoretical point of view, this causes no difficulty in application since we then proceed to use essentially only that portion of $\Gamma_{12}(\tau)$ which contributes to the radiation field in a region of narrow angular spread. From a measurement point of view, the matter is not so simple since the angular spectrum of the radiation is not easily decomposed before impinging on the screen holes; to date, measurement of the coherence of only a portion of an angular spectrum has not been performed. For purpose of this book, we shall always assume a theoretical form of $\Gamma_{12}(\tau)$ on the surface of an incoherent radiator. The measurement of $\Gamma_{12}(\tau)$ (or perhaps rather its appropriate vector generalization) under this condition is an outstanding problem.

Lastly, we note that the angular spread we can tolerate in measurement depends upon the size of the holes since implicit in our derivation in Chapter 1 was the fact that the phase variation of $V(t)$ over a pinhole, resulting from the angular spread of $V(t)$, results in a small angular spread compared to the angular spread introduced by diffraction from the hole. Again, however, if scalar theory is applicable, this restriction is easily satisfied in practice.

A theory of measurement of the full vector field has not yet been given. As is shown in Chapter 10, it is not difficult to consider polarization effects for fields of very narrow angular spread, but even in this restricted case, to our knowledge, a measurement procedure has not yet been developed to consider two-point mutual polarization effects for fields of arbitrary spectral spread.

Details of Measurement of $\Gamma_{12}(\tau)$

As we pointed out in Chapter 1, in principle, it is simple to measure $\Gamma_{12}(\tau)$ when the spectral width of the radiation is narrow; in fact, in many cases, we need only measure the visibility to find $|\gamma_{12}(\tau)|$. We shall now set out a method for measuring $\Gamma_{12}(\tau)$ when the spectral width of the radiation is finite. It should be noted, however, that as of the writing of this book the only measurements that have been made have been for radiation of narrow spectral width.

To measure $\Gamma_{12}(\tau)$, in general, it is necessary to measure the power spectrum of the radiation rather than simply an intensity distribution, as outlined in Chapter 1. We begin by returning again to Young's two pinhole experiments illustrated in Fig. 1–1.

We wish now to relate the power spectrum of the radiation at two points Q_1 and Q_2 [termed $\hat{I}(Q_1, \nu)$ and $\hat{I}(Q_2, \nu)$] to the mutual power spectrum, $\hat{\Gamma}(P_1, P_2, \nu)$. The relation we wish to establish is

$$\begin{aligned}\hat{I}(Q_i, \nu) &= |k_1(Q_i, \nu)|^2\, \hat{I}(P_1, \nu) + |k_2(Q_i, \nu)|^2\, \hat{I}(P_2, \nu) \\ &\quad + 2\mathrm{Re}\, k_1(Q_i, \nu)\, k_2^*(Q_i, \nu)\, \hat{\Gamma}(P_1, P_2, \nu) \qquad (i = 1, 2)\end{aligned} \tag{2–74}$$

where the k's are propagators that are known and depend only upon geometry and frequency. The propagators are given in Section 3–5. In this experiment, we, of course, set the distance, d, to be much larger than the pinhole diameters.

Let us suppose that the radiation $V(T, t)$ exists from $-T$ to T. We denote $\hat{V}(T, \nu)$ to be the Fourier transform of $V(T, t)$. Since $V(T, t)$ satisfies the wave equation, $\hat{V}(T, \nu)$ satisfies the Helmholtz equation:

$$\nabla^2 \hat{V}(T, \nu) + k^2 \hat{V}(T, \nu) = 0 \tag{2–75}$$

A formal solution of this equation, relating $\hat{V}(Q_i, T, \nu)$ to $\hat{V}(P_1, T, \nu)$ and $\hat{V}(P_2, T, \nu)$ is

$$\hat{V}(Q_i, T, \nu) = k_1(Q_i, \nu)\,\hat{V}(P_1, T, \nu) + k_2(Q_i, \nu)\,\hat{V}(P_2, T, \nu) \tag{2-76}$$

where k_1 and k_2 are known function of geometry and frequency.†

The frequency spectrum at Q_i is defined as

$$\hat{I}(Q_i, \nu) = \lim_{T\to\infty} \frac{1}{2T}\,\hat{V}(Q_i, T, \nu)\,\hat{V}^*(Q_i, T, \nu)\ddagger \tag{2-77}$$

Substitution of Eq. (2–76) into Eq. (2–77) yields

$$\begin{aligned}\hat{I}(Q_i, \nu) &= |k_1(Q_i, \nu)|^2\,\hat{I}(P_1, \nu) + |k_2(Q_i, \nu)|^2\,\hat{I}(P_2, \nu)\\ &\quad + 2\,\mathrm{Re}\,k_1(Q_i, \nu)\,k_2^*(Q_i, \nu)\left[\lim_{T\to\infty}\frac{1}{2T}\,\hat{V}(P_1, T, \nu)\,\hat{V}^*(P_2, T, \nu)\right]\end{aligned} \tag{2-78}$$

As shown in Section 2–3, the bracketed [ ] expression is simply $\hat{\Gamma}(P_1, P_2, \nu)$ and we have thus Eq. (2–74).

Now $\hat{I}(P_1, \nu)$ may be measured by closing the pinhole P_2 and $\hat{I}(P_2, \nu)$ may be measured by closing the pinhole P_1. For then,

$$\hat{I}(Q_1, \nu) = |k_j(Q_1, \nu)|^2\,\hat{I}(P_j, \nu) \qquad (j = 1, 2) \tag{2-79}$$

where $k_j(Q_1, \nu)$ is known.

To measure $\hat{\Gamma}(P_1, P_2, \nu)$, we write it in terms of its real and imaginary parts:

$$\hat{\Gamma}(P_1, P_2, \nu) = \hat{\Gamma}^r(P_1, P_2, \nu) + i\hat{\Gamma}^i(P_1, P_2, \nu)$$

Further, writing $k_1(Q_i, \nu)\,k_2^*(Q_i, \nu)$ as

$$k_1(Q_i, \nu)\,k_2^*(Q_i, \nu) = \alpha(Q_i, \nu) + i\beta(Q_i, \nu) \tag{2-80}$$

we have, using Eq. (2–74),

$$\begin{aligned}\hat{I}(Q_i, \nu) &= |k_1(Q_i, \nu)|^2\,\hat{I}(P_1, \nu) + |k_2(Q_i, \nu)|^2\,\hat{I}(P_2, \nu)\\ &\quad + 2\{\alpha(Q_i, \nu)\,\hat{\Gamma}^r(P_1, P_2, \nu) - \beta(Q_i, \nu)\,\hat{\Gamma}^i(P_1, P_2, \nu)\}\end{aligned} \tag{2-81}$$

Measurement of $\hat{I}(Q_i, \nu)$ at two points, Q_1 and Q_2 will then suffice to determine $\hat{\Gamma}^r(P_1, P_2, \nu)$ and $\hat{\Gamma}^i(P_1, P_2, \nu)$.

With $\hat{\Gamma}(P_1, P_2, \nu)$ thus determined, $\Gamma_{12}(\tau) \equiv \Gamma(P_1, P_2, \tau)$ may be found by taking its Fourier transform.

The propagators $k_i(Q_i, \nu)$ are explicitly determined in Section 3–5.

This completes our discussion of the measurement of $\Gamma_{12}(\tau)$ for radiation of unlimited spectral spread.

---

†The k's differ by exponential factors from those introduced in Chapter 1, since here they are defined with respect to $\hat{V}(P_1, T, \nu)$ rather than $V[P_1, t - r_1/c]$.

‡See Section 2.3 for a note on the existence of this function.

Although we consider the two-hole interference experiment as our primary measurement procedure when $\Delta\nu/\bar{\nu}$ is both large and small, there is another method of measurement that may be of more practical use under certain restricted conditions. We conclude this section with an outline of this method. (This subsection is given here in order to keep the discussion of measurement procedures in one section. If the discussion is not clear, however, we suggest that the reader first study Chapters 3, 4, and 5.)

Another method for measuring the mutual coherence function for quasi-monochromatic radiation from homogeneous plane sources

In practice, the technique of measuring $\Gamma_{12}(\tau)$ by interferometric methods may prove to be extremely cumbersome. This is clear since, for every pair of points, one would have to repeat this experiment in order to determine the boundary condition for, say, a diffraction problem.

We outline here a method of measuring $\Gamma_{12}(0)$ in the quasi-monochromatic approximation for all pairs of points on a plane surface in a single experiment. In particular, we should like to take a single photograph such that the intensity variation in the image is a one-to-one map of the mutual intensity function across the surface in question. It is, of course, not possible to do this in general, since the mutual intensity $\Gamma(\mathbf{x}_1, \mathbf{x}_2, 0)$ is a function of the coordinates of two points, whereas the intensity $I(\mathbf{x})$ is a function of the coordinates of one point only. In a large class of physically interesting problems, however, the mutual intensity is a function of the difference only,

$$\Gamma(\mathbf{x}_1, \mathbf{x}_2, 0) = \Gamma(\mathbf{x}_1 - \mathbf{x}_2, 0) \tag{2–82}$$

Obviously Eq. (2–82) cannot hold near the edge of the source, so that the method presupposes large sources where the end effects are negligible. Further, we note that on a surface where $\Gamma_{12}(0)$ in a function of separation only, the intensity $I(\mathbf{x})$ is constant.

If $\Gamma(\boldsymbol{\xi}_1, \boldsymbol{\xi}_2, 0)$ describes the mutual intensity across a plane surface, and if the surface is placed at the aperture plane of a lens, then the mutual intensity in the focal plane of the lens is given by†

$$\Gamma(\mathbf{x}_1, \mathbf{x}_2, 0) = \text{const} \int_S \int_S \Gamma(\boldsymbol{\xi}_1 - \boldsymbol{\xi}_2, 0)\, e^{[(2\pi i/\bar{\lambda} f)(\mathbf{x}_1 \cdot \boldsymbol{\xi}_1 - \mathbf{x}_2 \cdot \boldsymbol{\xi}_2)]}\, d\boldsymbol{\xi}_1\, d\boldsymbol{\xi}_2 \tag{2–83}$$

†See Chapters 3 and 4, Eqs. (4–30), (3–27), (3–28). We discuss there the relation between $\Gamma(\xi_1, \xi_2, 0)$ and $I(\mathbf{x})$. Expanding the exponential $e^{ik(r_1 - r_2)}$ as in Section 5–3 then gives a far-field approximation. Since placing a lens in front of the source allows you to obtain the far-field solution in the focal plane of the lens, the formulas given in those chapters apply here with only a slight change.

where $\bar{\lambda}$ is the mean radiation wavelength and f is the focal length of the lens.

Thus, the intensity in the focal plane of the lens is given by

$$I(\mathbf{x}) = \text{const} \int_S \int_S \Gamma(\boldsymbol{\xi}_1 - \boldsymbol{\xi}_2, 0)\, e^{[2\pi i \mathbf{x}\cdot(\boldsymbol{\xi}_1 - \boldsymbol{\xi}_2)/\bar{\lambda} f]}\, d\boldsymbol{\xi}_1\, d\boldsymbol{\xi}_2 \tag{2–84}$$

Introducing the change of variables,

$$\boldsymbol{\xi}_1 - \boldsymbol{\xi}_2 = \boldsymbol{\rho} \quad \text{and} \quad \boldsymbol{\xi}_1 + \boldsymbol{\xi}_2 = \boldsymbol{\sigma} \tag{2–85}$$

Eq. (2–84) becomes

$$I(\mathbf{x}) = \text{const} \iint_{-\infty}^{\infty} \Gamma(\boldsymbol{\rho}, 0)\, e^{(2\pi i \boldsymbol{\rho}\cdot\mathbf{x})/\bar{\lambda} f}\, d\boldsymbol{\rho} \tag{2–86}$$

Strictly speaking, the development of Eqs. (2–84)–(2–86) is justified only for infinite apertures. [For finite apertures, $I(\mathbf{x})$ is the convolution of $\tilde{\Gamma}(\boldsymbol{\rho})$ with the impulse response of the lens.] Physically, to justify this approximation, we require only that the aperture size be large compared to the coherence interval of the field to be measured.

Thus the intensity in the image is the Fourier transform of the mutual intensity function. If $I(\mathbf{x})$ is suitably recorded on film, the inverse Fourier transform $\Gamma(\boldsymbol{\xi}_1 - \boldsymbol{\xi}_2, 0)$ can be obtained optically. Moreover, the Fourier transform of $I(\mathbf{x})$, $\tilde{I}(\boldsymbol{\mu})$, is precisely the mutual intensity across the original source.

The physical significance of this method may be made quite clear from the following considerations: If the mutual intensity is a function of the coordinate differences only, then it follows that there is a uniquely determined fictitious incoherent source which, if placed at infinity, would produce the same mutual coherence function across the source plane. Arranging the optics such that the partially coherent source plane coincides with the principal plane of the lens yields a photograph of the intensity distribution of this fictitious source. Since the coherence in the far field of an incoherent source is the Fourier transform of the source intensity distribution (van Cittert-Zernike theorem, see Chapters 3, 5), the Fourier transform of this image yields the coherence of the original source plane.

Experiments using this technique have been performed by Bouche and Thompson (1964), and we refer the reader to their paper for a discussion of the actual experimental procedure.

chapter

3

Free Space Propagation of the Mutual Coherence Function $\Gamma_{12}(\tau)$

In this chapter, we shall derive the wave equations governing the propagation of $\Gamma_{12}(\tau)$ in free space and present formal solutions of the equations in integral form for radiation from a finite surface. In particular, we shall consider in more detail the case of radiation from a plane finite surface.

3.1 DERIVATION OF DIFFERENTIAL EQUATIONS GOVERNING $\Gamma_{12}(\tau)$

The equations governing the propagation of $\Gamma_{12}(\tau)$ in free space are found by assuming that the field is characterized by the real scalar function $V^r(t)$

which satisfies in free space the scalar wave equation:

$$\nabla^2 V^r(t) = \frac{1}{c^2}\frac{\partial^2 V^r(t)}{\partial t^2} \tag{3–1}$$

The analytic signal $V(t) = V^r(t) + iV^i(t)$ also satisfies the scalar wave equation. This follows from the linearity of the relations between V and V^r. Thus, if we multiply both sides of Eq. (3–1) by δ_+ and integrate, we obtain

$$\nabla^2 V(t) = \frac{1}{c^2}\frac{\partial^2}{\partial t^2} V(t) \tag{3–2}$$

The mutual coherence function is defined as

$$\Gamma_{12}(\tau) = \langle V_1(t+\tau)\, V_2^*(t)\rangle \tag{3–3}$$

To derive the governing equations for $\Gamma_{12}(\tau)$ take the laplacian with respect to P_1 of both sides of the defining equation (3–3). This yields, assuming the functions are sufficiently regular for differentiation and averaging to commute,

$$\nabla_1^2\Gamma_{12}(\tau) = \langle \nabla_1^2 V_1(t+\tau)\, V_2^*(t)\rangle \tag{3–4}$$

From Eq. (3–2), we find

$$\nabla_1^2 V_1(t+\tau) = \frac{1}{c^2}\frac{\partial^2 V_1(t+\tau)}{\partial(t+\tau)^2}$$

Since

$$\frac{\partial^2 V_1(t+\tau)}{\partial(t+\tau)^2} = \frac{\partial^2 V_1(t+\tau)}{\partial\tau^2}$$

$$\nabla_1^2\Gamma_{12}(\tau) = \left\langle \frac{\partial^2 V_1(t+\tau)}{c^2\partial\tau^2}\, V_2^*(t)\right\rangle \tag{3–5}$$

Since $V_2(t)$ is independent of τ,

$$\nabla_1^2\Gamma_{12}(\tau) = \frac{\partial^2}{c^2\,\partial\tau^2}\langle V_1(t+\tau)\, V_2^*(t)\rangle = \frac{\partial^2}{c^2\,\partial\tau^2}\Gamma_{12}(\tau) \tag{3–6}$$

A similar equation may be derived in terms of the laplacian taken with respect to point P_2. Taking the laplacian of Eq. (3–3) with respect to P_2 yields

$$\nabla_2^2\Gamma_{12}(\tau) = \langle V_1(t+\tau)\, \nabla_2^2 V_2^*(t)\rangle \tag{3–7}$$

Again using Eq. (3–2),

$$\nabla_2^2\Gamma_{12}(\tau) = \left\langle V_1(t+\tau)\, \frac{\partial^2 V_2^*(t)}{c^2\,\partial t^2}\right\rangle \tag{3–8}$$

The brackets $\langle\ \ \rangle$ represent the integral

$$\lim_{T\to\infty}\frac{1}{2T}\int_{-T}^{T}(\ \ )\,dt$$

The integral may be integrated twice by parts to yield

$$\nabla_2^2\Gamma_{12}(\tau) = \left\langle \frac{\partial^2 V_1(t+\tau)}{c^2\partial t^2}\, V_2^*(t)\right\rangle \tag{3–9}$$

since the integrated terms like

$$\lim_{T\to\infty} \frac{1}{T} \frac{\partial V_1(t+\tau)}{\partial t} \frac{\partial V_2^*(t)}{\partial t}\bigg|_{t=T} \to 0$$

the time derivatives being assumed finite.

Equation (3–9) yields finally,

$$\nabla_2^2 \Gamma_{12}(\tau) = \frac{\partial^2}{c^2\,\partial\tau^2}\,\Gamma_{12}(\tau) \tag{3–10}$$

by noting that

$$\frac{\partial^2 V_1(t+\tau)}{c^2\,\partial t^2} = \frac{\partial^2 V_1(t+\tau)}{c^2\,\partial\tau^2}$$

In summary then, the equations governing the propagation of $\Gamma_{12}(\tau)$ in free space are†

$$\nabla_s^2 \Gamma_{12}(\tau) = \frac{\partial^2}{c^2\,\partial\tau^2}\,\Gamma_{12}(\tau) \qquad (s = 1, 2) \tag{3–11}$$

$\Gamma_{12}(\tau)$ is a function of seven variables x_1, y_1, z_1, x_2, y_2, z_2, τ. Two wave equations are required, since each equation contains only four independent variables. The two equations may be combined into a single higher-order equation:

$$\nabla_1^2\,\nabla_2^2 \Gamma_{12}(\tau) = \frac{\partial^4}{c^4\,\partial\tau^4}\,\Gamma_{12}(\tau) \tag{3–12}$$

3.2 INTEGRAL SOLUTION FOR $\Gamma_{12}(\tau)$

As a boundary condition for Eq. (3–11), one usually specifies $\Gamma_{12}(\tau)$ for all pairs of points over some bounded surface S and imposes the radiation condition of Sommerfeld at infinity on the function $V(t)$. The radiation condition on $\Gamma_{12}(\tau)$ is obtained by applying the condition to $V_1(t+\tau)$ and $V_2^*(t)$ and appealing to the definition of $\Gamma_{12}(\tau)$. (This is discussed in more detail at the end of the section.) In Sections 3.2 and 3.3 we follow a development given by Parrent (1959b).

We now propose to solve Eq. (3–11) formally, subject to these conditions. The solution to Eq. (3–11) may be formally written in terms of two four-dimensional Green's functions. The authors think, however, that it is perhaps conceptually simpler first to Fourier decompose the mutual coherence in time and then write the solution in terms of three-dimensional Green's functions.

†This is, of course, not the only way these equations have been derived. In Chapter 11, when deriving the coherence tensors associated with full Maxwell equations, an alternate derivation will be used. Originally Wolf (1955) derived them using Fourier decomposition.

Let $\hat{\Gamma}_{12}(\nu)$ be the Fourier time transform of $\Gamma_{12}(\tau)$. Since $\Gamma_{12}(\tau)$ is an analytic signal (Chapter 2), it contains only positive frequencies; that is,

$$\Gamma_{12}(\tau) = \int_0^{\infty} \hat{\Gamma}_{12}(\nu)\, e^{-2\pi i\nu\tau}\, d\nu \tag{3–13}$$

$$\begin{aligned} \hat{\Gamma}_{12}(\nu) &= \int_{-\infty}^{\infty} \Gamma_{12}(\tau)\, e^{2\pi i\nu\tau}\, d\tau \qquad & \nu > 0 \\ &= 0 & \nu < 0 \end{aligned} \tag{3–14}$$

Substituting Eq. (3–13) into Eq. (3–11) and interchanging the order of integration and differentiation, we obtain

$$\int_0^{\infty} [\nabla_s^2 + k^2(\nu)]\, \hat{\Gamma}_{12}(\nu)\, e^{-2\pi i\nu\tau}\, d\nu = 0 \tag{3–15}$$

where
$$k(\nu) = \frac{2\pi\nu}{c}$$

Since Eq. (3–15) must hold for all τ, we have

$$[\nabla_s^2 + k^2(\nu)]\, \Gamma_{12}(\nu) = 0 \qquad (s = 1, 2) \tag{3–16}$$

Thus each spectral component of $\Gamma_{12}(\tau)$ satisfies the two scalar Helmholtz equations.

Equation (3–16) with $s = 1$ has the formal solution:†

$$\hat{\Gamma}(P_1, S_2, \nu) = -\int_s \hat{\Gamma}(S_1, S_2, \nu)\, \frac{\partial G_1(P_1, P_1', \nu)}{\partial n_{S_1}}\bigg|_{P_1'=S_1} dS_1 \tag{3–17}$$

Here G_1 is a Green's function satisfying the equation,

$$[\nabla_1^2 + k^2(\nu)]\, G(P_1, P_1', \nu) = -\delta(P_1 - P_1') \tag{3–18}$$

with boundary condition,

$$G(P_1, P_1', \nu)\Big|_{P_1'=S_1} = 0 \tag{3–19}$$

The function $\hat{\Gamma}(P_1, S_2, \nu)$ provides the boundary condition for solving Eq. (3–16) with $s = 2$. Thus,

$$\hat{\Gamma}(P_1, P_2, \nu) = -\int \hat{\Gamma}(P_1, S_2, \nu)\, \frac{\partial G_2(P_2, P_2', \nu)}{\partial n_{S_2}}\bigg|_{P_2'=S_2} dS_2 \tag{3–20}$$

where G_2 is a Green's function satisfying the same boundary conditions as G_1. Combining Eqs. (3–17) and (3–20) we have finally

$$\hat{\Gamma}(P_1, P_2, \nu) = \int_s \int_s \hat{\Gamma}(S_1, S_2, \nu)\, \frac{\partial G_2(P_2, P_2', \nu)}{\partial n_{S_2}}\bigg|_{P_2'=S_2} \frac{\partial G_1(P_1, P_1', \nu)}{\partial n_{S_1}}\bigg|_{P_1'=S_1} dS_1\, dS_2 \tag{3–21}$$

Thus $\hat{\Gamma}(P_1, P_2, \nu)$ is obtained formally in terms of $\hat{\Gamma}(S_1, S_2, \nu)$.

---

†We mention again that $\Gamma_{12}(\tau)$ and $\hat{\Gamma}_{12}(\nu)$ will be written as $\Gamma(P_1, P_2, \tau)$ and $\hat{\Gamma}(P_1, P_2, \nu)$ when necessary to stress the space dependence.

It is interesting to note that Eq. (3–17), which yields $\hat{\Gamma}(P_1, S_2, \nu)$ in terms of $\hat{\Gamma}(S_1, S_2, \nu)$, is itself often a useful result since it gives the coherence between a point on the surface and any point in space. It is particularly instructive if one wishes to determine the coherence between a point on the surface and a point on a line perpendicular to the surface. The properties of the coherence in this "longitudinal" direction are quite different from the coherence between points on the surface. A particular solution to illustrate this point will be given in Chapter 5 after the quasi-monochromatic approximation has been introduced.

Equation (3–21) with $P_1 = P_2$ is also a particularly useful form since it represents the power spectrum of the radiation at any point external to the surface. From this expression, we see that the power spectrum at any point in space is determined not in terms of the power spectrum over the surface but in terms of the function $\hat{\Gamma}(S_1, S_2, \nu)$ which is a mutual power spectrum, a function that depends on two points rather than one point. Similarly, $\Gamma(P_1, P_1, 0)$, twice the intensity at any point in space, depends on the two-point mutual coherence function $\Gamma(S_1, S_2, \tau)$ rather than simply the intensity $\Gamma(S_1, S_1, 0)$ across the surface.

The Sommerfeld radiation condition demands that $\hat{V}_1(\nu)$ and $\hat{V}_2^*(\nu)$ behave asymptotically as

$$f_1(\theta_1, \Phi_1, \nu)\frac{e^{ikr_1}}{r_1} \quad \text{and} \quad f_2(\theta_2, \Phi_2, \nu)\frac{e^{-ikr_2}}{r_2}$$

as $r_1, r_2 \to \infty$, where r_i is the distance from some point on the source surface. Since

$$\hat{\Gamma}(P_1, P_2, \nu) = \lim_{T\to\infty}\frac{1}{2T}\hat{V}_1(T, \nu)\,\hat{V}_2^*(T, \nu)\dagger$$

$$\hat{\Gamma}(P_1, P_2, \nu) \to f_{12}(\theta_1, \theta_2, \Phi_1, \Phi_2, \nu)\frac{e^{ik(r_1-r_2)}}{r_1 r_2}$$

as r_1 and $r_2 \to \infty$. This condition must be used in choosing the appropriate Green's functions.

In terms of $\Gamma(P_1, P_2, \tau)$, the solution is

$$\Gamma(P_1, P_2, \tau) = \int_0^\infty \int_S \int_S \hat{\Gamma}(S_1, S_2, \nu)\left.\frac{\partial G_1(P_1, P_1', \nu)}{\partial n_{S_1}}\right|_{P_1'=S_1}$$

$$\left.\frac{\partial G_2(P_2, P_2', \nu)}{\partial n_{S_2}}\right|_{P_2'=S_2} dS_1\; dS_2\, e^{-2\pi i\nu\tau}\, d\nu \qquad (3\text{–}22)$$

3.3 RADIATION FROM A PLANE FINITE SURFACE

Perhaps the simplest problem to solve is the propagation of the mutual

---

†See Section 2.3 for a note on the existence of this function.

coherence from plane finite surfaces, subject to the assumption that the radiation intensity drops rapidly to zero in the containing plane, for points outside S. For this condition to be realizable without specifically holding the intensity to zero in the plane outside of the source, we must assume that a characteristic source size d_c is much, much greater than λ_c, a characteristic radiation wavelength. If this is done, almost none of the radiation from the source will intersect the containing plane, and we have a realistic problem if we just specify $\Gamma(S_1, S_2, \tau)$ over a finite plane surface and assume it is zero elsewhere in the plane.

The Green's functions G_1 and G_2 which satisfy the radiation condition are, respectively,

$$G_1 = \frac{e^{ikr_1}}{4\pi r_1} - \frac{e^{ikr_1''}}{4\pi r_1''} \tag{3–23}$$

$$G_2 = \frac{e^{-ikr_2}}{4\pi r_2} - \frac{e^{-ikr_2''}}{4\pi r_2''} \tag{3–24}$$

where r_1 and r_2 are defined in Fig. 3–1. r_1'' and r_2'' are the distances to the mirror points of r_1 and r_2, respectively. That is,

$$r_1 = \sqrt{(z_1 - z_1')^2 + (x_1 - x_1')^2 + (y_1 - y_1')^2}$$

$$r_1'' = \sqrt{(z_1 + z_1')^2 + (x_1 - x_1')^2 + (y_1 - y_1')^2}$$

z_1' is considered positive.

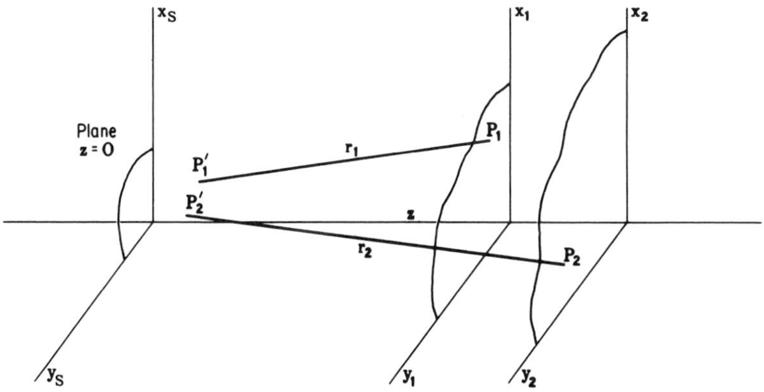

Figure 3-1. Geometry for describing radiation from a plane surface.

The normal derivative of G is

$$\frac{\partial G_1}{\partial n_{S_1}} = \frac{(ikr_1 - 1)}{4\pi}\frac{e^{ikr_1}}{r_1^2}\frac{\partial r_1}{\partial n_{S_1}} + \frac{(1 - ikr_1'')}{4\pi}\frac{e^{ikr_1''}}{r_1''^2}\frac{\partial r_1''}{\partial n_{S_1}} \tag{3–25}$$

and

(3–26)
$$\left.\frac{\partial r_1}{\partial n_{S_1}}\right|_{S_1} = -\left.\frac{\partial r_1}{\partial z_1'}\right|_{S_1} = \frac{z_1}{r_1} = \left.\frac{\partial r_1''}{\partial z_1'}\right|_{S_1}$$
$$\left.r_1\right|_{S_1} = \left.r_1''\right|_{S_1}$$

Thus, defining $\cos\theta_1 = z_1/r_1$, we find

(3–27)
$$\left.\frac{\partial G_1}{\partial n_{S_1}}\right|_{S_1} = -2\,\frac{(1 - ikr_1)}{4\pi}\cos\theta_1\,\frac{e^{+ikr_1}}{r_1^2}$$

Similarly,

(3–28)
$$\left.\frac{\partial G_2}{\partial n_{S_2}}\right|_{S_2} = -2\,\frac{(1 + ikr_2)}{4\pi}\cos\theta_2\,\frac{e^{-ikr_2}}{r_2^2}$$

Substituting into Eq. (3–29) yields, for each spectral component,

(3–29)
$$\hat{\Gamma}(P_1, P_2, \nu) = \frac{1}{4\pi^2}\int_s\int_s \hat{\Gamma}(S_1, S_2, \nu)(1 - ikr_1)(1 + ikr_2) \cos\theta_1\cos\theta_2\,\frac{e^{ik(r_1 - r_2)}}{r_1^2 r_2^2}\,dS_1\,dS_2$$

and taking the Fourier transform of Eq. (3–29), we find the general solution:

(3–30)
$$\Gamma(P_1, P_2, \tau) = \frac{1}{4\pi^2}\int_0^\infty\int_s\int_s \hat{\Gamma}(S_1, S_2, \nu)(1 - ikr_1)(1 + ikr_2) \cos\theta_1\cos\theta_2\,\frac{e^{ik(r_1 - r_2)}}{r_1^2 r_2^2}\,e^{-2\pi i\nu\tau}\,dS_1\,dS_2\,d\nu$$

Inverting the order of integration, this may be written

(3–31)
$$\Gamma(P_1, P_2, \tau) = \frac{1}{4\pi^2}\int_s\int_s \cos\theta_1\cos\theta_2\,\Omega_{12}(\tau)\,dS_1\,dS_2$$

where

$$\Omega_{12}(\tau) = \frac{1}{r_1^2 r_2^2}\int_0^\infty \hat{\Gamma}(S_1, S_2, \nu)\,e^{-2\pi i\nu[\tau - (r_1 - r_2)/c]}\,d\nu + \frac{(r_2 - r_1)}{r_1^2 r_2^2 c}\int_0^\infty 2\pi i\nu\hat{\Gamma}(S_1, S_2, \nu)\,e^{-2\pi i\nu[\tau - (r_1 - r_2)/c]}\,d\nu + \frac{r_1 r_2}{r_1^2 r_2^2 c^2}\int_0^\infty 4\pi^2\nu^2\hat{\Gamma}(S_1, S_2, \nu)\,e^{-2\pi i\nu[\tau - (r_1 - r_2)/c]}\,d\nu$$

Noting that if

(3–32)
$$f(t) = \int_0^\infty g(\nu)\,e^{-2\pi i\nu t}\,d\nu$$

then

(3–33)
$$\frac{d^n f(t)}{dt^n} = \int_0^\infty (-2\pi i\nu)^n g(\nu)\,e^{-2\pi i\nu t}\,d\nu$$

we find

$$\Omega_{12}(\tau) = \left(\frac{1}{r_1^2 r_2^2} + \frac{(r_1 - r_2)}{r_1^2 r_2^2} \frac{\partial}{c\,\partial\tau} - \frac{r_1 r_2}{r_1^2 r_2^2 c^2} \frac{\partial^2}{\partial\tau^2}\right) \cdot \left(\Gamma\left(S_1, S_2, \tau - \frac{(r_1 - r_2)}{c}\right)\right) \tag{3-34}$$

Thus, in simplified notation, Eq. (3–30) becomes

$$\Gamma(P_1, P_2, \tau) = \frac{1}{4\pi^2} \int_s \int_s \cos\theta_1 \cos\theta_2\, F\left[\Gamma\left(S_1, S_2, \tau - \frac{(r_1 - r_2)}{c}\right)\right] dS_1, dS_2 \tag{3-35}$$

where F is the differential operator

$$F = \frac{1}{r_1^2 r_2^2} + \frac{(r_1 - r_2)}{r_1^2 r_2^2} \frac{1}{c} \frac{\partial}{\partial\tau} - \frac{r_1 r_2}{r_1^2 r_2^2 c^2} \frac{\partial^2}{\partial\tau^2}$$

Equation (3–35) is the general solution for the mutual coherence in a field produced by a plane polychromatic partially coherent source. It is a generalization of the van Cittert-Zernike theorem for polychromatic partially coherent sources. It expresses the mutual coherence function, under the conditions stated, in terms of the mutual coherence across the source.

A simplified version of this theorem is used to determine the angular diameter of stars. The expression assumes a particularly simple form if the quasi-monochromatic approximation is applicable, and we shall, for this condition, explicitly integrate Eq. (3–35) in Chapter 5 for the case of a slit and circular aperture.

3.4 FREE SPACE PROPAGATORS

[Details of Measurement of $\Gamma_{12}(\tau)$, Sec. 2.6]

The formal solution for $\hat{V}_Q(T, \nu)$ from a plane finite surface is, in analogy to the foregoing calculations,

$$\hat{V}_Q(T, \nu) = \frac{1}{2\pi} \int \hat{V}_A(T, \nu)(1 - ikr) \cos\theta_1 \frac{e^{ikr}}{r^2}\, dA \tag{3-36}$$

If the holes P_1 and P_2 are small, $\hat{V}_A(T, \nu)$ is sensibly constant over both P_1 and P_2 and we assume that $(1 - ikr) \cos\theta_1 (e^{ikr}/r^2)$ need be evaluated only at P_1 and P_2 respectively. Thus

$$\hat{V}_Q(T, \nu) = \frac{1}{2\pi} \hat{V}_{P_1}(T, \nu)(1 - ikr_1) \cos\theta_1 \frac{e^{ikr_1}}{r_1^2} A + \frac{1}{2\pi} \hat{V}_{P_2}(T, \nu)(1 - ikr_2) \cos\theta_2 \frac{e^{ikr_2}}{r_2^2} A \tag{3-37}$$

where A is the hole area of P_1 or P_2. For simplicity, we take both hole areas equal but, of course, $\hat{V}_{P_1}(T, \nu)$ is not in general equal to $\hat{V}_{P_2}(T, \nu)$.

For $kr_1 \gg 1$, the case we are interested in, we may write

(3–38) $$\hat{V}_Q(T, \nu) = k_1(Q, \nu)\, \hat{V}_{P_1}(T, \nu) + k_2(Q, \nu)\, \hat{V}_{P_2}(T, \nu)$$

where $k_1(Q, \nu)$ and $k_2(Q, \nu)$ are the propagators defined as

(3–39) $$k_1(Q, \nu) \equiv -\frac{ik}{2\pi r_1} \cos\theta_1\, Ae^{ikr_1}$$
$$k_2(Q, \nu) \equiv -\frac{ik}{2\pi r_2} \cos\theta_2\, Ae^{ikr_2}$$

chapter

4

Limiting Forms of $\Gamma_{12}(\tau)$

In this chapter, we consider the incoherent and coherent limits of radiation fields in terms of the complex degree of coherence $\gamma_{12}(\tau)$. We pointed out in Chapter 2 that $0 \leq |\gamma_{12}(\tau)| \leq 1$ and termed $|\gamma_{12}(\tau)| = 1$ the coherent limit and $|\gamma_{12}(\tau)| = 0$ the incoherent limit.

These definitions apply to two *specific* points P_1 and P_2 and a *specific* time delay τ. Thus in a radiation field, $|\gamma_{12}(\tau)|$ may equal zero whereas $|\gamma_{1'2'}(\tau)|$ may equal to .5. We should, however, like to generalize the definitions of coherence and incoherence between two *specific* points and define coherent and incoherent fields and sources where P_1 and P_2 may be *any* points in the field or source and τ, *any* time delay.

A natural generalization of the coherence or incoherence of two points would be to call a field or source coherent or incoherent respectively if $|\gamma_{12}(\tau)| = 1$ or $|\gamma_{12}(\tau)| = 0$ for *all* pairs of points in the field or source and *all* time delays. These definitions, however, are unfortunately too restrictive.

We wish in this chapter to prove three theorems about fields and sources for which $|\gamma_{12}(\tau)|$ equals either 0 or 1 for *all* pairs of points P_1 and P_2 and *all* time delays τ. Two of these theorems will demonstrate the difficulties of considering such mathematically defined fields in physical situations. To circumvent the difficulties introduced by these definitions and in an attempt to preserve the concepts of coherence and incoherence when applied to whole fields and sources we shall then introduce the concept of quasi-monochromatic fields (a less restrictive type of coherent field) and discuss the proper form of $\Gamma_{12}(\tau)$ over an incoherent source surface.

To review, we begin the chapter by briefly discussing again the motivation for calling $|\gamma_{12}(\tau)| = 1$ the coherent limit of two specific points, and $|\gamma_{12}(\tau)| = 0$ the incoherent limit of two specific points.†

4.1 MOTIVATION FOR THE DEFINITIONS OF COHERENCE AND INCOHERENCE

The motivation for calling the limiting values of $|\gamma_{12}(\tau)|$ coherent and incoherent may be seen from a consideration of Young's interference experiment. Before any rigorous definitions, when one observed high visibility fringes on the screen, the radiation from the two holes was termed *coherent* and when there were no fringes on the screen, *incoherent*. The term *coherence* essentially denoted a cooperative effect between the two radiators. Hence, when a carefully defined function, such as $\gamma_{12}(\tau)$, was given, it was useful to interpret it in terms of the visibility of the fringes.

When the radiation from a single pinhole (say only P_1) (see Fig. 1–1) is observed over the central portion of the screen, the intensity is effectively a constant and there are no fringes. To be sure, as a result of the $1/R^2$ decay and the finite diameter of the hole, the intensity is not actually a constant, but for very small pinholes it is a good approximation, and in fact, a necessary one if the visibility of the fringes, as given by Eq. (1–8), is to have any real meaning. When the second pinhole is also opened, fringes may or may not appear, depending upon the degree of constructive interference between the radiation from the two holes. If the fringes are very sharp, the screen intensity going to zero in places, the radiations from P_1 and P_2 are called *coherent*. If no fringes appear, the screen intensity remaining constant, the radiations from P_1 and P_2 are called *incoherent*.

Referring to Eq. (1–19), we see the visibility $\mathcal{V}$ is given by

†For a definition of coherence in terms of ensemble averages and higher order moments, we refer the reader to Glauber (1963a).

(4–1) $$\mathcal{V} = |\gamma_{12}(\tau)|$$

for fields of narrow but finite spectral width, where $(\Delta\nu)\tau \ll 1$.

We recall that the visibility is defined by

(4–2) $$\mathcal{V} = \frac{I_{\max} - I_{\min}}{I_{\max} + I_{\min}}$$

Hence when $I_{\max} = I_{\min}$

$$\mathcal{V} = 0 \quad \text{and} \quad |\gamma_{12}(\tau)| = 0$$

This is the incoherent limit.

When $I_{\min} = 0$ (very sharp fringes),

$$\mathcal{V} = 1 \quad \text{and} \quad |\gamma_{12}(\tau)| = 1$$

This is the coherent limit.

The condition of narrow, but finite spectral width is necessary for the relation given in Eq. (4–1). No such simple relation can be given when the spectral width is finite. However, we carry over the definitions to finite spectral fields on the basis of this physical picture.

4.2 PROOF OF THREE THEOREMS

In this section, we prove the following three theorems:

I *An optical field has the property* $|\gamma_{12}(\tau)| = 1$ *for all pairs of points and time delays* τ *if and only if it is monochromatic. By monochromatic we mean that the complex disturbance* $V(t)$ *is of the form* $V(t) = Ae^{-(2\pi i\nu_0 t + \beta i)}$ *where* A *and* β *are functions only of position.*

II *A non-null field for which* $|\gamma_{12}(\tau)| = 0$ *for all pairs of points and time delays* τ *cannot exist in free space.*

Corollary: If $|\gamma_{12}(\tau)| = 0$ *for all pairs of points on some continuous closed surface, then the surface does not radiate.*

III *Spectral filtering of two source points whose mutual coherence is zero will not change the mutual coherence of the two points.*

In proving Theorems I and II we follow a development given by G. Parrent (1959c).

Proof of theorem I

We now prove that an optical field has the property $|\gamma_{12}(\tau)| = 1$ for all pairs of points and delay times τ, if and only if it is monochromatic.

That a monochromatic field is coherent is simple to show since, in this case, $V_j(t) = A_j e^{-(2\pi i\nu_0 t + \beta_j i)}$ where A_j and β_j are independent of t. Direct calculation of $|\gamma_{12}(\tau)|$ then yields the value 1.

Proof of the converse, however, is somewhat more difficult. Before formally proving it rigorously, we shall again return to Young's interference experiment to indicate the plausibility of the fact that only when the field is monochromatic will $|\gamma_{12}(\tau)| = 1$.

Referring to Fig. 1–1, let us suppose the source $\sum$ is on the axis approaching infinity and that it emits two discrete frequencies ν_1 and ν_2 such that

$$\left|\frac{\nu_1 - \nu_2}{\nu_1}\right| \ll 1.$$

Then two plane waves of frequencies ν_1 and ν_2 will impinge on A. Each wave alone will yield through interference of P_1 and P_2 a cosine pattern on the central portion of the screen, the maximum value of each pattern occurring on the axis. Since $\nu_1 \neq \nu_2$, the power patterns† on the screen rather than the amplitude patterns will add linearly.

Now the distance between peaks of intensity on the screen will be slightly different for the ν_1 wave and the ν_2 wave. Thus, whereas on the axis, the maximums of the two patterns will add, some distance away, the minimums of one pattern will add with the maximums of the other. This reduces the value of the visibility, and by the argument given in the preceding section, it reduces the value of $|\gamma_{12}(\tau)|$. Adding further frequencies to the initial source only worsens the situation; the visibility will remain 1 for all τ only when a single frequency is present in the illuminating source.

A more mathematical way of saying the same thing is actually to compute $\gamma_{12}(\tau)$ for two sources both emitting two discrete frequencies, ν_1 and ν_2. If source 1 emits a radiation of the form,

$$V_1(t) = A_{11}e^{-(2\pi i\nu_1 t + \Phi_{11}i)} + A_{12}e^{-(2\pi i\nu_2 t + \Phi_{12}i)}$$

and source 2 emits radiation of the form,

$$V_2(t) = A_{21}e^{-(2\pi i\nu_1 t + \Phi_{21}i)} + A_{22}e^{-(2\pi i\nu_2 t + \Phi_{22}i)}$$

then

$$|\gamma_{12}(\tau)| = \frac{|\langle V_1(t+\tau)V_2^*(t)\rangle|}{\sqrt{\langle V_1(t)V_1^*(t)\rangle\langle V_2(t)V_2^*(t)\rangle}}$$

$$= \frac{|A_{11}A_{21}e^{-2\pi i\nu_1\tau-(\Phi_{11}-\Phi_{21})i} + A_{12}A_{22}e^{-2\pi i\nu_2\tau-(\Phi_{12}-\Phi_{22})i}|}{\sqrt{(A_{11}^2 + A_{12}^2)(A_{21}^2 + A_{22}^2)}} \tag{4–3}$$

and

$$|\gamma_{12}(\tau)| = \frac{\sqrt{A_{11}^2A_{21}^2 + A_{12}^2A_{22}^2 + 2A_{11}A_{21}A_{12}A_{22}\cdot \cos[(2\pi\tau(\nu_1-\nu_2) + (\Phi_{11}-\Phi_{21}) - (\Phi_{12}-\Phi_{22})]}}{\sqrt{(A_{11}^2 + A_{12}^2)(A_{21}^2 + A_{22}^2)}} \tag{4–4}$$

If the cosine term is equal to 1, one can readily show that $|\gamma_{12}(\tau)| \leq 1$ since $(A_{11}A_{21} + A_{12}A_{22})^2 \leq (A_{11}^2 + A_{12}^2)(A_{21}^2 + A_{22}^2)$. For some τ, however,

†We remember that the power pattern is a time-averaged quantity.

the cosine is < 1 and thus $|\gamma_{12}(\tau)| < 1$ for some τ. We note that, if $\nu_1 = \nu_2$, A_{12} and A_{22} may be set equal to zero, and the ratio equals 1 for all τ.

One can show similarily that, if the field at each of two points, $i = 1, 2$, can be represented by a Fourier series in time of the form,

$$V_i^T(t) = \sum_{m=0}^{\infty} A_{im} \cos(2\pi m\nu t + \Phi_{im}) \tag{4-5}$$

then $|\gamma_{12}(\tau)| < 1$ for some τ.

If we were not dealing in general with the idealization of stationary random time series, the proof that $V_i^T(t)$ must equal $A_{im} \cos(2\pi m\nu t + \Phi_{im})$, if one starts with the assumption that

$$V_i^T(t) = \sum_{m} A_{im} \cos(2\pi m\nu t + \Phi_{im})$$

would be adequate to prove that the field is monochromatic if $|\gamma_{12}(\tau)| = 1$. The Fourier series representation, however, implies that the time series is periodic and thus a Fourier integral representation is needed in general.

This brings up the problem of the lack of convergence of the Fourier integrals of the function $V_i^T(t)$ since only its correlation function or power spectrum exists. To circumvent this difficulty, we shall directly show instead that if $|\gamma_{12}(\tau)| = 1$ for all τ, then

$$\Gamma_{11}(\tau) = A_1^2 e^{-i(\beta_1 + 2\pi\nu_0\tau)}$$

A_1, ν_0, and β_1 being functions only of position. Then we shall conclude that

$$V_1(t) = A_1 e^{-[2\pi i\nu_0 t + \beta_1 i]}$$

where A_1 and β_1 are only functions of position, and ν_0 is a constant independent of position.

The proofs rely on two rather complicated mathematical theorems which we will now state. The proofs may be found in Edwards and Parrent (1960).

(A) If $e^{i\Phi_{12}(\tau)}$ is a unimodular analytic signal, then it has the form

$$e^{i\Phi_{12}(\tau)} = e^{-i(\beta + 2\pi\nu_0\tau)} \prod_{n=1}^{\infty} \frac{a_n^*}{a_n} \left[\frac{a_n - \tau}{a_n^* - \tau}\right] \tag{4-6}$$

where a_n are complex numbers whose imaginary part is >0 and β and ν_0 are real constants independent of τ.

(B) If $\mathrm{Re}\,[e^{i\Phi_{11}(\tau)}] = \mathrm{Re}\,[e^{i(\Phi_{11}(-\tau))}]$ *(implying that*

$$\int_{-\infty}^{\infty} \cos\Phi_{11}(\tau) \sin 2\pi\nu_0\tau \, d\tau = 0$$

as it must for a stationary field), then $e^{i\Phi_{11}(\tau)}$ has the form $e^{-i(\beta + 2\pi\nu_0\tau)}$.

Since $|\gamma_{12}(\tau)| = 1$, then $\Gamma_{12}(\tau)$ must have the form

$$\Gamma_{12}(\tau) = \sqrt{\Gamma_{11}(0)}\sqrt{\Gamma_{22}(0)}\, e^{i\Phi_{12}(\tau)} \tag{4-7}$$

where, since $\Gamma_{12}(\tau)$ is an analytic singal, $\Phi_{12}(\tau)$ is an analytic signal. Further, of course, $e^{i\Phi_{12}(\tau)}$ is an unimodular analytic signal. Then, by Theorems A and B, $\Gamma_{11}(\tau)$ has the form

$$\Gamma_{11}(\tau) = A_1^2 e^{-i(\beta+2\pi\nu_0\tau)} \tag{4–8}$$

where $A_1 = \sqrt{\Gamma_{11}(0)}$, β and ν_0 may be functions of position, but not τ.

Since $\Gamma_{11}(\tau)$ is an autocorrelation function of a stationary process, then $\mathrm{Re}[\Gamma_{11}(0)] \geq \mathrm{Re}[\Gamma_{11}(\tau)]$ and hence $\beta = 0$. That is,

$$\Gamma_{11}(\tau) = A_1^2 e^{-2\pi i\nu_0\tau} \tag{4–9}$$

Though in general the correlation function cannot be inverted to give information about the complex disturbance $V_1(t)$, it can be in this degenerate case. To see this, consider a function $V_1(t)$ of the form

$$V_1 = A_1 e^{-[2\pi i\nu_0 t+\beta_1 i]} + f(t) \tag{4–10}$$

where A_1 and β_1 are functions only of position, and $f(t)$ is a function whose power spectrum exists but has a zero value at $\nu = \nu_0$. Then,

$$\Gamma_{11}(\tau) = \langle [A_1 e^{2\pi i\nu_0 t+\beta_1 i} + f^*(t)][A_1 e^{-2\pi i\nu_0(t+\tau)-\beta_1 i} + f(t+\tau)]\rangle \tag{4–11}$$

yielding,

$$\Gamma_{11}(\tau) = A_1^2 e^{-2\pi i\nu_0\tau} + \langle f^*(t) f(t+\tau)\rangle \tag{4–12}$$

since $\langle e^{+2\pi i\nu_0 t} f(t+\tau)\rangle$ and $\langle e^{-2\pi i\nu_0 t} f^*(t)\rangle$ equal zero by virtue of not having overlapping frequency components. Comparing Eqs. (4–9) and (4–12), when $\tau = 0$ shows that $f(t)$ must equal zero.

The last thing we must prove is that ν_0 is independent of position. This follows directly from the form in Eq. (4–10) with $f(t) = 0$. For if $\nu_{01} \neq \nu_{02}$

$$\Gamma_{12}(0) = \langle A_1 A_2 e^{-i(\beta_1-\beta_2)} e^{-2\pi i t(\nu_{01}-\nu_{02})}\rangle = 0 \tag{4–13}$$

in contradiction to the assertion that $|\gamma_{12}(\tau)| = 1$.

In summary, we have proved that $|\gamma_{12}(\tau)| = 1$ if and only if

$$V_1(t) = A_1 e^{-i(2\pi\nu_0 t+\beta_1)}$$

We note here that, in this case, $\Gamma_{12}(\tau)$ has the form

$$\Gamma_{12}(\tau) = U(P_1)U^*(P_2)e^{-2\pi i\nu_0\tau} \tag{4–14}$$

i.e., a simple periodic factor $e^{-2\pi i\nu_0\tau}$ multiplying the product of a wave function U evaluated at P_1 with its complex conjugate evaluated at P_2. We shall later indicate that the same form may be obtained when the field has the property $|\gamma_{12}(\tau)| = 1$, only for small τ.

Proof of theorem II

We wish to show now that $|\gamma_{12}(\tau)|$ cannot $= 0$ for all τ and all pairs of points in a non-null radiation field.

Let $\bar{V}$ be a finite volume of space throughout which the field is assumed to be incoherent. Let S be any closed surface centered in $\bar{V}$. By repeated application of Green's theorem (see Chapter 3), one obtains the formal solution for $\hat{\Gamma}(P_1, P_2, \nu)$, [$P_1, P_2$ are exterior to S] in terms of $\hat{\Gamma}(S_1, S_2, \nu)$, where S_1 and S_2 are points on S. It is

$$\hat{\Gamma}(P_1, P_2, \nu) = \int_S \int_S \hat{\Gamma}(S_1, S_2, \nu) \left.\frac{\partial G_1(P_1, P_1', \nu)}{\partial n_{S_1}}\right|_{P_1' = S_1} \left.\frac{\partial G_2(P_2, P_2', \nu)}{\partial n_{S_2}}\right|_{P_2' = S_2} dS_1\, dS_2 \tag{4–15}$$

where G_1 and G_2 are Green's functions satisfying the equation $[\nabla_j^2 + k^2]G = -\delta(P_j - P_j')$ and vanishing over S.

Since, in Eq. (4–15) we require S_1 and S_2 to explore the surface S independently, the integral is four-dimensional. By assumption, however, the integral is only two-dimensional since it is non-zero only when the two points S_1 and S_2 coincide.

$$\{|\gamma_{12}(\tau)| = 0 \Rightarrow \hat{\Gamma}(S_1, S_2, \nu) = 0\}$$

Therefore, if $\Gamma(S_1, S_2, \nu)$ is assumed to be everywhere finite, the integral is identically zero, that is,

$$\hat{\Gamma}(P_1, P_2, \nu) = 0 \tag{4–16}$$

for all P_1 and P_2 (including $P_1 = P_2$).

If the field is non-null, $\hat{\Gamma}(P_1, P_1, \nu)$, which represents the power spectrum of the field at P_1, cannot be zero for all ν; hence we find that it is contradictory to assume that an incoherent field can exist in free space.

As a corollary, we note that the foregoing reasoning shows that if $|\gamma_{12}(\tau)| = 0$ for all pairs of points on a continuous surface, the surface does not radiate.

The proof that an incoherent field cannot exist in all space is not too surprising, from even a cursory inspection, since any two points in a radiation field are fed by many of the same points, and we should expect coherence to develop in the field. What is more interesting, however, and perhaps more subtle, is the fact that there can be no incoherent continuous radiating surface.

Another way of seeing this latter fact is to consider a flat infinite plane embedded in free space with a tangential **E** field impressed upon it. Suppose the time and spatial Fourier analysis of **E** over the surface yields a function of the form $\tilde{\tilde{\mathbf{E}}}_\nu(\lambda_x, \lambda_y)$ and assume the radiation is quasi-monochromatic about $\bar{\nu}$. One can then show that when λ_x and λ_y are less than $\bar{\lambda} = c/\bar{\nu}$, $\tilde{\tilde{\mathbf{E}}}_\nu(\lambda_x, \lambda_y)$ will not contribute to the radiated field. (These are the evanescent waves. This type of analysis will be discussed further under "Radiation from an infinite plane surface.") Now, if $|\gamma_{12}(\tau)| = 0$ over the plane, the field must vary infinitely fast in spatial frequency and in the limit all the energy will be in spatial frequencies less than $\bar{\lambda} = c/\bar{\nu}$. Thus the surface cannot radiate.

Proof of theorem III

The last theorem to be proved states that frequency filtering of two points whose mutual coherence equals 0 ($\Gamma_{12}(\tau) = 0$) will not change the value of $\Gamma_{12}(\tau)$; that is, it will remain zero, and the points remain incoherent.

To show this, consider the Fourier transform of $\Gamma_{12}(\tau)$, $\hat{\Gamma}_{12}(\nu)$. The condition $\Gamma_{12}(\tau) = 0$ yields then

$$\int_0^\infty \hat{\Gamma}_{12}(\nu)\, e^{-2\pi i\nu\tau}\, d\nu = 0 \quad \text{(for all } \tau) \tag{4–17}$$

This implies that $\hat{\Gamma}_{12}(\nu) = 0$ for all ν.

By definition,

$$\hat{\Gamma}_{12}(\nu) = \lim_{T\to\infty} \frac{1}{2T} \hat{V}(P_1, T, \nu)\, \hat{V}^*(P_2, T, \nu).$$

Frequency filtering of $V(P, T, t)$ will yield

$$\begin{aligned} \hat{\Gamma}'_{12}(\nu) &= \lim_{T\to\infty} \frac{1}{2T} F_1(\nu)\, \hat{V}(P_1, T, \nu) F_2^*(\nu)\, \hat{V}^*(P_2, T, \nu) \\ &= F_1(\nu) F_2^*(\nu) \hat{\Gamma}_{12}(\nu) \end{aligned} \tag{4–18}$$

where $F_1(\nu)$ and $F_2(\nu)$ are the filtering functions. Since in Eq. (4–18), $\hat{\Gamma}_{12}(\nu) = 0$ implies $\hat{\Gamma}'_{12}(\nu) = 0$, $\Gamma'_{12}(\tau) = 0$ and this proves the theorem.

As noted in Section 2.3, one must be careful in using the foregoing definition for calculating $\hat{\Gamma}_{12}(\nu)$. To avoid difficulty, we may assume here that $F_i(\nu)$ varies slowly over frequency intervals of the order of $1/T$ in any real problem.

This theorem provides some justification for the filtering of radiation when interferometric techniques are used to measure incoherent source diameters. Since, however, we have proved in the previous section that continuous sources cannot have $\gamma_{12}(\tau) = 0$ over the surface for all pairs of points and time delays τ if the source radiates, we expect the mutual coherence across the source will change somewhat upon filtering. To demonstrate rigorously that the source remains incoherent in some sense upon filtering requires a knowledge of the true mutual coherence function and a knowledge of the characteristics of the filter.

4.3 QUASI-MONOCHROMATIC RADIATION

We have seen under "Proof of Theorem I" that the condition $|\gamma_{12}(\tau)| = 1$ for all pairs of points and all time delays τ implies that the field is strictly monochromatic. Now, no such fields exist in nature since all fields have some spectral spread. Fields do exist, however, such that $\Delta\nu$, the spectral spread of the radiation, is small compared to $\bar{\nu}$, the mean frequency of the radiation. Such fields are termed *quasi-monochromatic fields* and much of the theory of partial coherence is concerned with them. For the theory of such fields to be physically meaningful, the path differences between interfering components must be kept small.†

It turns out, however, that although quasi-monochromatic fields were introduced to give a more realistic interpretation of monochromaticity, such fields actually have some properties that are quite different from strictly monochromatic radiation. In particular, $|\gamma_{12}(\tau)|$ need not equal 1 in such fields and may in fact equal zero between some points. To study these fields further, let us give a more precise definition of quasi-monochromatic radiation. We define it as follows:

Quasi-monochromatic radiation has the property that the mutual power spectrum of the radiation, $\hat{\Gamma}_{12}(\nu)$, is appreciably different from zero only for the spectral components ν which satisfy the inequality $|\nu - \bar{\nu}| < \Delta\nu$, where $\Delta\nu$ is the spectral width satisfying the condition that $\Delta\nu/\bar{\nu} \ll 1$.

The mutual coherence function $\Gamma_{12}(\tau)$ is obtained from the relation

$$\Gamma_{12}(\tau) = \int_0^\infty \hat{\Gamma}_{12}(\nu) e^{-2\pi i\nu\tau}\, d\nu \tag{4–19}$$

This may be written as

$$\Gamma_{12}(\tau) = e^{-2\pi i\bar{\nu}\tau} \int_0^\infty \hat{\Gamma}_{12}(\nu) e^{-2\pi i(\nu-\bar{\nu})\tau}\, d\nu \tag{4–20}$$

If we now limit our attention to small τ such that the inequality $\Delta\nu|\tau| \ll 1$ holds, then the exponential factor is approximately 1 and we find

$$\Gamma_{12}(\tau) = e^{-2\pi i\bar{\nu}\tau} \int_0^\infty \hat{\Gamma}_{12}(\nu)\, d\nu \tag{4–21}$$

Upon integration, we have

$$\Gamma_{12}(\tau) = e^{-2\pi i\bar{\nu}\tau} \Gamma_{12}(0) \tag{4–22}$$

The choice of $\tau = 0$ is, of course, arbitrary and we may find an expression for $\Gamma_{12}(\tau)$ about some other point τ_0 if we choose to do so. We then find

$$\Gamma_{12}(\tau_0 + \tau') = e^{-2\pi i\bar{\nu}\tau'} \Gamma_{12}(\tau_0) \tag{4–23}$$

where $\tau = \tau_0 + \tau'$ and $\Delta\nu|\tau'| \ll 1$.

---

†See "Propagation of Quasi-Monochromatic Fields" for a more precise statement of this restriction.

Coherent quasi-monochromatic fields

The condition $\Delta\nu|\tau'| \ll 1$ is the key condition in utilizing the concept of a quasi-monochromatic field in the theory of partial coherence. By limiting the value of $|\tau|$ we choose to use in any particular problem, it now becomes physically meaningful to speak of coherent fields in a restricted sense. We now call a field *coherent* if for all pairs of points of interest there exists a $\tau_0(P_1, P_2)$ such that $|\gamma_{12}(\tau)| = 1$ if $|\tau'|\Delta\nu \ll 1$. If $\Delta\nu/\bar{\nu}$ is very small, the fields may act like a monochromatic field for all times of interest in any physical problem.

As in the case of a true mathematical monochromatic field, we may show that $\Gamma_{12}(\tau_0)$ is of the form,

$$\Gamma_{12}(\tau_0) = A_1 A_2 e^{i\Phi_{12}} \tag{4–24}$$

and analysis similar to that performed in Section 4.3 shows that, for

$$|\tau'|\Delta\nu \ll 1$$

$\Gamma_{12}(\tau)$ must be of the form,

$$\Gamma_{12}(\tau) = U(P_1)U^*(P_2)e^{-2\pi i\bar{\nu}\tau'} \tag{4–25}$$

where $U(P_1)$ is a wave function evaluated at P_1 and $U^*(P_2)$ is the complex conjugate of a wave function evaluated at P_2.

The physical significance of this theorem should not be overlooked. In light of coherence theory, it is this type of theorem which justifies the elementary treatment of optical phenomena. To clarify this point, consider that, in terms of coherence theory, the correct description of diffraction and interference phenomena as well as the correct description of an imaging system should involve the solution of two wave equations, i.e., those for $\Gamma_{12}(\tau)$. On the other hand, a great many experiments are adequately described by solving a single scalar wave equation and taking the squared modulus of the result as the intensity. The theorem expressed in Eq. (4–25) justifies this procedure, and the development of this theorem points out the conditions under which the treatment is valid. Thus, it is not sufficient for the radiation to have a narrow spectral width. (In fact in the next section, noncoherent quasi-monochromatic fields will be discussed.) In addition, it is necessary for the field to be coherent in a quasi-monochromatic sense. Only when both these conditions are satisfied do the two coupled wave equations separate into single uncoupled equations and only under these conditions is the calculation of the intensity as the squared modulus of a simple wave function justified. Furthermore, since Huygens' principle is simply an approximation to the solution of such a wave equation, this theorem, Eq. (4–25), is, from the point of view of coherence theory, the justification of Huygens' principle in the cases where it may in fact be applied.

Quasi-monochromatic fields that are not coherent

When the concept of a quasi-monochromatic field is introduced, the condition $(\Delta\nu/\bar{\nu}) \ll 1$ does not demand that $|\gamma_{12}(\tau)| = 1$ for $\Delta\nu\,|\tau'| \ll 1$. $|\gamma_{12}(\tau)|$ may have any value between 0 and 1. *A field with narrow spectral width is not necessarily coherent even over a limited range of* τ'. This has been a source of confusion in the literature and should be clearly understood. Skinner (1961 b) gives an example of a two-point source that is incoherent (between the two points) for arbitrarily narrow spectral width.

The field acts coherently if all points exhibit their spectral spread in an orderly manner. That is, viewing a quasi-monochromatic field as a field of the form,

$$V(t) = A(t)e^{-(2\pi i\bar{\nu}t + \beta(t)i)} \tag{4–26}$$

where $A(t)$ and $\beta(t)$ are very slowly varying functions of time (compared to $1/\nu$), we require that the time variation of $A(t)$ and $\beta(t)$ vary in a like manner for all points. The condition $\Delta\nu/\bar{\nu} \ll 1$ alone, however, in no way demands this, and thus $|\gamma_{12}(\tau)|$ may take any value between 0 and 1 for a quasi-monochromatic field. In particular, it may take the value 0 for a particular choice of two points. This possiblity is open since the time average taken in forming $|\gamma_{12}(\tau)|$ extends over $-\infty$ to ∞, or times long compared to $1/\Delta\nu$.

Propagation of quasi-monochromatic fields

The general solution for $\Gamma(P_1, P_2, \tau)$ in terms of $\Gamma(S_1, S_2, \tau)$ over some surface S is

$$\Gamma(P_1, P_2, \tau) = \int_0^\infty e^{-2\pi i\nu\tau}\,d\nu \int_S \int_S \hat{\Gamma}(S_1, S_2, \nu) \left.\frac{\partial G_1(P_1, P_1', \nu)}{\partial n_{S_1}}\right|_{P_1'=S_1} \left.\frac{\partial G_2(P_2, P_2', \nu)}{\partial n_{S_2}}\right|_{P_2'=S_2} dS_1\, dS_2 \tag{4–27}$$

We wish to make use of the fact that the spectral content of the field is very narrow. Proceeding as above, we write this as (choosing $\tau_0 = 0$ for convenience)

$$\Gamma(P_1, P_2, \tau) = e^{-2\pi i\bar{\nu}\tau} \int_0^\infty d\nu \int_S \int_S \hat{\Gamma}(S_1, S_2, \nu) \left.\frac{\partial G_1(P_1, P_1', \nu)}{\partial n_{S_1}}\right|_{P_1'=S_1} \left.\frac{\partial G_2(P_2, P_2', \nu)}{\partial n_{S_2}}\right|_{P_2'=S_2} dS_1\, dS_2 \tag{4–28}$$

where τ is the time difference and $|\tau|\,\Delta\nu \ll 1$. This has the form,

$$\Gamma(P_1, P_2, \tau) = e^{-2\pi i\bar{\nu}\tau}\Gamma(P_1, P_2, 0) \tag{4-29}$$

where

$$\Gamma(P_1 P_2, 0) = \int_0^\infty d\nu \int_S \int_S \hat{\Gamma}(S_1, S_2, \nu) \left.\frac{\partial G_1(P_1, P_1', \nu)}{\partial n_{S_1}}\right|_{P_1'=S_1} \left.\frac{\partial G_2(P_2, P_2', \nu)}{\partial n_{S_2}}\right|_{P_2'=S_1} dS_1\, dS_2$$

It is most desirable to put this latter expression in the form,

$$\begin{aligned}\Gamma(P_1, P_2, 0) &= \int_S \int_S dS_1\, dS_2 \left.\frac{\partial G_1(P_1, P_1', \bar{\nu})}{\partial n_{S_1}}\right|_{P_1'=S_1} \left.\frac{\partial G_2(P_2, P_2', \bar{\nu})}{\partial n_{S_2}}\right|_{P_2'=S_2} \int_0^\infty \hat{\Gamma}(S_1, S_2, \nu)\, d\nu \\ &= \int_S \int_S dS_1\, dS_2 \left.\frac{\partial G_1(P_1, P_1', \bar{\nu})}{\partial n_{S_1}}\right|_{P_1'=S_1} \left.\frac{\partial G_2(P_2, P_2', \bar{\nu})}{\partial n_{S_2}}\right|_{P_2'=S_2} \Gamma(S_1, S_2, 0)\end{aligned} \tag{4-30}$$

To do this, however, requires that the product

$$\left[\left.\frac{\partial G_1(P_1, P_1', \nu)}{\partial n_{S_1}}\right|_{P_1'=S_1} \left.\frac{\partial G_2(P_2, P_2', \nu)}{\partial n_{S_2}}\right|_{P_2'=S_2}\right]$$

be a slowly varying function of ν for all parameters. Now, in general, this is clearly not the case since, for example, in the far field the product will contribute a term of the form $e^{ik(r_1-r_2)}$, and $\Delta k(r_1 - r_2)$ need not necessarily be small. If $\Delta k(r_1 - r_2)$ is not small, the quasi-monochromatic approximation is not too useful.

It turns out, however, that in many important problems, $\Gamma(P_1, P_2, 0)$ is of great interest when $\Delta k(r_1 - r_2)$ is indeed much less than 1. In addition, we often find too that the other terms in k contributed by the product

$$\left[\left.\frac{\partial G_1(P_1, P_1', \nu)}{\partial n_{S_1}}\right|_{P_1'=S_1} \left.\frac{\partial G_2(P_2, P_2', \nu)}{\partial n_{S_2}}\right|_{P_2'=S_2}\right]$$

do not vary significantly if the condition $\Delta k(r_1 - r_2) \ll 1$ is met. The condition for neglecting the product other than the $e^{ik(r_1-r_2)}$ term must, however, be studied for each particular geometry.† We shall, in Chapter 5, consider the case of radiation from a plane finite source.

We note here that when $\Delta k(r_1 - r_2) \ll 1$ is the only criterion of importance this criterion may be relaxed somewhat by combination with

†In subsequent portions of this book we shall frequently refer to a condition like $\Delta k(r_1 - r_2) \ll 1$ by stating that the difference in radiation path lengths is small.

the criterion $|\tau|\,\Delta\nu \ll 1$. The combined condition as follows from Eq. (4–27) is

$$\Delta\nu\left|\tau - \frac{(r_1 - r_2)}{c}\right| \ll 1$$

4.4 INCOHERENT SOURCES

We have shown in Section 4.3 that a source will not radiate if $|\gamma_{12}(\tau)| = 0$ for all pairs of points and time delays τ on some enclosing surface S. To circumvent this difficulty, we often find in the literature that, when representing an incoherent source, $\Gamma_{12}(\tau)$ is given the form $I(S_1, \tau)\,\delta(S_1 - S_2)$, where $\delta(S_1 - S_2)$ is a Dirac delta function. This form does give a non-null field, and it gives results often in agreement with experiment. This form, however, imposes the condition of infinite intensity over the source surface. It is clearly a mathematical idealization, and in this section, we should like to give alternate definitions of an incoherent source, and at the same time justify in some measure the use of the δ function in calculations.

The criterion for an incoherent source in terms of an enclosing surface, S, is often taken to be that the intensity of the field external to S is a linear superposition of the intensity of all points on the source surface S. The implication here is that one calculates the intensity contribution from each infinitesimal element of the surface and then adds the result; there being no coherence between the various infinitesimal elements.

As Theorem II shows, however, this leads to a null result if the intensity remains finite over S. To get a non-null result and yet retain the notion of incoherence the assumption is often made that

$$\hat{\Gamma}(S_1, S_2, \nu) = \beta \hat{I}(S_1, \nu)\,\delta(S_1 - S_2) \tag{4–31}$$

where $\delta(S_1 - S_2)$ is a Dirac delta function; β is a constant included to allow $\hat{I}(S_1, \nu)$ to retain the units of a power spectrum. This assumption yields the following result, which is non-null

$$I(P_1) = \beta \int_0^\infty d\nu \int_S \hat{I}(S_1, \nu) \left.\frac{\partial G_1(P_1, P_1', \nu)}{\partial n_{S_1}}\right|_{P_1'=S_1} \left.\frac{\partial G_2(P_1, P_2', \nu)}{\partial n_{S_1}}\right|_{P_2'=S_1} dS_1 \tag{4–32}$$

The difficulty of this assumption is that the intensity over S is now infinite.

Recently, Beran and Parrent (1963a) have resolved the difficulty of infinite intensity by showing that, for surfaces which have characteristic radii of curvature that are large compared to a characteristic radiation wavelength, the form

$$\hat{\Gamma}(S_1, S_2, \nu) = \hat{I}(S_1, \nu)\, \frac{2J_1(k\,|S_1 - S_2|)}{(k\,|S_1 - S_2|)} \tag{4–33}$$

yields results in the radiation field which are identical to the assumption Eq. (4–31), if we set $\beta = 4\pi/k^2$.

Further, however, they showed, by considering the radiation from a volume composed of classical isotropic radiators that are mutually incoherent, that there are many forms similar to Eq. (4–33) that represent sources one would call incoherent. Thus for convenience one may use Eq. (4–31) to represent an incoherent source, but one must justify that this is the type of incoherent source that permits such a representation.

In this section, we show how Eq. (4–33) was derived and how similar forms may be derived by consideration of a volume of classical isotropic radiators. We shall conclude this section with a brief discussion of the present state of knowledge of incoherent sources. The following sections follow the development given by Beran and Parrent (1963a).

Derivation of Eq. (4-33)

The derivation Eq. (4–33) follows from consideration of radiation from an infinite plane surface. The application of the formula to curved surfaces of large radii of curvature is then made by qualitative argument. We thus begin by considering radiation from an infinite plane surface.

Radiation from an infinite plane surface: $\hat{\Gamma}(P_1, P_2, \nu)$ satisfies the equations,

$$\nabla_j^2 \hat{\Gamma}(P_1, P_2, \nu) + k^2 \hat{\Gamma}(P_1, P_2, \nu) = 0 \qquad (j = 1, 2) \tag{4–34}$$

The general solution of this equation is

$$\hat{\Gamma}(P_1, P_2, \nu) = \iint_{-\infty}^{\infty}\!\!\iint \tilde{\Gamma}(k_x, k_y, k_x', k_y', \nu)\, e^{i\mathbf{k}\cdot\mathbf{r}_1 - i\mathbf{k}'\cdot\mathbf{r}_2}\, dk_x\, dk_y\, dk_x'\, dk_y' \tag{4–35}$$

where $\mathbf{k}$ and $\mathbf{k}'$ have components k_x, k_y, k_z and k_x', k_y', k_z', respectively, and

$$k_z = \sqrt{k^2 - k_x^2 - k_y^2}, \quad k_z' = \sqrt{k^2 - k_x'^2 - k_y'^2}$$

$\mathbf{r}_i$ has components x_i, y_i, z_i.

Let us consider as a boundary condition that $\Gamma(P_1, P_2, \nu)$ is given over $z_1 = z_2 = 0$, which we call the radiating surface S. Then,

$$\hat{\Gamma}(S_1, S_2, \nu) = \iint_{-\infty}^{\infty}\!\!\iint \tilde{\Gamma}(k_x, k_y, k_x', k_y', \nu)\, e^{ik_x x_{1s} + ik_y y_{1s}}\, e^{-ik_x' x_{2s} - ik_y' y_{2s}}\, dk_x'\, dk_y'\, dk_x\, dk_y \tag{4–36}$$

This is a Fourier transform relation between $\hat{\Gamma}(S_1, S_2, \nu)$ and $\tilde{\Gamma}(k_x, k_y, k_x', k_y', \nu)$ and hence we may invert the relation to find

$\tilde{\Gamma}(k_x, k_y, k'_x, k'_y, \nu)$ if $\hat{\Gamma}(S_1, S_2, \nu)$ is given. To find $\hat{\Gamma}(P_1, P_2, \nu)$ we need then only substitute $\tilde{\Gamma}(k_x, k_y, k'_x, k'_y, \nu)$ into Eq. (4–35).

$\hat{\Gamma}(S_1, S_2, \nu)$ is arbitrary within wide limits and hence so is $\tilde{\Gamma}(k_x, k_y, k'_x, k'_y, \nu)$. In particular, $\hat{\Gamma}(S_1, S_2, \nu)$ may be so chosen that $\tilde{\Gamma}(k_x, k_y, k'_x, k'_y, \nu)$ is non-zero when $k_x^2 + k_y^2 > k^2$ or $k_x'^2 + k_y'^2 > k^2$. If this occurs, however, either $e^{ik_z z}$ or $e^{-ik'_z z}$ becomes a decreasing real exponential in Eq. (4-35) (we omit increasing exponentials as unphysical). This means that that portion of $\tilde{\Gamma}(k_x, k_y, k'_x, k'_y, \nu)$ for which either $k_x^2 + k_y^2$ or $k_x'^2 + k_y'^2$ is greater than k^2 will not radiate. These high values of (k_x, k_y) or (k'_x, k'_y) are called *evanescent waves.*

Consider now what happens if $\hat{\Gamma}(S_1, S_2, \nu)$ contains a Dirac delta function. To do this let us represent the delta function as a limit:

(4–37) $$\delta(S_1 - S_2) = \underset{\alpha \to 0}{\text{limit}}\, e^{[-(x_{1s}-x_{2s})^2-(y_{1s}-y_{2s})^2]/\alpha^2} \frac{L^2}{\alpha^2}\frac{1}{\pi}$$

where the L^2 is an arbitrary length introduced so that, in the expression,

(4–38) $$\hat{\Gamma}(S_1, S_2, \nu) = \hat{I}(S_1, \nu)\, \delta(S_1 - S_2)$$

$\hat{I}(S_1, \nu)$ has the dimensions of intensity/unit frequency.

Inverting Eq. (4–36) using Eq. (4–38), we have

(4–39) $$\tilde{\Gamma}(k_x, k_y, k'_x, k'_y, \nu) = \frac{L^2}{\pi(2\pi)^4} \lim_{\alpha \to 0} \frac{1}{\alpha^2} \iint_{-\infty}^{\infty}\iint \hat{I}(S_1, \nu)\, e^{-[(x_{1s}-x_{2s})^2-(y_{1s}-y_{2s})]^2/\alpha^2}\, e^{-ik_x x_{1s}-ik_y y_{1s}+ik'_x x_{2s}+ik'_y y_{2s}}\, dx_{1S}\, dy_{1S}\, dx_{2S}\, dy_{2S}$$

Changing to the variables:

$$\xi = x_{2S} - x_{1S}$$
$$\eta = y_{2S} - y_{1S}$$
$$x'_{1S} = x_{1S}$$
$$y'_{1S} = y_{1S}$$

we have, after integration over ξ and η,

(4–40) $$\tilde{\Gamma}(k_x, k_y, k'_x, k'_y, \nu) = \text{const}\, L^2 \lim_{\alpha \to 0} \left[\iint_{-\infty}^{\infty} \hat{I}(S'_1, \nu)\, e^{-ix'_{1s}(k_x-k'_x)}\, e^{-iy'_{1s}(k_y-k'_y)}\, dx'_{1S}\, dy'_{1S} \right] e^{-(k_x'^2+k_y'^2)\frac{\alpha^2}{4}}$$

As $\alpha \to 0$, this expression shows, through the last exponential term, that most of the energy is in spatial frequencies such that $k_x'^2 + k_y'^2 > k^2$. Thus, most of the energy will not radiate.

The portion of $\tilde{\Gamma}(k_x, k_y, k'_x, k'_y, \nu)$ that will radiate, $\tilde{\Gamma}^R(k_x, k_y, k'_x, k'_y, \nu)$, is in the limit $\alpha \to 0$:

$$\tilde{\Gamma}^R(k_x, k_y, k'_x, k'_y, \nu) = \text{const}\left[\iint_{-\infty}^{\infty} \hat{I}(S'_1, \nu)\, e^{-ix'_{1s}(k_x - k'_x)} e^{-iy'_{1s}(k_y - k'_y)}\, dx'_{1S}\, dy'_{1S}\right] \tag{4–41}$$

where $k'^2_x + k'^2_y < k^2$.

If we now ask for $\hat{\Gamma}^R(S_1, S_2, \nu)$ associated only with $\tilde{\Gamma}^R(k_x, k_y, k'_x, k'_y, \nu)$, we need only take the Fourier transform of $\tilde{\Gamma}^R(k_x, k_y, k'_x, k'_y, \nu)$. Straightforward manipulation then yields

$$\hat{\Gamma}^R(S_1, S_2, \nu) = [\hat{I}'(S_1, \nu)]\left[\frac{2J_1(k\sqrt{(x_{1S} - x_{2S})^2 + (y_{1S} - y_{2S})^2})}{k\sqrt{(x_{1S} - x_{2S})^2 + (y_{1S} - y_{2S})^2}}\right] \tag{4–42}$$

where all constants have been absorbed in $\hat{I}(S_1, \nu)$ and represented as $\hat{I}'(S_1, \nu)$.

By construction, $\hat{\Gamma}^R(S_1, S_2, \nu)$ contains no evanescent waves and gives the same radiated field as a Dirac delta function. Hence, it satisfies Eq. (4–32) and is everywhere finite. Moreover, the form of $\hat{\Gamma}^R(S_1, S_2, \nu)$ is independent of the delta function representation chosen and basically is equivalent to the simple assumption that the spatial frequency spectrum over S is constant from 0 to k.

β may be determined by substituting Eqs. (4–42) and (4–31) into Eq. (4–15) and comparing the results for radiation from a plane finite surface.

Radiation from curved surfaces: If the radiation is from an arbitrarily curved surface, a form such as Eq. (4–33) is not easily derived. When, however, the radii of curvature of S are very large compared to a characteristic wavelength, we should expect a form similar to Eq. (4–33) to emerge again. For then $\hat{\Gamma}^R(S_1, S_2, \nu)$ is effectively non-zero only for distances of the order of several wavelengths, and over this distance, S may be considered infinite and flat.

The surface integrals in Eq. (4–15) are not explored for arbitrary values of S_1 and S_2. S_1 must be nearly equal to S_2 and the two surfaces if curved can be segmented into a series of plane finite parts (of characteristic dimension very, very large compared to a wavelength) and corresponding parts may be paired. Thus the integral is simply the radiation from a series of plane finite surfaces, each surface of which is totally uncorrelated to all other surfaces.

The plane finite surface and the plane infinite surface act identically for $z \gg 1/k$ if a characteristic radius of curvature of S is much greater than z.

Derivation of the mutual coherence on the surface of a volume composed of classical isotropic radiators

To see how representative the form of $\hat{\Gamma}(S_1, S_2, \nu)$ given in Eq. (4–33) really is, we now determine $\hat{\Gamma}(S_1, S_2, \nu)$ by considering a volume of classical isotropic radiators that are mutually incoherent. We shall find from this simple model that $\hat{\Gamma}(S_1, S_2, \nu)$ depends upon the geometry of the volume.

For simplicity, we assume first that there is no absorption in the volume and that there are many radiators in a volume of the order of the characteristic wavelength cubed.

We suppose that each of the radiators radiates a function $V_T^i(t)$† of the form

$$V_T^i(\mathbf{r}_1, t) = \int_0^\infty \hat{S}_i(\nu, T)\frac{e^{ikR(\mathbf{r}_1, \mathbf{r}_i)-2\pi i\nu t}}{R(\mathbf{r}_1, \mathbf{r}_i)}\, d\nu \tag{4-43}$$

where $|S_i(\nu, T)|^2$ gives the weight of the various frequencies for the ith radiator and we assume that the radiation exists from $-T$ to T for convenience in taking limits. $\mathbf{r}_i$ is the coordinate vector of the ith radiator and $\mathbf{r}_1$ is the coordinate vector of the observation point.

Then

$$\begin{aligned}\Gamma(P_1, P_2, \tau) = \lim_{T\to\infty}\frac{1}{2T}\int_{-T}^{T} dt \sum_{j=1}^{N}\sum_{i=1}^{N}\int_0^\infty\int_0^\infty d\nu\, d\nu' \\ \frac{\hat{S}_i(\nu, T)\hat{S}_j^*(\nu', T)}{R(\mathbf{r}_1, \mathbf{r}_i)\, R(\mathbf{r}_2, \mathbf{r}_j)}\, e^{i[kR(\mathbf{r}_1, \mathbf{r}_i)-k'R(\mathbf{r}_2, \mathbf{r}_j)]-2\pi i[t(\nu-\nu')+\nu\tau]}\end{aligned} \tag{4-44}$$

Assuming we may interchange integrations, we have

$$\Gamma(P_1, P_2, \tau) = \int_0^\infty d\nu\, e^{-2\pi i\nu\tau}\sum_{i=1}^{N}\sum_{j=1}^{N}\frac{e^{ik[R(\mathbf{r}_1, \mathbf{r}_i)-R(\mathbf{r}_2, \mathbf{r}_j)]}}{R(\mathbf{r}_1, \mathbf{r}_i)\, R(\mathbf{r}_2, \mathbf{r}_j)}\hat{K}(i, j, \nu) \tag{4-45}$$

where

$$\hat{K}(i, j, \nu) = \lim_{T\to\infty}\frac{1}{2T}\hat{S}_i(\nu, T)\, \hat{S}_j^*(\nu, T)\text{‡}$$

and is in the form of a mutual power spectrum.

If the sources are mutually incoherent,

$$\begin{aligned}\hat{K}(i, j, \nu) &= \hat{K}(i, \nu) \qquad i = j \\ &= 0 \qquad\qquad i \neq j\end{aligned} \tag{4-46}$$

For convenience, we assume here that $\hat{K}(i, \nu)$ is independent of i.

Thus Eq. (4–45) reduces to:

$$\Gamma(P_1, P_2, \tau) = \int_0^\infty d\nu\, e^{-2\pi i\nu\tau}\hat{K}(\nu)\sum_{i=1}^{N}\frac{e^{ik[R(\mathbf{r}_1, \mathbf{r}_i)-R(\mathbf{r}_1, \mathbf{r}_i)]}}{R(\mathbf{r}_1, \mathbf{r}_i)\, R(\mathbf{r}_2, \mathbf{r}_i)} \tag{4-47}$$

If there are many radiators in a cubic wavelength, then the sum over i may be replaced by an integral. Let us consider two geometries: a sphere and a hemisphere. The summation is now replaced by the integral,

$$\hat{M}(\mathbf{r}_1, \mathbf{r}_2, \nu) = n\int_{\bar{V}}\frac{e^{ik[R(\mathbf{r}_1, \mathbf{r})-R(\mathbf{r}_2, \mathbf{r})]}}{R(\mathbf{r}_1, \mathbf{r})\, R(\mathbf{r}_2, \mathbf{r})}\, d\bar{V} \tag{4-48}$$

---

†We note that here the i denotes the ith radiator, not the imaginary part of $V_T(t)$.
‡See Section 2.3 for a note on the existence of this function.

where $\bar{V}$ is the volume of the source and n is the number of particles/unit volume. In the remainder of this section we shall be concerned with $\hat{M}(\mathbf{r}_1, \mathbf{r}_2, \nu)$. The physics of incoherent radiation is more easily studied in terms of ν rather than τ. $\Gamma(P_1, P_2, \tau)$ follows from $\hat{K}(\nu)\,\hat{M}(\mathbf{r}_1, \mathbf{r}_2, \nu)$ if the frequency spectrum of the radiation is known.

In analogy to the problem treated under "Radiation from an infinite plane surface," we wish to compute $\hat{K}(\nu)\,\hat{M}(\mathbf{r}_1, \mathbf{r}_2, \nu)$ between two points on the surface enclosing the volume. We assume that $V^{1/3} \gg \lambda$. For the sphere problem, we will take $\mathbf{r}_1$ to be the origin. Since we expect from our surface calculation that $\hat{M}(\mathbf{r}_1, \mathbf{r}_2, \nu)$ should be zero in distances of the order of several wavelengths, we shall assume that $|\mathbf{r}_2 - \mathbf{r}_1| \ll a$, where a is the radius of the sphere. After expanding the exponential, we arrive at the following expression:

$$\hat{M}(\mathbf{r}_1, \mathbf{r}_2, \nu) = n \int_{\bar{V}} \frac{e^{ikr_0 \sin\theta \cos\Phi}}{r^2}\, r^2\, dr\, d\theta\, d\Phi \sin\theta \tag{4–49}$$

where r_0 is the separation between two points on the sphere surface.

Integration of Eq. (4–49) yields:

$$\hat{M}(\mathbf{r}_1, \mathbf{r}_2, \nu) = \text{const}\,\frac{J_1(kr_0)}{kr_0} \tag{4–50}$$

This is identical to Eq. (4–33). The agreement, however, is a little too fortuitous. The infinite plane problem is perhaps somewhat more like finding the coherence between two points in the neighborhood of the origin of a hemisphere of radius a (that is, in the center of the flat side). Here the result is

$$\hat{M}(\mathbf{r}_1, \mathbf{r}_2, \nu) = \text{const}\,\frac{\sin kr_0}{kr_0} \tag{4–51}$$

In general, one may arrive at a series of $\hat{M}(\mathbf{r}_1, \mathbf{r}_2, \nu)$ if one replaces $\hat{K}(\nu)$ by $\hat{K}(\nu, r)$, that is, makes the volume intensity a function of r. Then Eq. (4–49) becomes

$$\hat{M}(\mathbf{r}_1, \mathbf{r}_2, \nu) = n \int_0^{2\pi}\int_0^{\pi/2}\int_0^{G(\theta)} \frac{e^{ikr_0 \sin\theta \cos\Phi}}{r^2}\,\hat{K}(\nu, r) r^2\, dr \sin\theta\, d\theta\, d\Phi \tag{4–52}$$

where $G(\theta)$ represents the geometry. To arrive at Eq. (4–50), $G(\theta)$ equals $2a\cos\theta$ whereas to arrive at Eq. (4–51) $G(\theta) = a$ (a being the radius of the sphere). In general, then

$$\hat{M}(\mathbf{r}_1, \mathbf{r}_2, \nu) = n \int_0^{2\pi}\int_0^{\pi/2} e^{ikr_0 \sin\theta \cos\Phi}\, F(\theta) \sin\theta\, d\theta\, d\Phi \tag{4–53}$$

where

$$F(\theta) = \int_0^{G(\theta)} \hat{K}(\nu, r)\, dr$$

and finally,

$$\hat{M}(\mathbf{r}_1, \mathbf{r}_2, \nu) = \text{const} \int_0^{\pi/2} J_0(kr_0 \sin \theta) F(\theta) \sin \theta \, d\theta \tag{4–54}$$

One may arrive at the intensity spectrum per unit solid angle by letting $r_0 = 0$. Then we have

$$\hat{M}(\mathbf{r}_1, \mathbf{r}_1, \nu) = \text{const} \int_0^{\pi/2} F(\theta) \sin \theta \, d\theta \tag{4–55}$$

The intensity angular spectrum is then $F(\theta) \cos \theta$, the $\cos \theta$ arising from the angle between the surface and the direction of propagation.

Types of incoherent sources

The independent radiator model described in the previous section indicates that

$$\hat{\Gamma}(S_1, S_2, \nu) = K(\nu)\, M(S_1, S_2, \nu)$$

depends upon the geometry of the source. With little difficulty, one can extend the model to include self-absorption effects, the effect being represented in the function $F(\theta)$. We may thus conclude from this model that there is no unique incoherent source.

Perhaps the most that can be said is that, in any physical source, the coherence function $\hat{\Gamma}(S_1, S_2, \nu)$ will probably resemble functions like

$$\frac{2J_1(kr_{12})}{kr_{12}} \quad \text{and} \quad \frac{\sin kr_{12}}{kr_{12}}$$

in that their first zero will occur in the order of a wavelength and that they will reach a small fraction of their maximum value in several wavelengths.

$\hat{\Gamma}(S_1, S_2, \nu)$ must be determined by careful consideration of each particular source, theoretically or experimentally. In this evaluation, the validity of scalar theory must, of course, be considered.

It turns out that in many problems (see Chapter 5) it is unimportant which function of $\hat{\Gamma}(S_1, S_2, \nu)$ is used provided that it resembles

$$\frac{2J_1(kr_{12})}{kr_{12}} \quad \text{or} \quad \frac{\sin kr_{12}}{kr_{12}}$$

and thus it is most convenient to use a delta function representation. One must, however, prove this to be the case. For example, in considering the radiation from a plane finite source for small angles of observation, it can be shown that the delta function representation is appropriate (to within a constant).

At this writing, little has been done from a coherence point of view to distinguish the various types of incoherent sources except implicitly in considering phenomena like limb darkening of the sun. For curved surfaces, the form of $\hat{\Gamma}(S_1, S_2, \nu)$ critically determines the far-field intensity pattern resulting from each element on the surface (which in turn determines the total far field coherence function).

We conclude by stating that, in our opinion, incoherent sources can best be studied theoretically from a treatment of the radiation as it emanates from the source volume rather than as it passes through a surface enclosing the source. It appears that scalar theory may then be used consistently for far-field calculations, whereas in treating the intermediate step of radiation from a curved surface it may be necessary to consider the full vector equations. Experimentally, it appears that it will be necessary to consider the radiation as it passes through a surface surrounding the source since it is difficult to measure inside most radiating sources.

chapter

5

Radiation under Various Conditions of Coherence

Here we wish to explore radiation from sources under various conditions of coherence of the source. We wish to show the simplifications that are introduced when the source is either coherent or incoherent and when, in the latter case, the radiation is quasi-monochromatic. In particular, we consider in detail the far-field radiation from a plane finite source for small angles under these simplifying conditions. For simplicity, we shall use a delta function representation for the source. The starting points of this chapter are Eqs. (3–22) and (3–30). We conclude the chapter with a discussion of the measurement of the angular diameter of nonresolvable objects like stars and a description of a laboratory experiment.

5.1 RADIATION FROM A COHERENT SOURCE

When the radiation is coherent,† and hence, as shown in Chapter 4, strictly monochromatic, the study of $\Gamma(P_1, P_2, \tau)$ reduces to the study of the propagation of $V(\mathbf{x}, t)$ itself. The general expression for $\Gamma(P_1, P_2, \tau)$ is Eq. (3–22):

$$\Gamma(P_1, P_2, \tau) = \int_0^\infty \int_S \int_S \hat{\Gamma}(S_1, S_2, \nu) \left.\frac{\partial G_1(P_1, P_1', \nu)}{\partial n_{S_1}}\right|_{P_1'=S_1} \left.\frac{\partial G_2(P_2, P_2', \nu)}{\partial n_{S_2}}\right|_{P_2'=S_2} \cdot dS_1\, dS_2\, e^{-2\pi i\nu\tau}\, d\nu \tag{5–1}$$

For a monochromatic source, we have shown in Chapter 4 that

$$\Gamma(S_1, S_2, \tau) = \hat{V}(S_1)\, \hat{V}^*(S_2)\, e^{-2\pi i\nu_0\tau} \tag{5–2}$$

Taking the Fourier transform of Eq. (5–2) yields

$$\hat{\Gamma}(S_1, S_2, \nu) = \hat{V}(S_1)\, \hat{V}^*(S_2)\, \delta(\nu - \nu_0) \tag{5–3}$$

Substituting Eq. (5–3) into Eq. (5–1) gives

$$\Gamma(P_1, P_2, \tau) = \int_0^\infty \left[\int_S \hat{V}(S_1) \left.\frac{\partial G_1(P_1, P_1', \nu)}{\partial n_{S_1}}\right|_{P_1'=S_1} dS_1\right] \left[\int_S \hat{V}^*(S_2) \left.\frac{\partial G_2(P_2, P_2', \nu)}{\partial n_{S_2}}\right|_{P_2'=S_2} dS_2\right] e^{-2\pi i\nu\tau}\, \delta(\nu - \nu_0)\, d\nu \tag{5–4}$$

This may be written as

$$\Gamma(P_1, P_2, \tau) = \hat{V}(P_1)\, \hat{V}^*(P_2)\, e^{-2\pi i\nu_0\tau} \tag{5–5}$$

where

$$\hat{V}(P_1) = \int_S \hat{V}(S_1) \left.\frac{\partial G_1(P_1, P_1', \nu_0)}{\partial n_{S_1}}\right|_{P_1'=S_1} dS_1$$

$$V^*(P_2) = \int_S \hat{V}^*(S_2) \left.\frac{\partial G_2(P_2, P_2', \nu_0)}{\partial n_{S_2}}\right|_{P_2'=S_2} dS_2$$

Thus the problem is most simply treated directly in terms of $\hat{V}(P)$. This problem is familiar to students of electromagnetic theory and we shall not go into the form of the solution obtained.

†This means coherent for all values of τ. This is, of course, too restrictive a definition to be of physical use (as we discussed in Chapter 4).

5.2 RADIATION FROM INCOHERENT SOURCES REPRESENTABLE BY EQ. 4-31

We have shown in Chapter 4 that, under some conditions, it is allowable to represent incoherent sources by

$$\Gamma(S_1, S_2, \tau) = \int_0^\infty \frac{4\pi}{k^2} \hat{I}(S_1, \nu)\, \delta(S_1 - S_2)\, e^{-2\pi i\nu\tau}\, d\nu \tag{5–6}$$

In this case,

$$\hat{\Gamma}(S_1, S_2, \nu) = \frac{4\pi}{k^2} \hat{I}(S_1, \nu)\, \delta(S_1 - S_2) \tag{5–7}$$

Substituting this expression into Eq. (5–1) then yields

$$\Gamma(P_1, P_2, \tau) = \int_0^\infty e^{-2\pi i\nu\tau}\, d\nu \int_S \hat{I}(S_1, \nu) \frac{4\pi}{k^2} \left.\frac{\partial G_1(P_1, P_1', \nu)}{\partial n_{S_1}}\right|_{P_1'=S_1} \left.\frac{\partial G_2(P_2, P_2', \nu)}{\partial n_{S_1}}\right|_{P_2'=S_1} dS_1 \tag{5–8}$$

We now have one less integral to compute and we shall explore this solution further considering radiation from a plane finite source.†

Radiation from a plane finite incoherent surface

Solution of Eq. (5–8) for radiation from other than plane surfaces is extremely difficult, and little has been done in this area. The difficulty is that a closed form solution for G_i is not obtainable for a curved surface like a sphere. We shall thus restrict our attention here to radiation from a plane finite surface. Fortunately, for an incoherent surface, this type of solution indicates the type of result we might expect for any large finite incoherent radiating surface.

As we showed in Chapter 3

$$\left.\frac{\partial G_1(P_1, P_1', \nu)}{\partial n_{S_1}}\right|_{P_1'=S_1} = \frac{-2(1 - ikr_1)}{4\pi} \frac{z_1}{r_1} \frac{e^{ikr_1}}{r_1^2} \tag{5–9}$$

where

$$r_1 = \sqrt{(x_1 - x_{1S})^2 + (y_1 - y_{1S})^2 + z_1^2}$$

---

†It may be shown that, under the conditions that we solve the plane finite surface problem in the next section, any coherence function which goes to zero in the order of wavelengths will yield the same result as the delta function approximation. To prove this, one simply expands the exponential term $e^{ik(r_1 - r_2)}$ in Eq. (3–30) in the manner shown in the next section and then integrates over the difference coordinates $\mathbf{x}_{1S} - \mathbf{x}_{2S}$. The small-angle assumption then yields the desired result.

with a similar expression for the normal derivative of $G_2(P_2, P_2', \nu) = G_1^*(P_2, P_2', \nu)$.

We thus find for $\Gamma(P_1, P_2, \tau)$,

$$\Gamma(P_1, P_2, \tau) = \frac{1}{\pi}\int_0^\infty e^{-2\pi i\nu\tau}\frac{1}{k^2}\,d\nu \int_S \hat{I}(S_1, \nu) \tag{5-10}$$
$$(1 - ikr_1)(1 + ikr_2)\frac{z_1 z_2}{r_1 r_2}\frac{e^{ik(r_1 - r_2)}}{r_1^2 r_2^2}\,dS_1$$

where

$$r_2 = \sqrt{(x_2 - x_{1S})^2 + (y_2 - y_{1S})^2 + z_2^2}$$

We stated in the introduction that we shall be interested in the far-field radiation. Unfortunately the condition $kr \gg 1$ or even $R/d \gg 1$ (where d is a characteristic source dimension and R is a characteristic dimension from the source to the measuring point) is not sufficient to obtain a simple solution. We must assume further that

$$\frac{x_1 - x_2}{R_1}, \quad \frac{y_1 - y_2}{R_1}, \quad \text{and} \quad \frac{\sqrt{x_1^2 + y_1^2}}{R_1} \text{ are} \ll 1$$

and $z_1 = z_2 = z$. (This latter condition may be relaxed somewhat, but we will consider the relaxation after the solution for $z_1 = z_2$ is obtained.) The conditions

$$\frac{x_1 - x_2}{R_1} \quad \text{and} \quad \frac{y_1 - y_2}{R} \ll 1$$

are reasonable conditions in the light of the solution obtained and we shall see that we require these ratios to be of the order of $1/kd$. We shall also always consider $kd \gg 1$, but this is implicit in our definition of an incoherent source. Further, we note that the assumption of $\sqrt{(x_1^2 + y_1^2)}/R_1 \ll 1$ is consistent with our use of scalar theory if our scalar theory results from using a single cartesian component of the electric field.

If the condition $R/d \gg 1$, $z_1 = z_2 = z$ is met, the integral over the surface may be somewhat simplified since we may remove the nonexponential r_i terms from under the integral. This yields

$$\Gamma(P_1, P_2, \tau) = \frac{1}{\pi}\frac{z^2}{R_1^4}\int_0^\infty e^{-2\pi i\nu\tau}\,d\nu \int_S \hat{I}(S_1, \nu)\, e^{ik(r_1 - r_2)}\,dS_1 \tag{5-11}$$

where we let $R_2 \approx R_1$.

The remaining assumptions are necessary to simplify the exponential term $e^{ik(r_1 - r_2)}$. We remember that

$$\begin{aligned} r_1 &= \sqrt{(x_1 - x_{1S})^2 + (y_1 - y_{1S})^2 + z^2} \\ r_2 &= \sqrt{(x_2 - x_{1S})^2 + (y_2 - y_{1S})^2 + z^2} \end{aligned} \tag{5-12}$$

The difference of these expressions may be expanded as

$$r_1 - r_2 \approx -\frac{x_{1S}(x_1 - x_2)}{R_1} - \frac{y_{1S}(y_1 - y_2)}{R_1} + R_1 - R_2 \tag{5-13}$$

where

$$R_p = \sqrt{x_p^2 + y_p^2 + z^2}$$

The remaining terms may be neglected because of the foregoing assumptions. That is, when they are multiplied by k they are $\ll 1$.

Neglect of the term $k(R_1 - R_2)$ depends upon the order of magnitude of $\sqrt{(x_1^2 + y_1^2)}/d$ and R/kd^2. Since it may be removed from the surface integration, we shall keep it in our calculations.

Our expression for $\Gamma(P_1, P_2, \tau)$ is now

$$\Gamma(P_1, P_2, \tau) = \frac{1}{\pi}\frac{z^2}{R_1^4}\int_0^\infty e^{-2\pi i\nu\{\tau - [(R_1 - R_2)/c]\}}\, d\nu \int_S \hat{I}(S_1, \nu) e^{-i[(k/R_1)(x_{1s}x_{12} + y_{1s}y_{12})]}\, dS_1 \tag{5-14}$$

where we have set $x_{12} \equiv x_1 - x_2$, $y_{12} \equiv y_1 - y_2$.

We note here that we have not needed the usual far-field assumption $kd^2/R \ll 1$ to derive the preceding expression. This is a consequence of the assumption of incoherence.

The surface integral may be solved for various geometries, if we assume $\hat{I}(S_1, \nu)$ is independent of S_1 over the surface. Then we have

$$\Gamma(P_1, P_2, \tau) = \frac{1}{\pi}\frac{z^2}{R_1^4}\int_0^\infty e^{-2\pi i\nu\{\tau - [(R_1 - R_2)/c]\}}\, I(\nu)\, d\nu \int_S e^{-i[(k/R_1)(x_{1s}x_{12} + y_{1s}y_{12})]}\, dS_1 \tag{5-15}$$

For a rectangular source surface ($2a \times 2b$), the surface integral may be separated and is

$$\left(\int_{-a}^{a} e^{-i(k/R_1)x_{12}x_{1s}}\, dx_{1S}\right)\left(\int_{-b}^{b} e^{-i(k/R_1)y_{12}y_{1s}}\, dy_{1S}\right) \tag{5-16}$$

This yields

$$4\left(\frac{\sin[(kx_{12}a)/R_1]}{kx_{12}/R_1}\right)\left(\frac{\sin[(ky_{12}b)/R_1]}{ky_{12}/R_1}\right) \equiv 4ab \operatorname{sinc}\left[\frac{kx_{12}a}{R_1}\right]\operatorname{sinc}\left[\frac{ky_{12}b}{R_1}\right] \tag{5-17}$$

where $\operatorname{sinc} x = \sin x/x$

The expression for $\Gamma(P_1, P_2, \tau)$ is then

$$\Gamma(P_1, P_2, \tau) = \frac{4}{\pi}\frac{z^2}{R_1^4}ab\int_0^\infty e^{-2\pi i\nu\{\tau - [(R_1 - R_2)/c]\}}\, \hat{I}(\nu)\, d\nu \operatorname{sinc}\left[\frac{kx_{12}a}{R_1}\right]\operatorname{sinc}\left[\frac{ky_{12}b}{R_1}\right] \tag{5-18}$$

For a circular source surface (radius a), the surface integral may be solved by using polar coordinates, that is,

$$x_{1S} = r_S \cos \Phi$$
$$y_{1S} = r_S \sin \Phi \tag{5–19}$$

This yields, for the surface integral,

$$\int_0^{2\pi} \int_0^a d\Phi \, dr_S r_S \, e^{-i[(k/R_1)(r_s \cos \Phi x_{12} + r_s \sin \Phi y_{12})]} \tag{5–20}$$

The expression,

$$\int_0^{2\pi} e^{-i[(k/R_1)r_s(x_{12} \cos \Phi + y_{12} \sin \Phi)]} \, d\Phi$$

integrates to

$$2\pi J_0 \left(\frac{k}{R_1} r_{12} r_S\right) \tag{5–21}$$

where

$$r_{12} = \sqrt{x_{12}^2 + y_{12}^2}$$

The remaining integral,

$$2\pi \int_0^a r_S \, dr_S \, J_0 \left(\frac{k}{R_1} r_{12} r_S\right) \tag{5–22}$$

yields

$$2\pi a^2 \frac{J_1[(k/R_1) \, r_{12} a]}{(k/R_1) \, r_{12} a} \tag{5–23}$$

The final expression for $\Gamma(P_1, P_2, \tau)$ is then

$$\Gamma(P_1, P_2, \tau) = 2a^2 \frac{z^2}{R_1^4} \int_0^\infty e^{-2\pi i\nu\{\tau - [(R_1 - R_2)/c]\}} \, \hat{I}(\nu) \frac{J_1[(k/R_1) \, r_{12} a]}{(k/R_1) \, r_{12} a} \, d\nu \tag{5–24}$$

For both the rectangular and circular aperture, the mutual power spectrum functions $\hat{\Gamma}(P_1, P_2, \nu)$ go to zero when r_{12}/R is of the order $1/kd$, where d is a characteristic source dimension and decays with at least $1/r_{12}$ beyond that point. If the condition that $r_{12}/r \leq 1/kd$ is used in evaluating the higher-order terms in the binomial expansion of $r_1 - r_2$ (together with the other assumptions), it will be seen that the higher-order terms may indeed be neglected.

The coherence in the longitudinal direction

$$(x_1 - x_2 = 0, \quad y_1 - y_2 = 0, \quad z_1 - z_2 = z_{12})$$

differs markedly from the coherence in the transverse direction

$$(x_1 - x_2) = x_{12}, \quad (y_1 - y_2) = y_{12}, \quad (z_1 - z_2) = 0$$

If z_{12} is not assumed to be zero but to be of the order of x_{12} and y_{12}, then Eq. (5–14) is unchanged, except that $R_1 - R_2$ now contains the z dependence. If now we set $x_{12} = y_{12} = 0$, then this expression becomes

(5–25) $$\Gamma(P_1, P_2, \tau) = \frac{1}{\pi}\frac{z^2}{R_1^4}\int_0^\infty e^{-2\pi i\nu[\tau-(z_{12}/c)]}\,d\nu\int_S \hat{I}(S_1\,\nu)\,dS_1$$

The z_{12} dependence is simply represented by an oscillating term $e^{ikz_{12}}$. The restriction $z_{12} \approx x_{12} \approx R_1/kd$ has no direct effect on the longitudinal correlation function except that, within this bound, $\hat{\Gamma}(P_1, P_1, \nu)$ behaves as a simple periodic function for each frequency. This result is not surprising, since in the longitudinal direction, we expect the field to propagate like a superposition of plane waves over a limited distance: this distance being at least the transverse correlation distance.

Without further knowledge of $\hat{I}(\nu)$ or $\hat{I}(S_1, \nu)$, Eq. (5–14) may be considered as our final answer. When the radiation has a narrow spectral spread, however, Eq. (5–14) may be further simplified by using the quasi-monochromatic approximation. We shall consider this in the next section.

Quasi-monochromatic approximation

Let us assume that $\hat{I}(\nu, S)$ is a function that is appreciable when $\bar{\nu} - \Delta\nu \leq \nu \leq \bar{\nu} + \Delta\nu$ and effectively zero outside this region. This assumes that the integral,

(5–26) $$K(P_1, P_2, \nu) = \int_S \hat{I}(\nu, S_1)\, e^{-i[(k/R_1)(x_{1s}x_{12}+y_{1s}y_{12})]}\,dS_1$$

is effectively zero for all ν outside the region $\bar{\nu} \pm \Delta\nu$.

Now if $\hat{I}(\nu, S_1)$ may be approximated by a form,

(5–27) $$\hat{I}(\nu, S_1) = \hat{\eta}(\nu)\, G(S_1)$$

then, as is evidenced by Eqs. (5–18) and (5–24) the integral

$$L(P_1, P_2, \nu) = \int_S G(S_1)\, e^{-i[(k/R_1)(x_{1s}x_{12}+y_{1s}y_{12})]}\,dS_1$$

may often be insensitive to small changes in k. We shall consider here those sources for which the condition is met. For then Eq. (5–14) may be written as

(5–28) $$\Gamma(P_1, P_2, \tau) = \frac{1}{\pi}\frac{z^2}{R_1^4}L(P_1, P_2, \bar{\nu})\int_0^\infty \hat{\eta}(\nu)\, e^{-2\pi i\nu\{\tau-[(R_1-R_2)/c]\}}\,d\nu$$

where $\hat{\eta}(\nu)$ is appreciable only when $\bar{\nu} - \Delta\nu \leq \nu \leq \bar{\nu} + \Delta\nu$.

As we discussed in Chapter 4, the problem simplifies further if

$$\Delta\nu\left|\left(\tau - \frac{R_1 - R_2}{c}\right)\right| \ll 1$$

for then we have

(5–29) $$\Gamma(P_1, P_2, \tau) = \frac{1}{\pi}\frac{z^2}{R_1^4}L(P_1, P_2, \bar{\nu})\, e^{-2\pi i\bar{\nu}\{\tau-[(R_1-R_2)/c]\}}\int_0^\infty \hat{\eta}(\nu)\,d\nu$$

From a measurement point of view, it is simple to meet the condition

$$\Delta\nu\left|\left(\tau - \frac{R_1 - R_2}{c}\right)\right| \ll 1$$

when we measure $|\Gamma(P_1, P_2, 0|$. We simply perform a Young's interference experiment and measure the maximum visibility. The alignment of the base line is not too critical since small inaccuracies in alignment only shift the fringes laterally. This is the procedure generally followed when measuring the angular diameter of stars.

To measure $\text{Re}[\Gamma(P_1, P_2, 0)]$ is much more difficult since the absolute position of the fringes must be known. It is of some interest to see the conditions on $\Delta\nu$ if we are explicitly forced to hold

$$\Delta\nu\left|\frac{(R_1 - R_2)}{c}\right| \ll 1.$$

In making a series of measurements with one point fixed, as is natural, $R_1 - R_2$ changes if we use a linear base line so we cannot set $R_1 = R_2$ once and for all. To see the conditions we must place on $R_1 - R_2$, let us examine the series expansion of $R_1 - R_2$. It is to the first order

$$R_1 - R_2 \approx \frac{r_{12}^2}{2R_1} + \frac{(x_1 x_{12} + y_1 y_{12} + z_1 z_{12})}{R_1} \tag{5–30}$$

where

$$r_{12} = \sqrt{(x_1 - x_2)^2 + (y_1 - y_2)^2 + (z_1 - z_2)^2}$$

The term $(\Delta k r_{12}^2)/R_1$ is of order

$$\frac{\Delta k r_{12}}{kd} \approx \frac{R}{kd^2}\frac{\Delta k}{k}\dagger$$

The terms

$$\frac{\Delta k x_1 x_{12}}{R_1} \quad \text{and} \quad \frac{\Delta k y_1 y_{12}}{R_1}$$

are of order

$$\frac{\Delta k}{k}\frac{x_1}{d} \quad \text{and} \quad \frac{\Delta k}{k}\frac{y_1}{d}$$

The term $\Delta k z_1 z_{12}/R_1$ is of order $\Delta k z_{12}$ since

$$\frac{z_1}{R_1} \approx 1$$

Thus for $\Delta k(R_1 - R_2)$ to be $\ll 1$, we require

$$\frac{R}{kd^2}\frac{\Delta k}{k} \ll 1, \quad \frac{\sqrt{x_1^2 + y_1^2}}{d}\frac{\Delta k}{k} \ll 1, \quad \text{and} \quad \Delta k z_{12} \ll 1$$

We note immediately that the condition

---

†We assume that z_{12} is at most of the same order as $\sqrt{x_{12}^2 + y_{12}^2}$.

$$\frac{R}{kd^2}\frac{\Delta k}{k} \ll 1$$

is contrary to the usual far-field condition $R/kd^2 \gg 1$ unless $\Delta k/k \lll 1$. This condition is, however, fortuitous for viewing stars from the earth since the condition $R/kd^2 \ll 1$ is fulfilled. (That is, if one replaces the radiating sphere by an equivalent disk. This will be discussed in the next section.)

The conditions

$$\frac{\sqrt{x_1^2 + y_1^2}}{d}\frac{\Delta k}{k} \ll 1 \quad \text{and} \quad \Delta k z_{12} \ll 1$$

can be met by careful alignment of the base line when making coherence measurements.

It is extremely useful to meet the condition

$$\Delta\nu \left|\left(\tau - \frac{R_1 - R_2}{c}\right)\right| \ll 1$$

since integration of the expression,

$$\int_0^\infty \hat{\eta}(\nu)\, e^{-2\pi i\nu\{\tau - [(R_1 - R_2)/c]\}}\, d\nu \tag{5–31}$$

is difficult analytically and without an analytical guide, experiments are useless for interpretation of the source characteristics. Thus, in practice, the light from an incoherent source is often filtered to obtain the desired simplification.

5.3 MEASUREMENT OF NONRESOLVABLE OBJECTS

Angular diameter of two incoherent point sources

It is impossible to resolve the nearest star in a telescope. Hence in order to obtain the angular diameter of a star, one makes coherence measurements on the radiation received from a star. To understand physically the utility of such measurements let us consider the measurement of the distance between two incoherent point sources such as, perhaps, a double star system.

Referring to Fig. 5-1, we suppose the radiation marked S_1 is coming from source S_1 and the radiation marked S_2 is coming from source S_2. The angle θ between the directions of radiation is the angular diameter between the two point sources. If D is the distance between the sources and R is the distance to the measuring points P_1 and P_2 then $\theta \approx D/R$. In these measurements we assume $\theta \ll 1$ and thus the radiation impinging on the plane A is essentially two plane waves with directions that differ by θ. For simplicity, we assume that the radiation is quasi-monochromatic.

The measurement of θ will take place by observing the fringes on B

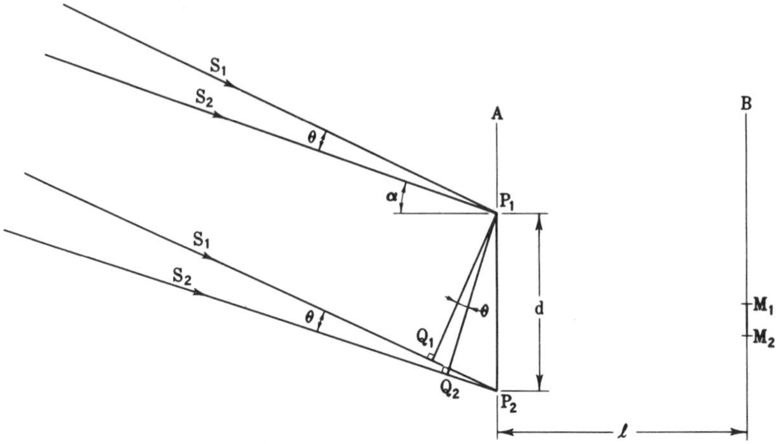

Figure 5-1. Interference measurement of radiation from two distant point sources.

as a function of the distance between P_1 and P_2. The source S_1 will give a cosine pattern on B with a maximum at some point M_1. At this point, the distances P_1M_1 and $Q_1P_2M_1$ differ by an integral number of wavelengths. The source S_2 will have a maximum at point M_2 where the distances P_1M_2 and $Q_2P_2M_2$ differ by an integral number of wavelengths. Let us suppose M_1 and M_2 are adjacent maximums.

Now if α is small, as we usually take it to be, then the distances Q_1P_2 and Q_2P_2 differ by a distance $\approx \theta d$. If $\theta d \ll \bar{\lambda}$ then M_1 and M_2 are very close and they form together essentially a single cosine pattern. However, as d becomes larger, the maximums M_1 and M_2 move apart until when $\theta d = \bar{\lambda}/2$ the maximum point M_1 coincides with the minimum point of the cosine pattern of which M_2 is a maximum. When this occurs there are no fringes on the screen. (If the intensity at A of the two sources is equal, as we assume it is here.)

Thus to find θ, simply separate P_1 and P_2 until there are no fringes on screen B. Then since at that point $\theta d = \bar{\lambda}/2$; $\theta = \bar{\lambda}/2d$.

This result could have been obtained formally from Eq. (5–14), since we remember that, for quasi-monochromatic light, the visibility is equal to $|\gamma_{12}(0)|$. Thus we could first determine $\Gamma(P_1, P_2, 0)$ for the radiation from two incoherent point sources and then seek the point where $\Gamma(P_1, P_2, 0) = 0$.

For two point sources, $\hat{I}(S_1, \nu) = C_1\hat{I}(\nu)\delta(S_1 - S_{10}) + C_2\hat{I}(\nu)\delta(S_1 - S_{20})$.† Hence in the quasi-monochromatic approximation, we have [assuming $\alpha = 0$, $S_{10} = (x_{10}, 0)$, $S_{20} = (x_{20}, 0)$, $C_1 = C_2$]:

†C_1 and C_2 are constants determined by the total intensity emitted form the holes. We assume $C_1 = C_2$ for convenience.

(5–32)
$$\Gamma(P_1, P_2, 0) = \frac{1}{\pi}\frac{z^2}{R_1^4} e^{-2\pi i\nu[(R_1-R_2)/c]} \text{ const}$$
$$\left[\int \hat{I}(\nu)\, e^{-i[(k/R_1)(x_{10}x_{12})]}\, d\nu + \int \hat{I}(\nu)\, e^{-i[(k/R_1)(x_{20}x_{12})]}\, d\nu\right]$$

Assuming $(\Delta k/R_1)(x_{10}\, x_{12})$ and $(\Delta k/R_1)(x_{20}\, x_{12})$ are $\ll 1$ we have

(5–33)
$$\Gamma(P_1, P_2, 0) = C\,[e^{-i[(\bar{k}/R_1)(x_{10}x_{12})]} + e^{-i[(\bar{k}/R_1)(x_{20}x_{12})]}]$$

where C is a function of all the parameters not dependent upon x_{10}, x_{20}, and x_{12}.

Let $x_{20} = x_{10} + D$. This yields

(5–34)
$$\Gamma(P_1, P_2, 0) = C e^{-i[(\bar{k}/R_1)(x_{10}x_{12})]}\,[1 + e^{-i(\bar{k}/R_1)Dx_{12}}]$$

When $(\bar{k}/R_1)Dx_{12} = \pi n$ (n odd), $\Gamma(P_1, P_2, 0) = 0$. The first zero occurs for $n = 1$. Thus $D/R_1 = \theta$ is

(5–35)
$$\theta = \frac{\bar{\lambda}}{2x_{12}}$$

This is the same result as obtained previously by more direct arguments.

Angular diameter of a uniformly illuminated incoherent disk

When the source becomes a distribution of continuous points rather than two discrete points, it is necessary to use more formal arguments to determine the angular size of the source. For a disk $\Gamma_{12}(0)$ is no longer zero when

$$x_{12} = \frac{\lambda}{2(D/R)}$$

where D is the disk diameter. Reference to Eq. (5–24) shows that a zero occurs when $J_1[(k/R)r_{12}\, a] = 0$. That is, when

$$\frac{k}{R}\, r_{12} a = \frac{\pi r_{12} D}{\lambda R} = 3.83$$

or

(5–36)
$$\theta = \frac{3.83}{\pi}\frac{\lambda}{r_{12}} = 1.22\,\frac{\lambda}{r_{12}}$$

The mutual interference of many point source patterns rather than just two accounts for the difference of over a factor of two between the two results.

Angular diameter of a uniformly illuminated incoherent sphere

As previously mentioned, the formal solution to the sphere problem is very difficult since we cannot find a closed form solution for the Green's function. One way to find an approximate solution when the source surface is incoherent is to replace the spherical surface by an equivalent disk of radius equal to that of the sphere and with the appropriate intensity distribution.

To find the equivalent intensity distribution, we first note that the sphere surface may be broken up into a finite number of approximately plane finite surfaces. The power radiated from each surface has a distribution represented by $F(\theta)$. Thus we have

$$I(P_1) = \frac{CF(\theta)}{R^2} \tag{5-37}$$

where C is determined from the total radiation intensity.

We refer now to Fig. 5-2. We wish to replace all the radiation from the sphere in the direction $\theta = 0$† by radiation from the equivalent disk. The element dA on the disk is replaced by an element $dA/\cos\theta$ on the sphere but, by Eq. (5-37), the intensity radiated in the $\theta = 0$ direction is changed by $F(\theta)$. Thus the disk intensity in the $\theta = 0$ direction is changed by a factor, $F(\theta)/\cos\theta$.

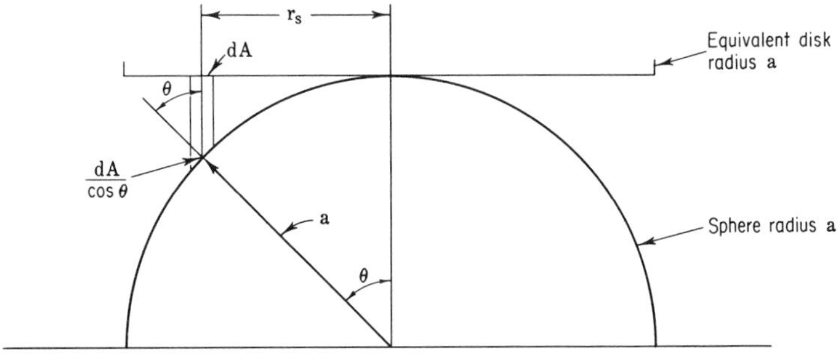

Figure 5-2. Equivalent disk used in describing radiation from a sphere.

We have concentrated on the $\theta = 0$ direction, since it is the simplest case and we are restricted to small angles in the disk solution. We remember that $\theta = 0$ is the mean angle of radiation that we are interested in. It is, of course, the small radiation about $\theta = 0$ that gives the coherence its value. To transform the intensity distribution from a sphere to an osculating disk, however, this variation may be discarded.

†Actually in a solid angle about $\theta = 0$.

The intensity distribution I over the disk is now replaced by $IF(\theta)/\cos\theta$. For a lambertian source, $F(\theta) = \cos\theta$ and the disk illumination is constant so that the solution Eq. (5–24) is appropriate. If the source incoherence is representable by Eq. (4–33), $F(\theta) = \cos^2\theta$, and Eq. (5–22) becomes

(5–38) $$2\pi \int_0^a r_S\sqrt{1 - r_S^2/a^2}\, J_0\left(\frac{k}{R_1} r_{12} r_S\right) dr_S$$

with the solution,

(5–39) $$2^{3/2}\pi\, a^2 \Gamma\left(\frac{3}{2}\right)\left(\frac{kr_{12}a}{R_1}\right)^{-3/2} J_{3/2}\left(\frac{kr_{12}a}{R_1}\right)$$

Thus here

(5–40) $$\theta = 1.4\frac{\lambda}{r_{12}}\ \dagger$$

rather than $\theta = 1.22(\lambda/r_{12})$.

Measurement of the angular diameter of stars

In order to measure the angular diameter of visible stars, we assume that the star is spherical and that the surface radiation on a surface immediately surrounding the star is incoherent and uniform. Moreover, in practice, some assumption must be made about the intensity distribution of the incoherent radiation on a disk tangent to the sphere.‡ For the sun, the phenomenon of limb darkening has been carefully studied and it is found that the intensity distribution is very wavelength dependent. In order to give the reader an idea of the dimensions involved in measurement of stars, we shall assume, however, that the intensity is uniform over the disk. Equation (5–36) applies if we use filtering to insure validity of the quasi-monochromatic approximation. [Actually, because of intensity limitations, too much filtering is not possible in practical measurements.]

To get an idea of the dimensions of r_{12}, consider the measurement of a star of the sun's radius (6.95×10^{10}cm) at distances of 4 light years (the approximate distance of the nearest star), 100 light years, and, say, 10^6 light years.

For a mean radiation wavelength of, say, 5×10^{-5} cm this yields for r_{12}; 17, 420, and 4.2×10^6 meters for 4, 10^2, and 10^6 light years, respectively.

It thus is practical to measure the angular diameter of only near stars

---

†θ here is again the angular diameter and must not be confused with the angle θ used above in Fig. 5-2 and Eq. (5–37).

‡As opposed to theory, since knowledge of the shape of $\Gamma(P_1, P_2, \tau)$ (for the quasi-monochromatic case) allows one to calculate the intensity distribution by inverting the Fourier transform relation in Eq. (5–28). In practice, we do not have sufficient confidence in our measurements to distinguish between various intensity distributions.

much larger than the sun. One of the first stars measured was α Orionis, Michelson and Pease (1921). They found $\theta = 0.055$ sec, which yielded a star diameter of almost 300 sun diameters. The distance to the star was obtained by triangulation.

Note that the intensity distribution over the star (or equivalent disk) changes the zero point noticeably. There is about a 17 per cent change between a uniformly illuminated disk and one with a $\sqrt{1 - (r_S^2/a^2)}$ intensity distribution. Further, it changes all successive zeros, and (as Michelson and Pease point out) in principle, if not in practice, it should be possible to get a good idea of the intensity distribution by measuring many zeros.

The same type of measurement may be made for radio sources, but here the source shapes are not simple spheres. The characteristic angular diameters are often much larger than for stars. The intense portion of the radio source Cygnus A has a characteristic angular diameter of the order of minutes. For 3-meter radio waves, an interferometer system with a base separation of the order of 10 km is needed. The question of determining the intensity distribution across the source is a difficult one. Whereas again in principle it is possible to find the distribution from coherence measurements, in practice it is somewhat uncertain.

Recently star and radio source diameters have been measured by measuring the coherence of the local intensity at two points rather than the complex amplitudes. If the star statistics are gaussian, this yields the same information as ordinary interference measurements. We shall discuss this concept of intensity coherence in Chapter 12.

5.4 LABORATORY EXPERIMENT

In the quasi-monochromatic approximation it may be easily shown that Eq. (5–24) yields for $\gamma_{12}(0)$ the following form:

$$\gamma_{12}(0) = \frac{2J_1(x)}{x} \tag{5–41}$$

where $x = \bar{k}r_{12}a/R_1$. That is, the far-field complex degree of coherence resulting from a self-luminous incoherent circular source is 2 times a first-order Bessel function divided by its argument. $|\gamma_{12}(0)|$ is plotted in Fig. 1-2. As we mentioned in Chapter 1, $|\gamma_{12}(0)|$ is equal to the visibility $\mathcal{V}$ under the restricted conditions given above. It is, however, instructive to note that $\gamma_{12}(0)$ takes on both positive and negative values and to make measurements on partially coherent light taking into account the phase β_{12} [$\beta = 0$ or π, for positive and negative values of $\gamma_{12}(0)$ respectively] in addition to $|\gamma_{12}(0)|$. This change in phase produces measurable effects.

As an illustration of this point, consider Figs. 5-3a—5-3d from Thompson (1958). Thompson let light from three incoherent circular sources fall on two

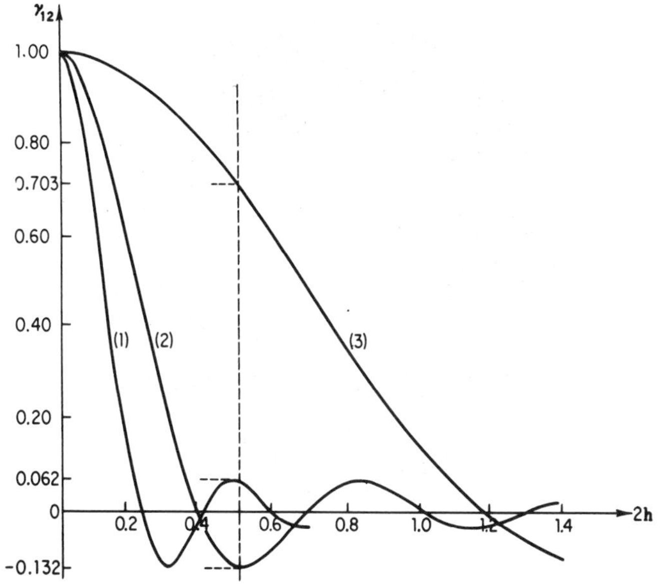

Figure 5-3a. The degree of coherence, γ_{12}, as a function of the separation of two points, $2h$, for three cases of source diameter: (1) 480 microns, (2) 280 microns, (3) 90 microns. [Figures 5-3 (a-d) taken by permission from B. Thompson, *J.O.S.A.*, vol. 48, no. 2, p. 95.]

small circular apertures separated by 0.5 cm and observed the far field intensity pattern. The fringes in the intensity pattern are shown for the three different source sizes (Figs. 5-3b—5-3d). The source sizes are so chosen that $\gamma_{12}(0)$ is alternately positive and negative.

Figure 5-3a shows the variation in the degree of coherence between two points plotted against the separation of the points for each source diameter. The vertical dotted line represents the separation of the circular apertures used in the experiment (i.e., 0.5 cm). At 0.5 cm, $\beta_{12} = 0$ for the 480 micron source, $\beta = \pi$ for the 280 micron source and $\beta_{12} = 0$ for the 90 micron source. In Figs. 5-3b—5-3d, the observed fringe systems and the calculated intensity distributions are shown. The chain lines represent the maximum and minimum of intensity and the fall-off is due to the diffraction envelope associated with the individual apertures. In Fig. 5-3b the fringes have good visibility with a central *maximum* ($\beta_{12} = 0$); in Fig. 5-3c the visibility has fallen considerably, and the fringes have a central *minimum* ($\beta_{12} = \pi$); finally in Fig. 5-3d the visibility is very poor but there is an unmistakable central *maximum* ($\beta_{12} = 0$).

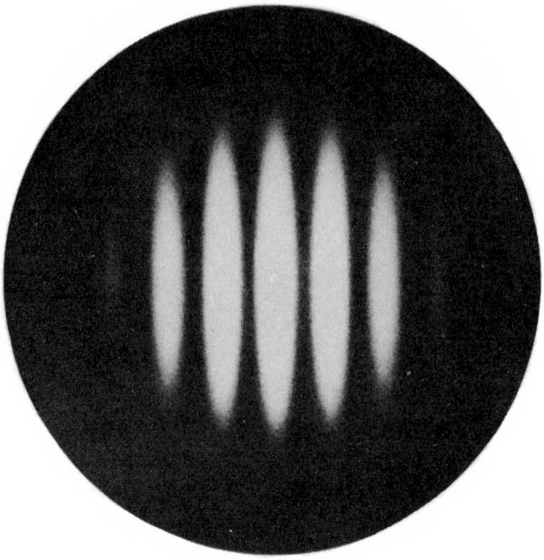

(i)

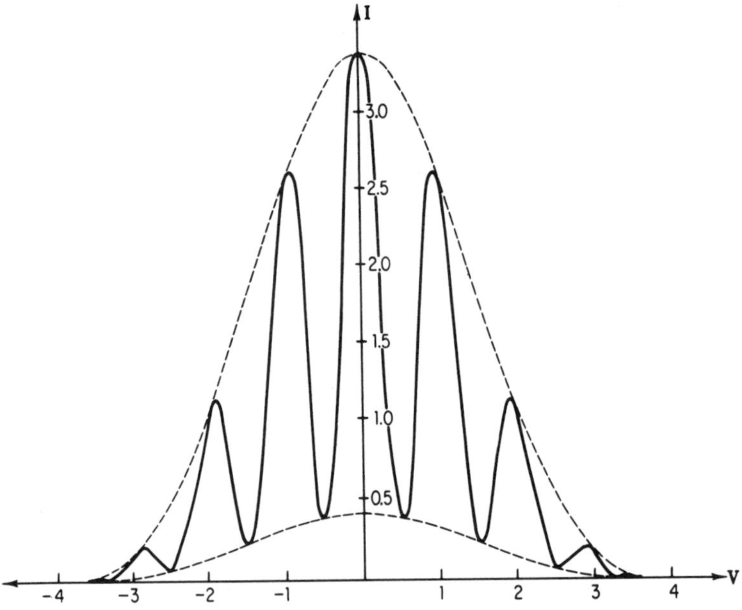

(ii)

Figure 5-3b. Two-beam interference with partially coherent light, showing the change of phase. (i) Observed patterns. (ii) Theoretical intentisty curves. The chain lines represent the curves I_{max} and I_{min}. ($2h = 0.5$ cm, $|\gamma_{12}| = 0.703$, $\beta_{12} = 0$.)

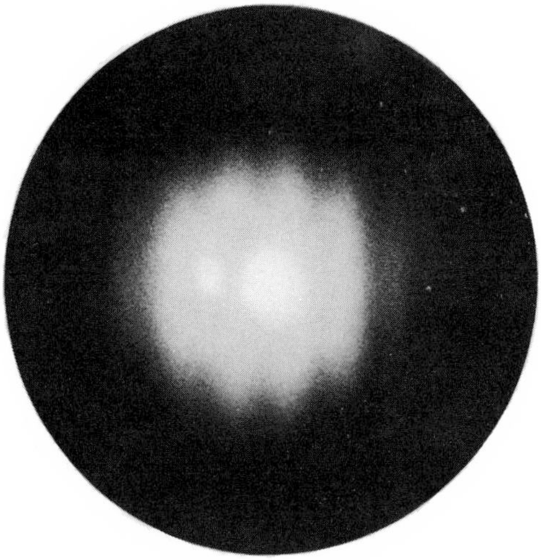

(i)

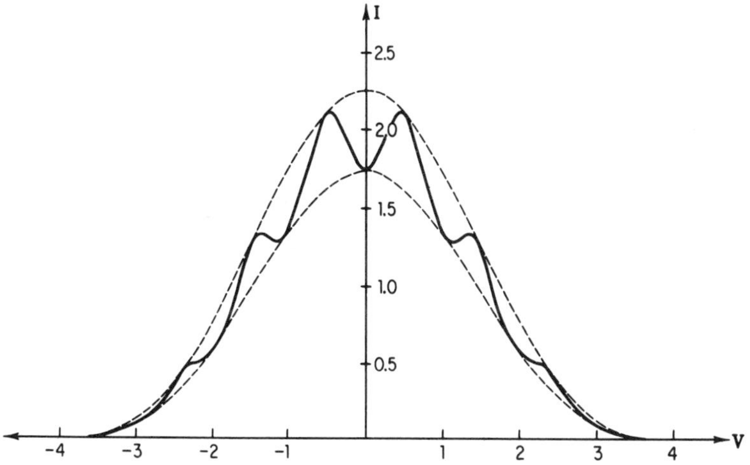

(ii)

Figure 5-3c. Two-beam interference with partially coherent light, showing the change of phase. (i) Observed patterns. (ii) Theoretical intensity curves. The chain lines represent the curves I_{max} and I_{min}. ($2h=0.5$ cm, $|\gamma_{12}| = 0.132$, $\beta_{12} = \pi$.)

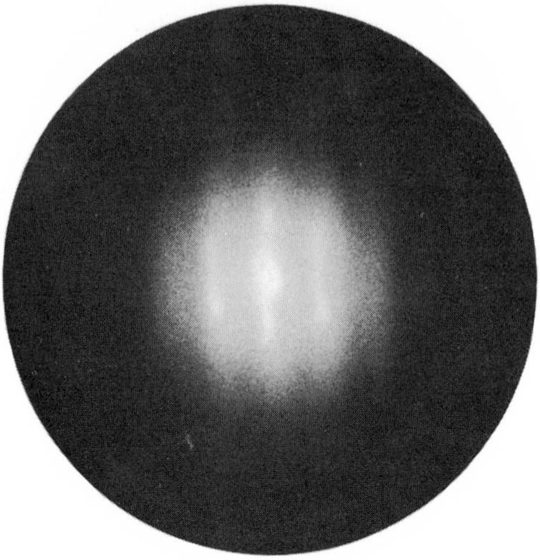

(i)

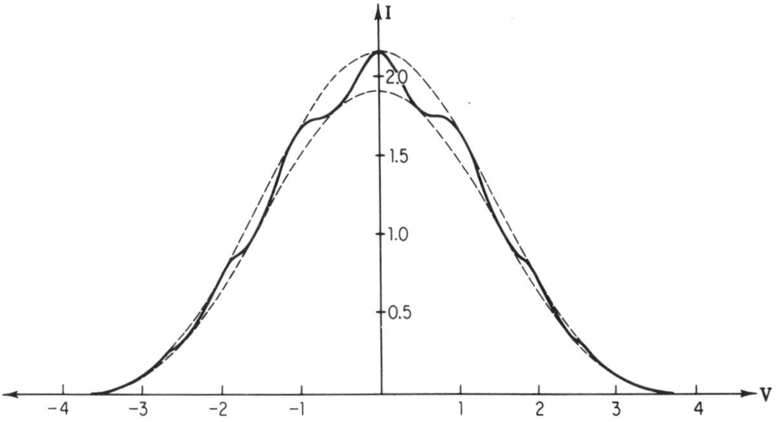

(ii)

Figure 5-3d. Two-beam interference with partially coherent light, showing the change of phase. (i) Observed patterns. (ii) Theoretical intensity curves. The chain lines represent the curves $I_{\max}$ and $I_{\min}$. ($2h = 0.5$ cm, $|\gamma_{12}| = 0.062$, $\beta_{12} = 0$.)

chapter

6

Propagation through Media with Variable Index of Refraction

When considering the propagation of the mutual coherence function through free space, we were able to derive partial differential equations which governed its development. To solve any radiation problem in terms of $\Gamma_{12}(\tau)$ it was only necessary to specify $\Gamma_{12}(\tau)$ on the boundary surfaces.

It is clear that one need not proceed in this manner. Integral solutions of $V(t)$ could have been obtained directly and $\Gamma_{12}(\tau)$ found by averaging two such integral solutions. Since, however, in both cases the object is to obtain a solution of $\Gamma_{12}(\tau)$ in terms of boundary conditions on $\Gamma_{12}(\tau)$ itself, it seemed desirable to cast the theory in the more versatile differential equation form. The latter form permits easy passage to an integral solution if desired and allows simpler treatment of problems with no finite boundary surface (see Chapter 11).

When considering propagation through media with variable index of refraction, however, we sometimes do not find it convenient or even possible to formulate the problem in terms of a differential equation. To explore the problem of appropriate formulation for the determination of $\Gamma_{12}(\tau)$, we shall, for the purpose of this chapter, consider a medium to be defined by specification of its index of refraction, and we consider three cases: (1) The index of refraction of the medium is a nonrandom function of position. (2) The index of refraction of the medium is a function of both time and position. (3) The index of refraction of the medium is defined in terms of an ensemble, the index being a function only of position in each member of the ensemble. In all cases we shall neglect dispersion effects.

The first case offers no difficulty in formulation, and we shall simply state the relevant governing equations. Much work has been done on this type of problem for which coherent radiation has been assumed, but there is little analysis available for partially coherent radiation except in connection with optical imaging systems. For solutions of the coherent problem in layered media, we refer the reader to Brekhovskikh (1960). The second case offers considerable difficulty in formulation, and we shall outline the difficulties. Since we know of no significant work done directly on this problem, we present none. Most of our attention is given to the third case where, although difficulties appear similar to those arising in the second case, various formulations are available for special cases and a number of solutions have been obtained.

We shall present a solution to a far-field scattering problem in the limit of small perturbations in the index of refraction. For purposes of simplicity, we shall use scalar theory throughout this chapter, and thus only forward scattering problems may be properly treated. However, a vector theory may be formally developed in exactly the same manner as the scalar theory. In the literature the vector solution is commonly used in integral formulations.

We conclude the chapter with a discussion of a laboratory experiment in which radiation is propagated through ground glass. This experiment will directly illustrate the effect of taking an ensemble average.

6.1 NON-RANDOM SPATIAL VARIATION OF THE INDEX OF REFRACTION

This case offers no difficulty in formulating a complete theory for $\Gamma_{12}(\tau)$

in terms of differential equations in a manner analogous to our free space derivation. The difficulty is only in the solution of the resultant equations. The resultant equations for $\Gamma_{12}(\tau)$ are:†

$$\nabla_i^2 \Gamma_{12}(\tau) = \frac{1}{c^2} n_i^2(\mathbf{x}_i) \frac{\partial^2}{\partial \tau^2} \Gamma_{12}(\tau) \qquad (i = 1, 2) \tag{6–1}$$

$n_i(\mathbf{x}_i)$ being the index of refraction.

Equation (6-1) is actually a key equation in a description of optical imaging systems. For a multiple lens system, for example, $n_i(\mathbf{x}_i)$ is a discontinuous function describing the index variation from one optical element to the next. From a formal point of view, it is Eq. (6-1) which justifies the treatment of image forming systems as linear systems (see Chap. 7). The spatial non-stationarity of image forming systems follows from the fact that in Eq. (6-1) $n_i(\mathbf{x}_i)$ is a function of $\mathbf{x}_i$. (This point is also discussed in Chap. 7).

If $n_i(\mathbf{x}_i)$ was a spatially random function, Eq. (6–1) would not be a useful formulation of the problem. The ensemble formulation given in Section 6.4 is intended to treat such a problem.

6.2 SPATIAL AND TEMPORAL VARIATION OF THE INDEX OF REFRACTION

When the index of refraction is time varying, the simple formulation just given is impossible.

If we write‡

$$\nabla^2 V(\mathbf{x}, t) = \frac{1}{c^2} \frac{\partial^2}{\partial t^2} n^2(\mathbf{x}, t)\, V(\mathbf{x}, t) \tag{6–2}$$

Then we find

$$\nabla_1^2 \Gamma_{12}(\tau) = \frac{1}{c^2} \frac{\partial^2}{\partial \tau^2} \langle n_1^2(\mathbf{x}_1, t + \tau)\, V_1(t + \tau)\, V_2^*(t) \rangle \tag{6–3††}$$

Since in general, V_1 and V_2 are not independent of n_1^2, we do not have an equation governing $\Gamma_{12}(\tau)$ alone. This is a problem that arises in many statistical formulations. It occurs in turbulent diffusion problems and problems in inhomogeneous elastic media. It is characterized by inability to find a determinate set of differential equations for an average function, like $\Gamma_{12}(\tau)$, when a coefficient in the equations, like $n(\mathbf{x}, t)$, has the same variable dependence as the functions, like $V(\mathbf{x}, t)$, that are used to formulate

†Since we are using a scalar theory, we have assumed that terms involving gradients of n_i are negligible in this and succeeding sections.

‡We assume that characteristic time variations in $n(\mathbf{x}, t)$ are slow compared to $1/\bar{\nu}$.

††It is assumed here that $\langle n_1^2(\mathbf{x}_1, t + \tau)\, V_1(t + \tau)\, V_2(t) \rangle$ and hence $\Gamma_{12}(\tau)$ exist.

the average. That is, since the average needed to form $\Gamma_{12}(\tau)$ is over t and both $V(\mathbf{x}, t)$ and $n(\mathbf{x}, t)$ are functions of t, it appears impossible in general to find a single finite differential equation governing $\Gamma_{12}(\tau)$ that depends only upon average functions of $n(\mathbf{x}, t)$.

The same result may be seen here in an integral formulation. In order to solve this problem in integral form, we return to Eq. (6–2). Since Eq. (6–2) is linear, we may formally write

$$V(\mathbf{x}, t) = \int_{S'} \int_{-\infty}^{\infty} G(\mathbf{x}, t; \mathbf{x}'_S, t')\, V(\mathbf{x}'_S, t)\, dt\, dS' \tag{6–4}$$

where $G(\mathbf{x}, t; \mathbf{x}'_S, t')$ is a Green's function which gives $V(\mathbf{x}, t)$ due to a unit potential at surface point $\mathbf{x}_S$ at time t. We consider $G(\mathbf{x}, t; \mathbf{x}'_S, t')$ to equal 0 when $t - t' < 0$; hence the limits of integration are $-\infty$ to $+\infty$. As in Section 2.3, we will also use $V_{S'T}(\mathbf{x}'_S, t')$ a function that is zero when $|t| > T$.† We do so for convenience in taking limits. Then $\Gamma_{12}(\tau)$ takes the form‡

$$\Gamma_{12}(\tau) = \lim_{T\to\infty} \frac{1}{2T} \int_{-T}^{T} \int_{S''} \int_{S'} \iint_{-\infty}^{\infty} dt\, dS''\, dS'\, dt''\, dt' \cdot \tag{6–5}$$
$$G^*(\mathbf{x}_2, t; \mathbf{x}''_S, t'')\, G(\mathbf{x}_1, t + \tau; \mathbf{x}'_S, t')\, V_{S''T}(\mathbf{x}''_S, t'')\, V_{S'T}(\mathbf{x}'_S, t')$$

In general, $G(\mathbf{x}_i, t_i; \mathbf{x}'_S, t'_S)$ depends upon both t_i and t'_S and not upon just the difference $t_i - t'_S$, since we have assumed the medium to be time varying. Thus, in general, $\Gamma_{12}(\tau)$ *cannot* be written in the form

$$\Gamma_{12}(\tau) = O(\mathbf{x}_1, \mathbf{x}_2, \tau; \mathbf{x}_{1S}, \mathbf{x}_{2S}, \delta)\, \Gamma_{1S,\, 2S}(\delta) \tag{6–6}$$

where O is some operator which depends *only* upon the properties of the medium.§

For this case therefore, we find that in general an integral or a differential equation for $\Gamma_{12}(\tau)$ cannot be formulated. As we have stated, almost no work has been done to solve this problem, in this form.†† When $n(\mathbf{x}, t)$ is a statistical variable, however, an ensemble formulation of this problem is sometimes possible and a considerable amount of work has been done in this direction. As we shall see in the next section a formulation problem still exists in the ensemble case even though a single integral equation of

†We keep T as a subscript here, rather than as an argument, as in Section 2.3.

‡Again, we assume that $\Gamma_{12}(\tau)$ exists.

§If $G(\mathbf{x}_i\; t_i; \mathbf{x}_S, t_S) = G(\mathbf{x}_i; t_i - t_S; \mathbf{x}_S, 0)$ it can be shown that

$$\Gamma_{12}(\tau) = \int_{S''} \int_{S'} \iint_{-\infty}^{\infty} dS''\, dS'\, d\beta\, d\alpha\, G^*(\mathbf{x}_2, \beta; \mathbf{x}''_S, 0)\, G(\mathbf{x}_1, \beta + \alpha + \tau; \mathbf{x}'_S, 0)\, \Gamma_{S'S''}(\alpha)$$

and there is no difficulty.

††An interesting article by Adomian (1963) does, however, considerably clarify this type of problem.

the form of Eq. (6–6) is now possible. Here, however, perturbation procedures have been developed to overcome the difficulties.†

6.3 STATISTICAL VARIATION OF THE INDEX OF REFRACTION

When the time variations of the index of refraction are random and very slow compared to the characteristic times of the radiation $(1/\bar{\nu}, 1/\Delta\nu)$ and propagation (l/c), the problem simplifies, since we may then approximate the physical situation by a time invariant ensemble formulation; i.e., by a formulation that essentially uncouples the radiation and media time variations.

We assume that the long-time average over the medium variation may be replaced by an ensemble average over many media systems such that in each system there is only a spatial variation of index of refraction. Systems of the ensemble are found by (1) considering a medium as fixed during times long compared to characteristic radiation times but short compared to characteristic times of medium variation and (2) considering the medium at successive times, $t_1, t_2 \ldots t_n$, where $t_{k+1} - t_k$ is long compared to characteristic times of medium variation. Each time, t_j, denotes a new system of the ensemble. Each member of the ensemble produces a different field coherence function, say, ${}^i\Gamma_{12}(\tau)$, corresponding to the spatially varying index of refraction of that member (the ith) of the ensemble. $\overline{{}^i\Gamma_{12}(\tau)}$, where the bar indicates ensemble averaging, yields the combined effect of both radiation and media variations.

The ensemble formalism is rigorously correct if we are considering propagation through time-independent spatially random media. Here we know only the statistical properties of the media and wish to know the average result of many experiments, i.e., over an ensemble. Propagation of radiation through ground glass would require such a formulation.

To present the formalism, we write Eq. (6–3) as

$$\nabla_1^2\, {}^i\Gamma_{12}(\tau) = \frac{{}^in_1^2(\mathbf{x}_1)}{c^2}\frac{\partial^{2\,i}\Gamma_{12}(\tau)}{\partial\tau^2} \tag{6–7}$$

Differentiating this equation with respect to ∇_2^2, we find

$$\nabla_2^2\nabla_1^2\, {}^i\Gamma_{12}(\tau) = \frac{{}^in_1^2(\mathbf{x}_1)\,{}^in_2^2(\mathbf{x}_2)}{c^4}\frac{\partial^4}{\partial\tau^4}\, {}^i\Gamma_{12}(\tau) \tag{6–8}$$

It would now be desirable to take an ensemble average of both sides of Eq. (6–8), but as we noted in Section 6.3 since ${}^i\Gamma_{12}(\tau)$ and ${}^in_1^2(\mathbf{x}_1)\, {}^in_2^2(\mathbf{x}_2)$ are not independent, this would not yield an equation governing $\Gamma_{12}(\tau)$ alone.

†Presumably, when the time varying problem can be converted to an ensemble formulation and thence solved, it can be solved directly in the time domain. Nevertheless, in these cases the ensemble formulation is used in general.

A single differential equation governing the propagation of $\overline{{}^i\Gamma_{12}(\tau)}$ cannot be obtained in general. A single integral representation for $\overline{{}^i\Gamma_{12}(\tau)}$ is possible, however, in terms of a Green's function of the form, $\overline{{}^iK(\mathbf{x}_1, \mathbf{x}_2; \mathbf{x}_{1S}, \mathbf{x}_{2S}; \nu)}$ where ${}^iK$ is a Green's function for the ith medium representation. ${}^iK$ contains all the information about ${}^in^2(\mathbf{x})$. Proceeding as in Section 6.3, we would find

$$\overline{{}^i\Gamma_{12}(\tau)} = \int_0^\infty e^{-2\pi i\nu\tau}\, d\nu \int_S \int_S dS''\, dS'\, \overline{{}^iK(\mathbf{x}_1, \mathbf{x}_2; \mathbf{x}_{1S}, \mathbf{x}_{2S}; \nu)} \cdot \hat{\Gamma}_{1S,\,2S}(\nu) \tag{6–9}$$

Unfortunately, from an analytical point of view (as distinct from an experimental point of view—see Section. 9.3), this expression is of little use since $\overline{{}^iK(\mathbf{x}_1, \mathbf{x}_2; \mathbf{x}_{1S}, \mathbf{x}_{2S}; \nu)}$ cannot be directly calculated. Instead, it has proved necessary to develop perturbation procedures which essentially determine $\overline{{}^iK}$ in an iterative manner.

The perturbation procedure using an integral formulation has been fully developed in a paper by Parrent, Shore, and Skinner (1962) and they find an expression for $\overline{{}^i\Gamma_{12}(\tau)}$ in terms of $\Gamma_{1S,2S}(\tau)$ and all order correlations of ${}^in_1(\mathbf{x}_1)$. The analogous perturbation procedure using a sequence of differential equations has not yet been formulated, although no difficulty is anticipated. A first-order theory, however, is very simply derived and this will be presented under "Formulation of perturbation equations."

An alternate approach to the perturbation technique is possible, if one assumes statistical independence at one point in the formulation of the differential equations. We present this approach at the conclusion of this section but shall give no solutions, since the method is only currently being studied for continuous random media.

Formulation of perturbation equations

Since obtaining any but a first approximation to the perturbation solution of ${}^i\Gamma_{12}(\tau)$ requires almost prohibitive work, we restrict ourselves to the first approximation of the perturbation series in this chapter. When only the first approximation is needed a differential equation formalism is again convenient and we present this approach here. We refer the reader to Parrent, Shore, and Skinner (1962) for a more complete formulation.

Assume the variation of ${}^in_j^2(\mathbf{x}_j)$ from n_0^2, the mean value, is small. Write

$${}^in_j^2(\mathbf{x}_j) = n_0^2 + \epsilon\, {}^in_{j1}^2(\mathbf{x}_j)$$

where the ${}^in_{j1}^2(\mathbf{x}_j)$ are of the order of n_0^2 and have zero mean values; ϵ is a small parameter. Assume a solution for ${}^i\Gamma_{12}(\tau)$ of the form

$${}^i\Gamma_{12}(\tau) = \Gamma_{12}^{(0)}(\tau) + \epsilon\, {}^i\Gamma_{12}^{(1)}(\tau) + \epsilon^2\, {}^i\Gamma_{12}^{(2)}(\tau) + \cdots \tag{6–10}$$

where ${}^i\Gamma_{12}^{(j)}(\tau)$, $j > 0$ is assumed of order $\Gamma_{12}^{(0)}(\tau)$. $\Gamma_{12}^{(0)}(\tau)$ is independent of the variation in index of refraction. Then substituting back in Eq. (6–8) and comparing coefficients, we find for $\Gamma_{12}^{(0)}(\tau)$, ${}^i\Gamma_{12}^{(1)}(\tau)$, ${}^i\Gamma_{12}^{(2)}(\tau)$, after ensemble averaging

(6–11)
$$\nabla_1^2 \nabla_2^2 \Gamma_{12}^{(0)}(\tau) = \frac{1}{c^4} n_0^4 \frac{\partial^4 \Gamma_{12}^{(0)}(\tau)}{\partial \tau^4}$$

$$\overline{{}^i\Gamma_{12}^{(1)}(\tau)} = 0$$

$$\nabla_1^2 \nabla_2^2 \overline{{}^i\Gamma_{12}^{(2)}(\tau)} = \frac{n_0^4}{c^4} \frac{\partial^4}{\partial \tau^4} \overline{{}^i\Gamma_{12}^{(2)}(\tau)} + \frac{n_0^2}{c^2} \frac{\partial^4}{\partial \tau^4} \overline{{}^i\Gamma_{12}^{(1)}(\tau)(n_{11}^2(\mathbf{x}_1) + n_{21}^2(\mathbf{x}_2))} + \overline{{}^i n_{11}^2(\mathbf{x}_1)\, {}^i n_{21}^2(\mathbf{x}_2)} \frac{1}{c^4} \frac{\partial^4}{\partial \tau^4} \Gamma_{12}^{(0)}(\tau)$$

We note here that though

$$\overline{{}^i\Gamma_{12}^{(1)}(\tau)} = 0, \quad \overline{{}^i\Gamma_{12}^{(1)}(\tau)(n_{11}^2(\mathbf{x}_1) + n_{21}^2(\mathbf{x}_2))} \neq 0$$

The term

$$\frac{n_0^2}{c^2} \frac{\partial^4}{\partial \tau^4} \overline{{}^i\Gamma_{12}^{(1)}(\tau)(n_{11}^2(\mathbf{x}_1) + n_{21}^2(\mathbf{x}_2))}$$

may be eliminated from this equation by using the perturbation procedure on Eq. (6–7) to obtain a relation between

$$\frac{\partial^2\, {}^i\Gamma_{12}^{(1)}(\tau)}{\partial \tau^2}$$

and derivatives of ${}^i\Gamma_{12}^{(2)}(\tau)$. The final equation is

(6–12)
$$\nabla_1^2 \nabla_2^2 \overline{{}^i\Gamma_{12}^{(2)}(\tau)} - \frac{n_0^2}{c^2} \nabla_1^2 \frac{\partial^2}{\partial \tau^2} \overline{{}^i\Gamma_{12}^{(2)}(\tau)} - \frac{n_0^2}{c^2} \nabla_2^2 \frac{\partial^2}{\partial \tau^2} \overline{{}^i\Gamma_{12}^{(2)}(\tau)} + \frac{n_0^4}{c^4} \frac{\partial^4}{\partial \tau^4} \overline{{}^i\Gamma_{12}^{(2)}(\tau)} = \overline{{}^i n_{11}^2(\mathbf{x}_1)\, {}^i n_{21}^2(\mathbf{x}_2)} \frac{1}{c^4} \frac{\partial^4}{\partial \tau^4} \Gamma_{12}^{(0)}(\tau)$$

We note again that

(6–13)
$$\overline{{}^i\Gamma_{12}(\tau)} = \Gamma_{12}^{(0)}(\tau) + \epsilon\, \overline{{}^i\Gamma_{12}^{(1)}(\tau)} + \epsilon^2\, \overline{{}^i\Gamma_{12}^{(2)}(\tau)} + \cdots$$

Formulation of equations assuming statistical independence of $\overline{{}^i\Gamma_{12}(\tau)}$ and $\overline{{}^i n_1(\mathbf{x}_1)\, {}^i n_2(\mathbf{x}_2)}$

In Eq. (6–7) we let

(6–14)
$$\begin{aligned} {}^i n_1^2(\mathbf{x}_1) &= n_0^2 + {}^i n_1'^2(\mathbf{x}_1) \\ {}^i n_2^2(\mathbf{x}_2) &= n_0^2 + {}^i n_2'^2(\mathbf{x}_2) \end{aligned}$$

where now ${}^i n_1'$ and ${}^i n_2'$ are not necessarily small.

Substituting Eq. (6–14) into Eq. (6–8) and performing manipulations similar to those necessary to obtain Eq. (6–12) from Eq. (6–11) yields

$$\nabla_1^2 \nabla_2^2 \overline{{}^i\Gamma_{12}(\tau)} - \frac{n_0^2}{c^2} \nabla_1^2 \frac{\partial^2}{\partial\tau^2} \overline{{}^i\Gamma_{12}(\tau)}$$

$$(6\text{–}15) \qquad - \frac{n_0^2}{c^2} \nabla_2^2 \frac{\partial^2}{\partial\tau^2} \overline{{}^i\Gamma_{12}(\tau)} + \frac{n_0^4}{c^4} \frac{\partial^4}{\partial\tau^4} \overline{{}^i\Gamma_{12}(\tau)}$$

$$= \overline{{}^i n_1'^2(\mathbf{x}_1)\, {}^i n_2'^2(\mathbf{x}_2) \frac{1}{c^4} \frac{\partial^4}{\partial\tau^4} {}^i\Gamma_{12}(\tau)}$$

This equation is indeterminate as it stands, since the right-hand side cannot in general be expressed in terms of $\overline{{}^i\Gamma_{12}(\tau)}$. To accomplish this, we make the assumption:

$$(6\text{–}16) \qquad \overline{{}^i n_1'^2(\mathbf{x}_1)\, {}^i n_2'^2(\mathbf{x}_1)\, {}^i\Gamma_{12}(\tau)} = \overline{{}^i n_1'^2(\mathbf{x}_1)\, {}^i n_2'^2(\mathbf{x}_2)}\, [\overline{{}^i\Gamma_{12}(\tau)}]$$

This assumption requires considerable justification. If correct, it allows a very simple finite formulation of a problem that ordinarily must be formulated in terms of an infinite series.

To first order this equation gives the same equation as the perturbation treatment. The conditions for the justification of this assumption for large deviations has not received serious study for a continuous random medium. We will give below a one paragraph pictorial justification for this assumption when l_n, a characteristic length representing the statistical variation of $n(\mathbf{x})$, is very small compared to a characteristic volume dimension. As stated earlier, we present no solutions using this approach.

The field $V(\mathbf{x}, t)$ at some point in the volume is made up of the field that would exist if ${}^i n(\mathbf{x})$ where a constant, plus a scattered field. The scattered field at, say, $\mathbf{x}_1$, is made up of scattered radiation from the whole volume, $\bar{V}$. Thus ${}^i\Gamma_{12}(\tau)$ is affected by the entire variation of ${}^i n(\mathbf{x})$ over all $\bar{V}$. (Of course, since we assume a scalar theory, the scattering must be principally forward.) On the other hand, ${}^i n(\mathbf{x}_1)$ is correlated to ${}^i n(\mathbf{x}_2)$ only over distances l_n which are small compared to $\bar{V}^{1/3}$. Therefore, we may expect ${}^i n_1'^2(\mathbf{x}_1)\, {}^i n_2'^2(\mathbf{x}_2)$ to be only very weakly correlated to ${}^i\Gamma_{12}(\tau)$. As a first approximation, we neglect this correlation in Eq. 6–15.

6.4 SOLUTION OF EQUATIONS

From the standpoint of the theory of partial coherence, the only work on propagation through variable media known to the authors (with the exception of optical imaging systems) is from an ensemble point of view. Considering plane wave monochromatic radiation as a special case of partially coherent radiation, however, considerable work has been done on propagation through layered media (as previously mentioned).

Here we consider only the case of propagation through random media from an ensemble point of view. The development will include the work done on plane wave monochromatic radiation as a special case when the perturbation solutions used for monochromatic radiation studies are similar to those given in Section 6.4.

To obtain a solution, we shall further restrict ourselves to finite media of real random index of refraction and study the scattered radiation in the far field of the media. When the radiation impinging on a random medium is partially coherent, it is extremely difficult to find the correct form of the coherence function if the radiation surface is adjacent to the random medium. Thus we shall also assume that the random medium is in the far field of the radiating source and that the source boundary condition does not affect the scattered radiation. This difficulty does not enter when considering plane wave monochromatic radiation if no finite boundary conditions are given.

The quantity we wish to study is $\overline{{}^i\Gamma_{12}^{(2)}(\tau)}$ which is governed by the equation:

$$\nabla_1^2 \nabla_2^2 \overline{{}^i\Gamma_{12}^{(2)}(\tau)} + \frac{n_0^4}{c^4}\frac{\partial^4}{\partial\tau^4}\overline{{}^i\Gamma_{12}^{(2)}(\tau)} - \frac{n_0^2}{c^2}\nabla_1^2\frac{\partial^2}{\partial\tau^2}\overline{{}^i\Gamma_{12}^{(2)}(\tau)} - \frac{n_0^2}{c^4}\nabla_2^2\frac{\partial^2}{\partial\tau^2}\overline{{}^i\Gamma_{12}^{(2)}(\tau)} = \frac{\overline{{}^in_{11}^2(\mathbf{x}_1)\,{}^in_{21}^2(\mathbf{x}_2)}}{c^4}\frac{\partial^4}{\partial\tau^4}\Gamma_{12}^{(0)}(\tau) \tag{6–17}$$

To simplify the notation slightly let us define

$$\overline{{}^i\Gamma_{12}^{(2)}(\tau)} \equiv \alpha_{12}(\tau) \quad \text{and} \quad \overline{{}^in_{11}^2(\mathbf{x}_1)\,{}^in_{21}^2(\mathbf{x}_2)} \equiv \sigma(\mathbf{x}_1, \mathbf{x}_2)$$

Then we have

$$\nabla_1^2\nabla_2^2\alpha_{12}(\tau) + \frac{n_0^4}{c^4}\frac{\partial^4}{\partial\tau^4}\alpha_{12}(\tau) - \frac{n_0^2}{c^2}\nabla_1^2\frac{\partial^2}{\partial\tau^2}\alpha_{12}(\tau) - \frac{n_0^2}{c^2}\nabla_2^2\frac{\partial^2}{\partial\tau^2}\alpha_{12}(\tau) = \frac{\sigma(\mathbf{x}_1, \mathbf{x}_2)}{c^4}\frac{\partial^4}{\partial\tau^4}\Gamma_{12}^{(0)}(\tau) \tag{6–18}$$

In this equation, $\sigma(\mathbf{x}_1, \mathbf{x}_2)$ and $\Gamma_{12}^{(0)}(\tau)$ are assumed known. To solve Eq. (6–18), we take the Fourier transform with respect to ν. This yields

$$(\nabla_1^2 + k_n^2)(\nabla_2^2 + k_n^2)\,\hat{\alpha}_{12}(\nu) = \sigma(\mathbf{x}_1, \mathbf{x}_2)k^4\hat{\Gamma}_{12}^{(0)}(\nu) \tag{6–19}$$

where

$$k_n^4 = \frac{n_0^4}{c^4}(2\pi\nu)^4; \qquad k^4 = \frac{(2\pi\nu)^4}{c^4}$$

and

$$\hat{\alpha}_{12}(\nu) = \int_{-\infty}^{\infty} e^{2\pi i\nu\tau}\,\alpha_{12}(\tau)\,d\tau$$

$$\hat{\Gamma}_{12}^{(0)}(\nu) = \int_{-\infty}^{\infty} e^{2\pi i\nu\tau}\,\Gamma_{12}^{(0)}(\tau)\,d\tau$$

For simplicity, to avoid having refraction effects at the boundary of the

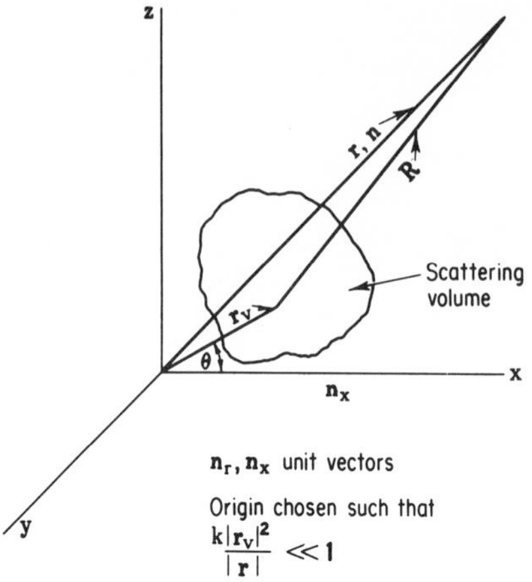

Figure 6-1. Geometry of a scattering volume.

random medium, we will let n_0 equal the index of refraction in the non-scattering region. Further, we will let $n_0 = 1$ in this development. To let n_0 equal a value other than 1, simply multiply the right-hand side of Eq. (6–19) by n_0^4/n_0^4 and remember that, in the subsequent development, k must be replaced by k_n and $\sigma(\mathbf{x}_1, \mathbf{x}_2)$ by $[\sigma(\mathbf{x}_1, \mathbf{x}_2)]/n_0^4$.

Since $\hat{\alpha}_{12}(\nu)$ is not fixed on any boundary, but results only from the interaction of $\Gamma_{12}^{(0)}(\tau)$ and the random media, the solution of Eq. (6–19) may be represented as a volume integral. The volume Green's function for the operator $(\nabla_1^2 + k^2)(\nabla_2^2 + k^2)$ is equal to†

$$\frac{1}{(4\pi)^2}\,\frac{e^{-ikR(\mathbf{x}_2,\,\mathbf{x}_{V''})+ikR(\mathbf{x}_1,\mathbf{x}_{V'})}}{R(\mathbf{x}_2, \mathbf{x}_{V''})R(\mathbf{x}_1, \mathbf{x}_{V'})}$$

where R is the distance between the field and volume points. Thus $\hat{\alpha}_{12}(\nu)$ has the form:

$$\hat{\alpha}(\mathbf{x}_1, \mathbf{x}_2, \nu) = \frac{1}{(4\pi)^2} \int_{V''}\int_{V'} \frac{k^4\, e^{-ikR(\mathbf{x}_2,\mathbf{x}_{V''})+ikR(\mathbf{x}_1,\mathbf{x}_{V'})}\,\sigma(\mathbf{x}_{V'}, \mathbf{x}_{V''})\hat{\Gamma}^{(0)}(\mathbf{x}_{V'}, \mathbf{x}_{V''}, \nu)}{R(\mathbf{x}_2, \mathbf{x}_{V''})\,R(\mathbf{x}_1, \mathbf{x}_{V'})}\,dV'\,dV'' \tag{6–20}$$

Now in the foregoing, we have assumed that R is very large; hence we expect to simplify Eq. (6–20). Referring to Fig. 6-1, we have

---

†The minus sign is necessary in one of the exponents, since $\Gamma_{12}(\tau)$ was formed from V and its complex conjugate.

$$R^2 = (r^2 + r_V^2 - 2\mathbf{r}\cdot\mathbf{r}_V) \tag{6–21}$$

Expanding this in a series, we obtain:

$$R \approx r\left\{1 - \frac{\mathbf{n}_r\cdot\mathbf{r}_V}{r} + \frac{1}{2r^2}[r_V^2 - (\mathbf{n}_r\cdot\mathbf{r}_V)^2] + \cdots\right\} \tag{6–22}$$

Assuming $(kl^2/r) \ll 1$, where l is a characteristic length of the scattering volume, we obtain

$$R \approx r - \mathbf{n}_r\cdot\mathbf{r}_V \tag{6–23}$$

Equation (6–20) is then approximately

$$\begin{aligned}\hat{\alpha}(\mathbf{x}_1, \mathbf{x}_2, \nu) &= \frac{1}{(4\pi)^2}\frac{k^4 e^{ik(r_1(\mathbf{x}_1)-r_2(\mathbf{x}_2))}}{r^2}\cdot \\ &\int_{V''}\int_{V'} e^{-ik(\mathbf{n}_{r_1}\cdot\mathbf{r}_{V'}-\mathbf{n}_{r_2}\cdot\mathbf{r}_{V''})}\,\sigma(\mathbf{x}_{V'}, \mathbf{x}_{V''})\hat{\Gamma}^{(0)}(\mathbf{x}_{V'}, \mathbf{x}_{V''}, \nu)\,dV'\,dV''\end{aligned} \tag{6–24}$$

where we have assumed

$$\frac{1}{R_1 R_2} = \frac{1}{r_1 r_2} = \frac{1}{r^2}$$

To find $\alpha(\mathbf{x}_1, \mathbf{x}_2, \tau)$ we take the inverse Fourier transform of $\hat{\alpha}(\mathbf{x}_1, \mathbf{x}_2, \nu)$.

Scattering of plane wave monochromatic radiation

When the radiation may be approximated by a plane monochromatic wave, Eq. (6–24) simplifies considerably. For a wave along the x axis, $\hat{\Gamma}^{(0)}(\mathbf{x}_{V'}, \mathbf{x}_{V''}, \nu) = \hat{I}(\nu_0)\,\delta(\nu - \nu_0)\,e^{ik_0(x_{V'}-x_{V''})}$. Then

$$\begin{aligned}\hat{\alpha}(\mathbf{x}_1, \mathbf{x}_2, \nu) &= \frac{\hat{I}(\nu_0)k_0^4}{(4\pi)^2 r^2}\delta(\nu - \nu_0)\,e^{ik_0[r_1(\mathbf{x}_1)-r_2(\mathbf{x}_2)]} \\ &\int_{V''}\int_{V'} \sigma(\mathbf{x}_{V'}, \mathbf{x}_{V''})\,e^{-ik_0(\mathbf{n}_{r_1}\cdot\mathbf{r}_{V'}-\mathbf{n}_{r_2}\cdot\mathbf{r}_{V''})}\,e^{ik_0(x_{V'}-x_{V''})}\,dV'\,dV''\end{aligned} \tag{6–25}$$

We let $k = k_0$ in anticipation of integration of the delta function over ν.

The problem is simplified further if we let $\sigma(\mathbf{x}_{V'}, \mathbf{x}_{V''})$ have the form $\sigma(\mathbf{x}_{V'}, \mathbf{x}_{V''}) = \eta(\mathbf{x}_{V'})\,\gamma(|\mathbf{x}_{V'} - \mathbf{x}_{V''}|)$, where $\eta(\mathbf{x}_{V'})$ varies little in distances over which $\gamma(|\mathbf{x}_{V'} - \mathbf{x}_{V''}|)$ is of appreciable magnitude. In other words, we assume that only the turbulent intensity is non-homogeneous.

We next make the transformation to the coordinate system:

$$\begin{aligned}\mathbf{s} &= \mathbf{r}_{V'} - \mathbf{r}_{V''} \\ \mathbf{p} &= \mathbf{r}_{V'}\end{aligned} \tag{6–26}$$

It is also usual to let $\mathbf{K} = k_0(\mathbf{n}_{r_2} - \mathbf{n}_x)$, where we note that

$$|\mathbf{K}| = 2k_0 \sin\frac{\theta}{2}$$

where θ is the angle between $\mathbf{r}_i$ and $\mathbf{x}$.

Thus we have

$$\hat{\alpha}(\mathbf{x}_1, \mathbf{x}_2, \nu) = \frac{\hat{I}(\nu_0)k_0^4}{(4\pi)^2 r^2}\,\delta(\nu - \nu_0)\, e^{ik_0(r_1(\mathbf{x}_1)-r_2(\mathbf{x}_2))} \int_{V_p} \eta(\mathbf{p})\, e^{-ik_0\mathbf{p}\cdot(\mathbf{n}_{r_1}-\mathbf{n}_{r_2})}\, dV_p \int_{V_s} \gamma(|\mathbf{s}|)\, e^{-i\mathbf{K}\cdot\mathbf{s}}\, dV_s \tag{6–27}$$

We have previously assumed that $\gamma(|\mathbf{s}|)$ is effectively zero in distances small compared to $\bar{V}^{1/3}$. We note that the jacobian of the transformation Eq. (6–26) is 1.

From the foregoing expression, we see that the effect of the statistical index of refraction variations is reflected in the intensity at $\mathbf{x}$, whereas the size of the scattering volume and the effect of large-scale inhomogeneities are reflected in the coherence between points $\mathbf{x}_1$ and $\mathbf{x}_2$. This may be seen directly since the intensity transform, $\hat{\alpha}(\mathbf{x}_1, \mathbf{x}_1, \nu)$, is

$$\hat{\alpha}(\mathbf{x}_1, \mathbf{x}_2, \nu) = \frac{\hat{I}(\nu_0)k_0^4}{(4\pi)^2 r^2}\,\delta(\nu - \nu_0) \int_{V_p} \eta(\mathbf{p})\, dV_p \int_{V_s} \gamma(|\mathbf{s}|)\, e^{-i\mathbf{K}\cdot\mathbf{s}}\, dV_s \tag{6–28}$$

Further assuming the intensity between nearby points varies slowly in distances for which the coherence drops to zero we may set

$$\hat{\alpha}(\mathbf{x}_1, \mathbf{x}_2, \nu) = \hat{\alpha}(\mathbf{x}_1, \mathbf{x}_1, \nu)\, e^{ik_0(r_1(\mathbf{x}_1)-r_2(\mathbf{x}_2))} \frac{1}{\int_{V_p} \eta(\mathbf{p})\, dV_p} \int_{V_p} \eta(\mathbf{p})\, e^{-ik_0\mathbf{p}\cdot(\mathbf{n}_{r_1}-\mathbf{n}_{r_2})}\, dV_p \tag{6–29}$$

showing the dependence of $\hat{\alpha}(\mathbf{x}_1, \mathbf{x}_2, \nu)$ upon the volume size through the integral over $\eta(\mathbf{p})e^{-ik_0\mathbf{p}\cdot(\mathbf{n}_{r_1}-\mathbf{n}_{r_2})}$.

The integral

$$J_1 = \int_{V_s} \gamma(|\mathbf{s}|)\, e^{-i\mathbf{K}\cdot\mathbf{s}}\, dV_s$$

may be simplified further by going to spherical coordinates. Integration then gives for this integral the form

$$J_1 = 4\pi \int_0^\infty \gamma(r) \frac{[\sin(|\mathbf{K}|r)]r^2}{|\mathbf{K}|r}\, dr \tag{6–30}$$

If $\gamma(r)$ has a characteristic dimension a, then if $k_0 a \ll 1$, the integral is independent of θ and the scattering is isotropic. If $k_0 a \gg 1$, the major part of the contribution comes when $\theta < 1/k_0 a$. This can be seen explicitly by letting, for example,

$$\gamma(r) = \gamma_0\, e^{-r^2/a^2}$$

and evaluating the integral of Eq. (6–30).

Since we have used a scalar theory, the theory is not expected to have too much validity for the former case, but it should prove essentially correct when the scattering is principally forward.

To show the effect of the integral over p, let us assume the volume is a cube of sides $2L$ along the x, y, and z axis, $\eta(\mathbf{p}) = 1$ and let

$$\mathbf{n}_{r_1} = \left(\frac{x_1}{r}, \frac{y_1}{r}, 0\right), \quad \mathbf{n}_{r_2} = \left(\frac{x_1}{r}, \frac{y_2}{r}, 0\right)$$

Then this integral, say, J_2, is

$$\begin{aligned} J_2 &= L^2 \int_{-L}^{L} e^{-k_0 p_y [(y_1 - y_2)/r]}\, dp_y \\ &= 2L^3 \frac{\sin B}{B} \end{aligned} \tag{6–31}$$

where

$$B = \frac{k_0 L (y_1 - y_2)}{r}$$

The $(\sin B)/B$ function is of the same origin as that derived in Eq. (5–18). The only difference is that now we have integrated over a volume rather than a surface. The more intuitive picture of Michelson given in Chapter 5 may be also used here to gain physical insight into this problem.

To conclude this section, we remember that $\alpha(\mathbf{x}_1, \mathbf{x}_2, \tau)$ is the Fourier transform of $\hat{\alpha}(\mathbf{x}_1, \mathbf{x}_2, \nu)$; hence from Eq. (6–27), we have

$$\begin{aligned} \alpha(\mathbf{x}_1, \mathbf{x}_2, \tau) &= \text{const}\, e^{2\pi i \nu_0 \tau} \frac{k_0^4}{r^2}\, e^{ik_0(r_1(\mathbf{x}_1) - r_2(\mathbf{x}_2))} \\ &\quad \int_{V_p} \eta(\mathbf{p})\, e^{-ik_0 \mathbf{p}\cdot(\mathbf{n}_{r_1} - \mathbf{n}_{r_2})}\, dV_p \int_{V_s} \gamma(|\mathbf{s}|)\, e^{-i\mathbf{K}\cdot\mathbf{s}}\, dV_s \end{aligned} \tag{6–32}$$

For a more complete treatment of this problem, see Skinner (1964) and the monographs by Chernov (1960) and Tatarski (1961). In the monographs, the two-point amplitude and phase coherence is studied rather than the more general function $\hat{\alpha}(\mathbf{x}_1, \mathbf{x}_2, \nu)$. We also refer the reader to the basic paper of Booker and Gordon (1950) in which scattering of radio waves by the troposphere is discussed.

6.5 PROPAGATION OF RADIATION THROUGH GROUND GLASS; AN EXPERIMENT

In this section we consider the propagation of radiation through a piece of ground glass. Figure 6-2a represents the far-field diffraction pattern of a hole illuminated by a quasi-monochromatic coherent plane wave from a gaseous laser. Figure 6-2b represents the diffraction pattern of the same radiation on this same hole when a piece of Kodak fine ground glass is placed behind the hole. Figure 6-2c represents the diffraction pattern of the hole when the ground glass is very slowly moved behind the hole; this procedure yields an ensemble average over many different pieces of ground

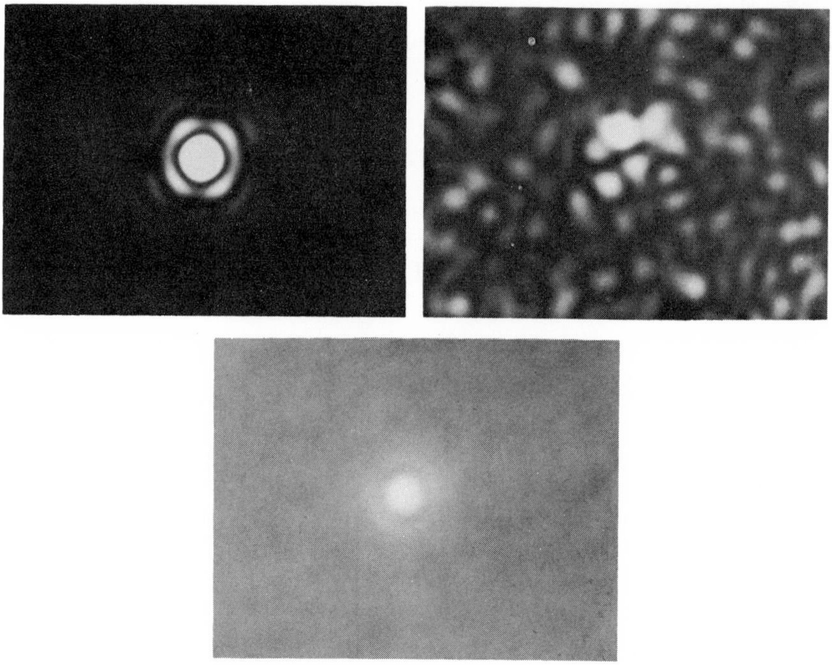

Figure 6-2 (a-c). Single-hole diffraction experiment using ground glass. (*Photographs by P. Considine, Technical Operations, Burlington, Mass.*)

glass. The hole dimension is significantly greater than a characteristic dimension of ground glass variation.

In Fig. 6-2a we observe the classical diffraction pattern made when coherent quasi-monochromatic radiation impinges on a hole. Assuming $l \ll (c/\Delta\nu)$, the presence of ground glass in Fig. 6-2b does not effect the coherence of the radiation. Thus, in Fig. 6-2b we see a diffraction pattern that shows high contrast intensity variations; this, in spite of the fact that the radiation is now spread over a wide angular field. Since the ground glass variations are random, the light and dark regions of the diffraction pattern change when a different piece of ground glass is placed behind the hole. Therefore, if the ground glass is slowly moved behind the hole, thus essentially placing a succession of different pieces of ground glass behind the hole and averaging over the different pieces, the sharp contrasts evident in Fig. 6-2b disappear. Instead we find the pattern given in Fig. 6-2c. Ensemble averaging *effectively* destroys the coherence of the radiation over the hole; $\overline{{}^j\Gamma(S_1, S_2, \tau)}$ is quite different from ${}^j\Gamma(S_1, S_2, \tau)$.

Figures 6-3(a-c) illustrate even more dramatically the coherence of the radiation after passing through ground glass. This set of figures represents the effect of the illumination on two holes. Again, Fig. 6-3a corresponds to

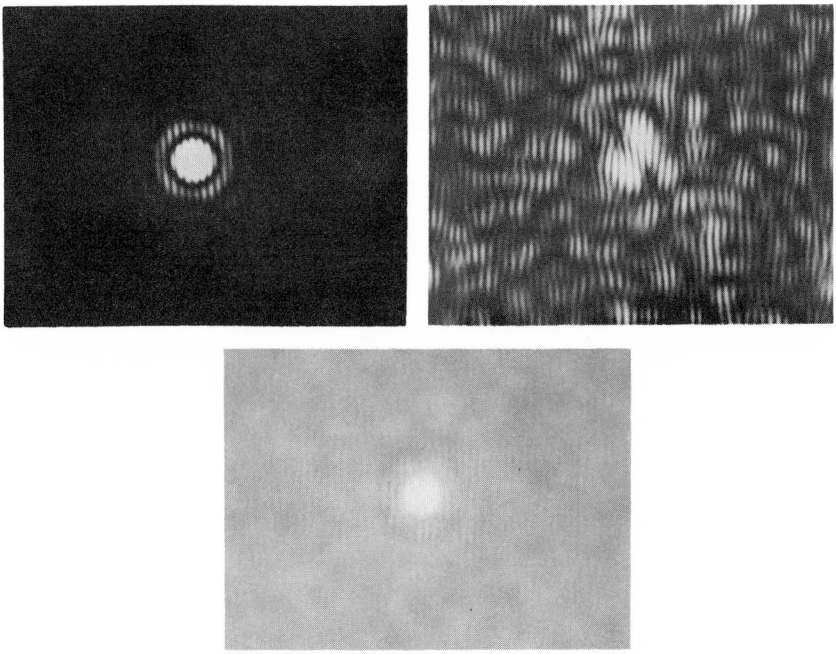

Figure 6-3 (a-c). Two-hole diffraction experiment using ground glass. (*Photographs by P. Considine, Technical Operations, Burlington, Mass.*)

the classical diffraction pattern with no ground glass; Fig. 6-3b, to the introduction of ground glass; Fig. 6-3c, to an average over an ensemble of pieces of ground glass. The sharp fringes in Fig. 6-3b again show that in a single experiment the radiation is coherent despite the spatial randomness of the pattern. In Fig. 6-3c, however, the fringes are now of very low contrast and barely visible, inasmuch as after ensemble averaging the coherence between points in different holes is significantly reduced.

The measurements presented above are preliminary, and thus we have given only a qualitative rather than quantitative discussion of the results. However, it was felt that some mention of them was warranted, for they clearly display the need for ensemble averaging if fields of the form

$$V_j(\mathbf{x}, t) = A_j(\mathbf{x})\, e^{2\pi i \bar{\nu} t + i\varphi_j(\mathbf{x})}$$

are to be considered as other than coherent.

chapter

7

Imaging with Partially Coherent Light

In this chapter, we apply the theorems and results of the earlier chapters to the determination of the relation between object and image for systems which image extended polychromatic objects. We shall treat the problem primarily in the spatial frequency domain, an approach introduced by Duffieux in 1946. Since its introduction, the frequency domain analysis has proved very powerful in the study of imaging systems both in optics and in radio astronomy—for example, see Bracewell and Roberts (1954).

In this analysis, the imaging system is described by a transfer function (also called modulation function, transmission factor, transmission function, contrast rendition function, frequency response function). The imaging problem is then solved as follows: the object and image are described in terms of the distribution of a suitable physical characterisitic of the optical disturbance, which characteristic is determined by the degree of coherence of the object illumination. (For example, an incoherently illuminated object is described in terms of the intensity distribution across it.) The spatial spectrum of the image is then obtained as the product of the transfer function with the spatial spectrum of the object, i.e., the optical system is treated as a spatial frequency filter.

This analysis is particularly promising in the study of cascaded systems as exemplified by Schade's (1953) treatment of television systems. In cascaded systems, the final image in the frequency domain is obtained by multiplying the spectrum of the object with the product of the transfer functions describing each stage of the system.

The essential step in this approach is the recognition that many optical systems may to a good approximation be treated as linear stationary systems in terms of their *spatial* as well as their *temporal* dependence. All the advantages, familiar to electronics engineers, of performing linear system analysis in the freuqency domain may then be realized in imaging problems. There are, of course, some difficulties confronting this approach in that some imaging systems of practical interest are not "stationary" in their spatial variation. The most significant difficulty, however, is the fact that the form of the transfer function is determined by the degree of coherence of the object illumination.

The realization that imaging systems can, under suitable conditions, be analyzed as linear stationary systems suggests strongly the application of the techniques of information and communication theory. Here again, however, several basic difficulties are encountered. Apart from the considerations already mentioned, an imaging device is not in general a *communication system* (since no opportunity of encoding the input exists) but rather an observation system. The difficulties confronting the analysis of such a system in terms of information and communication theory are discussed and illustrated by Woodward (1953) and lie outside the domain of our present discussion.

Some interesting results have, nonetheless, been obtained from the application of information theory to imaging systems. The chief contributions of this theory to the study of image formation are (1) the demonstration that an optical image has a finite number of degrees of freedom [see Fellgett and Linfoot (1955) and Gabor (1956)]; (2) the demonstration that the criteria for judging the quality of an imaging device must take account of the objects that the system is to image [see Fellgett and Linfoot (1955) and Schade (1953)]. The first of these conclusions follows immediately from Shannon's Sampling theorem [cf. Woodward (1953)] and from the fact that an imaging system behaves as a low-pass filter with a finite cut-off frequency. The second consideration will become evident from the subsequent discussion of this chapter.

Some of the various quality criteria for imaging devices which were introduced by Fellgett and Linfoot and Schade have been evaluated for aberrated optical systems [see O'Neill (1956a), Fukui (1957), and Parrent and Drane (1956)] and for antenna systems employing Dolph-Tchebysheff apodization† [see Drane (1957)]. The results obtained in each case were in good qualitative agreement with experience.

In spite of the difficulties mentioned, the transfer function analysis has contributed to the understanding of the problems of image formation. Among the interesting consequences of the application of the transfer function analysis to optical systems are the spatial filtering techniques developed by O'Neill (1956b,c) and Marechal and Croce (1953) for sharpening blurred edges and recovering wanted detail from an image containing noise (e.g., photographic grain).

The computation of the transfer function of any given system often leads to numerical integration; for this reason, detailed analysis has been limited to relatively simple systems, utilizing strictly coherent or incoherent illumination, with small aberrations [see Steel (1953)] or with a single aberration [Parrent (1955), Hopkins (1955), De (1955), O, Neill (1956a)].

The limitation to coherent or incoherent illumination is, however, very basic in itself and stems not from computational difficulties but rather from the following considerations: (1) A system imaging an incoherently illuminated object may be regarded as linear in *intensity;* (2) a system imaging a coherently illuminated object may be regarded as linear in amplitude if detection of the image is not included as part of the imaging system; (3) systems using partially coherent illumination are linear in neither of these quantities. H. H. Hopkins (1956) and Dumontet (1954) extended the transfer function analysis to systems imaging partially coherent objects by showing that such systems may be regarded as linear in *mutual intensity* provided that the illumination is quasi-monochromatic. The transfer functions for systems with small aberrations and partially coherent objects have been computed by Steele (1957), using the Hopkins formulation.

Most of the work on this subject has been limited to quasi-monochromatic light. As shown by Parrent (1961a), however, one can treat the more general

†It can be shown [see Dolph (1946)] that, if the currents in the elements of a linear (antenna) array are proportional to the coefficients of the Tchebysheff polynomials, the resulting diffraction pattern has the minimum possible side-lobe level for a given beam width. These polynomials provide a means of varying the apodization continuously from edge illumination (which gives the cosine squared diffraction pattern of a simple interferometer and hence the minimum beam width for a given aperture size) to a binomial distribution of currents which gives a diffraction pattern consisting of a main lobe with no side lobes.

problem of polychromatic illumination. We shall provide here a general formulation of the problem and then use the results of the preceding chapters to derive the more familiar solutions obtained in quasi-monochromatic imaging problems. It is hoped that, in addition to providing the mathematical framework for the solutions to these general problems, this approach will eliminate the frequently eccountered confusion concerning the significance and interpretation of the various transfer functions.† In Chapter 8, we shall consider applications of the theory presented here.

7.1 GENERAL FORMULATION OF THE IMAGING PROBLEM

In this section it will be shown that the general scalar imaging problem, involving partially coherent polychromatic objects, can be completely solved in terms of the observable, $\Gamma_{12}(\tau)$, in object and image space with no recourse to the disturbance, $V^r(t)$, itself. By dealing solely with the mutual coherence function, and functions simply derivable from it, our entire analysis, apart from the limiting forms, will involve as in other parts of the book only square-integrable functions.

It will be shown here how to use this general solution to define generalized transfer functions. Further, it will be shown that these new functions are simply derivable from the aperture illumination function (pupil function) of the imaging system. We shall closely follow the development given by Parrent (1961a).

Mathematical conventions and notations

In the development that follows, extensive use is made of multi-dimensional Fourier transforms. To prevent the equations from becoming too unwieldy, the following conventions and condensed notations are used.

Cartesian coordinates are denoted by (ξ, η) in object space; (x, y) in image space; and (α, β) in the exit pupil. The coordinates in image space are normalized by the lateral magnification of the imaging system. This is done to make the coordinates of a given object point equal in magnitude to those of the corresponding image point. The conventions regarding functional representation are

(7–1) $$f(\mathbf{x}) \equiv f(x, y)$$

(7–2) $$f(\mathbf{x}_1 - \mathbf{x}_2) \equiv f(x_1 - x_2, y_1 - y_2)$$

(7–3) $$d\mathbf{x}_1 \equiv dx_1\, dy_1$$

†This confusion is discussed and illustrated by F. J. Zucker (1957) in his summary comments.

and

$$\mathbf{x}_1 \equiv x_1 \mathbf{x}^0 + y_1 \mathbf{y}^0 \tag{7–4}$$

Here the subscripts 1 and 2 denote the point, P_1 or P_2, whose coordinates are used, and $\mathbf{x}^0$ and $\mathbf{y}^0$ are unit vectors in the direction of the x and y axis respectively. The same conventions, of course, apply in the aperture and object planes (see Fig. 7-1).

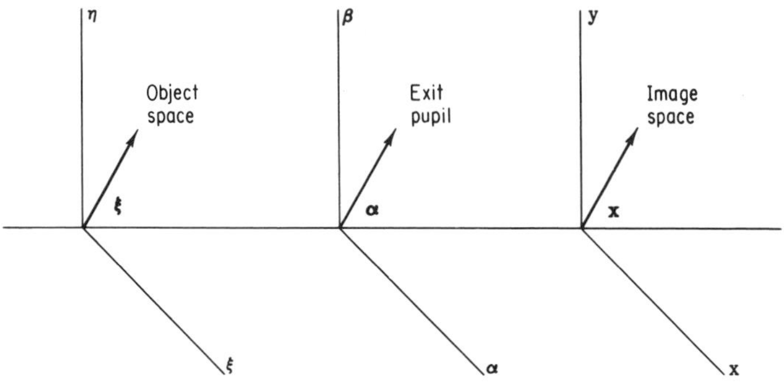

Figure 7-1. Coordinate systems used in imaging analysis.

We shall be concerned with the transmission of distributions from object space to image space and subscripts o and i will denote that the distribution is an object or image respectively, that is,

(7–5)
$f_0(\boldsymbol{\xi})$ distribution in object space
$f_i(\mathbf{x})$ corresponding distribution in image space

Since we shall require the Fourier transform of spatial functions, we associate with each space coordinate a spatial frequency coordinate using the following convention: μ_{1x} is the spatial frequency associated with the cartesian coordinate x_1, and μ_{1y} is associated with y_1. The functional conventions introduced for the space functions will, of course, also be used for the spatial frequency functions; that is,

$$f(\boldsymbol{\mu}_1) \equiv f(\mu_{1x}, \mu_{1y}) \tag{7–6}$$

$$\boldsymbol{\mu}_1 = \mu_{1x}\mathbf{x}^0 + \mu_{1y}\mathbf{y}^0 \tag{7–7}$$

and

$$d\boldsymbol{\mu}_1 = d\mu_{1x}\, d\mu_{1y} \tag{7–8}$$

The time coordinate is denoted by t and the time delay coordinate by τ. The associated temporal frequency is denoted by ν.

As we sometimes did in the preceding chapters, the mutual coherence function will be written here with its full argument rather than with the subscript 12.

Associated with every function of the space-time coordinates, $F(\mathbf{x}_1, \mathbf{x}_2, \tau)$, will be three other functions: namely, its "spatial" Fourier transform, $\tilde{F}(\boldsymbol{\mu}_1, \boldsymbol{\mu}_2, \tau)$; its "temporal" Fourier transform, $\hat{F}(\mathbf{x}_1, \mathbf{x}_2, \nu)$; and its total Fourier transform, $\mathring{F}(\boldsymbol{\mu}_1, \boldsymbol{\mu}_2, \nu)$; that is,

$$\tilde{F}(\boldsymbol{\mu}_1, \boldsymbol{\mu}_2, \tau) = \iiiint_{-\infty}^{\infty} F(\mathbf{x}_1, \mathbf{x}_2, \tau)\, e^{2\pi i(\boldsymbol{\mu}_1 \cdot \mathbf{x}_1 + \boldsymbol{\mu}_2 \cdot \mathbf{x}_2)}\, d\mathbf{x}_1\, d\mathbf{x}_2 \tag{7–9}$$

$$\hat{F}(\mathbf{x}_1, \mathbf{x}_2, \nu) = \int_{-\infty}^{\infty} F(\mathbf{x}_1, \mathbf{x}_2, \tau)\, e^{2\pi i \nu \tau}\, d\tau \tag{7–10}$$

$$\mathring{F}(\boldsymbol{\mu}_1, \boldsymbol{\mu}_2, \nu) = \int\!\!\iiiint_{-\infty}^{\infty} F(\mathbf{x}_1, \mathbf{x}_2, \tau)\, e^{2\pi i(\boldsymbol{\mu}_1 \cdot \mathbf{x}_1 + \boldsymbol{\mu}_2 \cdot \mathbf{x}_2 + \nu\tau)}\, d\mathbf{x}_1\, d\mathbf{x}_2\, d\tau \tag{7–11}$$

Throughout the rest of the chapter, all integrals will be written with a single integral sign without limits. The order of the integration will be implied by the differentials.

A generalized transfer function

In this section, we discuss the problem of determining the image of an extended polychromatic object and the inverse problem, namely, that of determining the object from a knowledge of the image. We shall show that the solution of this latter problem is fundamentally impossible with systems of finite aperture and radiation of finite wavelength. The object is considered to be planar and is specified by its mutual coherence function, $\Gamma_o(\boldsymbol{\xi}_1, \boldsymbol{\xi}_2, \tau)$. The central problem is formulating the relation between $\Gamma_o(\boldsymbol{\xi}_1, \boldsymbol{\xi}_2, \tau)$ and $\Gamma_i(\mathbf{x}_1, \mathbf{x}_2, \tau)$ in terms of the aperture illumination function. No assumptions concerning the spectral width or degree of coherence will be made in this section. We shall show that, although the evaluation of the integrals might prove somewhat formidable in certain practical applications, a solution in closed form can be obtained and a transfer function defined which is simply related to the pupil function.

From the linearity of Maxwell's equations it follows that, if there are no nonlinear devices in the imaging system, the mutual spectral density will be propagated through the system in accordance with two linear differential equations; that is,

$$D_s[\hat{\Gamma}_{12}(\nu)] = 0 \qquad (s = 1, 2) \tag{7–12}$$

where D_s is a linear differential operator in the coordinates of P_s (see

Chapter 3). Solving the first of these equations, we obtain the mutual spectral density, $\hat{\Gamma}_{io}(\mathbf{x}_1, \boldsymbol{\xi}_2, \nu)$, between the oscillations at a typical object point $\boldsymbol{\xi}_2$ and those at a typical image point $\mathbf{x}_1$. Here the subscript *io* denotes that the function depends upon a point in the object space and a point in the image space. This partial solution may be obtained by using only the linearity of Eq. (7–31) as follows: Let the contribution to the "complex disturbance" at $\mathbf{x}_1$ due to the "disturbance" from an element $d\boldsymbol{\xi}_1$, of the source around $\boldsymbol{\xi}_1$ be $\hat{\Gamma}_o(\boldsymbol{\xi}_1, \boldsymbol{\xi}_2, \nu)\ K(\mathbf{x}_1, \boldsymbol{\xi}_1, \nu)\ d\boldsymbol{\xi}_1$. The function $K(\mathbf{x}_1, \boldsymbol{\xi}_1, \nu)$ describes the optical imaging system; it is essentially the Green's function for D_1 with the appropriate boundary conditions. Then, since Eq. (7–12) is a linear differential equation, the total "disturbance" at $\mathbf{x}_1$ is given by

$$\hat{\Gamma}_{io}(\mathbf{x}_1, \boldsymbol{\xi}_2, \nu) = \int \hat{\Gamma}_o(\boldsymbol{\xi}_1, \boldsymbol{\xi}_2, \nu)\ K(\mathbf{x}_1, \boldsymbol{\xi}_1, \nu)\ d\boldsymbol{\xi}_1 \tag{7–13}$$

Next we repeat the argument just used, solving this time the second of the equations in (7–12). For the sake of generality, we assume the optical system to be characterized by a second function, $J(\mathbf{x}_2, \boldsymbol{\xi}_2, \nu)$. The relation between J and K will be determined shortly. Using the linearity of the remaining equation, we obtain the image as

$$\hat{\Gamma}_i(\mathbf{x}_1, \mathbf{x}_2, \nu) = \int \hat{\Gamma}_{io}(\mathbf{x}_1, \boldsymbol{\xi}_2, \nu)\ J(\mathbf{x}_2, \boldsymbol{\xi}_2, \nu)\ d\boldsymbol{\xi}_2 \tag{7–14}$$

Substituting from Eq. (7–13) into Eq. (7–14), we obtain finally

$$\hat{\Gamma}_i(\mathbf{x}_1, \mathbf{x}_2, \nu) = \iint \hat{\Gamma}_o(\boldsymbol{\xi}_1, \boldsymbol{\xi}_2, \nu)\ J(\mathbf{x}_2, \boldsymbol{\xi}_2, \nu)\ K(\mathbf{x}_1, \boldsymbol{\xi}_1, \nu)\ d\boldsymbol{\xi}_1\ d\boldsymbol{\xi}_2 \tag{7–15}$$

Before discussing the physical significance of the functions J and K, we shall show that there is a simple relation between them. To this end, we interchange the roles of $\mathbf{x}_1$ and $\mathbf{x}_2$ and of $\boldsymbol{\xi}_1$ and $\boldsymbol{\xi}_2$ in Eq. (7–15) obtaining

$$\hat{\Gamma}_1(\mathbf{x}_2, \mathbf{x}_1, \nu) = \iint K(\mathbf{x}_2, \boldsymbol{\xi}_2, \nu)\ J(\mathbf{x}_1, \boldsymbol{\xi}_1, \nu)\ \hat{\Gamma}_o(\boldsymbol{\xi}_2, \boldsymbol{\xi}_1, \nu)\ d\boldsymbol{\xi}_2\ d\boldsymbol{\xi}_1 \tag{7–16}$$

However,

$$\hat{\Gamma}_i(\mathbf{x}_2, \mathbf{x}_1, \nu) = \hat{\Gamma}_i^*(\mathbf{x}_1, \mathbf{x}_2, \nu) \quad \text{and} \quad \hat{\Gamma}_o(\boldsymbol{\xi}_2, \boldsymbol{\xi}_1, \nu) = \hat{\Gamma}_o^*(\boldsymbol{\xi}_1, \boldsymbol{\xi}_2, \nu)$$

Using these two relations, comparison of Eq. (7–16) and Eq. (7–15) shows that

$$[K(\mathbf{x}_1, \boldsymbol{\xi}_1, \nu)\ J(\mathbf{x}_2, \boldsymbol{\xi}_2, \nu)]^* = K(\mathbf{x}_2, \boldsymbol{\xi}_2, \nu)\ J(\mathbf{x}_1, \boldsymbol{\xi}_1, \nu) \tag{7–17}$$

From Eq. (7–17) it follows immediately that

$$J(\mathbf{x}_1, \boldsymbol{\xi}_1, \nu) = K^*(\mathbf{x}_1, \boldsymbol{\xi}_1, \nu) \tag{7–18}$$

Using the result of Eq. (7–13), we may rewrite Eq. (7–15) as

$$\hat{\Gamma}_i(\mathbf{x}_1, \mathbf{x}_2, \nu) = \iint K(\mathbf{x}_1, \boldsymbol{\xi}_1, \nu)\ K^*(\mathbf{x}_2, \boldsymbol{\xi}_2, \nu)\ \hat{\Gamma}_o(\boldsymbol{\xi}_1, \boldsymbol{\xi}_2, \nu)\ d\boldsymbol{\xi}_1\ d\boldsymbol{\xi}_2 \tag{7–19}$$

Equation (7–19) is the basic relation of this analysis. It expresses the temporal mutual spectral density of the image in terms of the temporal mutual spectral density of the object and a function K which characterizes the imaging system.

Until now, we have not specified the position of the image plane. Since there are by definition no imaging elements between the exit pupil and the image plane, it is clear that Eq. (7–19) is valid throughout this entire region. Since the form of K in the exit pupil varies significantly from its form in the gaussian image plane,† however, and since its behavior in each of these planes is of particular physical importance, it will prove convenient to designate by two different symbols the form of $K(\mathbf{x}_1, \boldsymbol{\xi}_1, \nu)$ on these two surfaces. Accordingly, we shall denote by $A(\boldsymbol{\alpha}, \boldsymbol{\xi}, \nu)$ the form of K in the plane of the exit pupil. Thus $A(\boldsymbol{\alpha}, \boldsymbol{\xi}, \nu)$ is the complex disturbance at a point $\boldsymbol{\alpha}$ in exit pupil due to the monochromatic point source of frequency ν at a point in the object plane. We retain the symbol $K(\mathbf{x}, \boldsymbol{\xi}, \nu)$ to denote the function in the image plane. Using this convention, $K(\mathbf{x}, \boldsymbol{\xi}, \nu)$ may be thought of as the distribution in the image plane due to a monochromatic point source of complex amplitude in the plane of the exit pupil, remembering, of course, that the distribution in the exit pupil is determined by the object. The relation between these two functions may then be expressed as

$$K(\mathbf{x}, \boldsymbol{\xi}, \nu) = \int A(\alpha, \boldsymbol{\xi}, \nu) \frac{\partial G(\mathbf{x}, \boldsymbol{\alpha}, \nu)}{\partial n} \, d\boldsymbol{\alpha} \tag{7–20}$$

Here $\boldsymbol{\alpha}$ is a point in the aperture of the system; G is a Green's function satisfying the Helmholtz equation and vanishing over the plane of the exit pupil.

Under the conditions characterizing most imaging systems, Eq. (7–20) takes a particularly simple form; but before discussing this point, we shall continue the development up to the introduction of the general transfer function. This we do in order to avoid the erroneous impression that the transfer function analysis involves the Fraunhofer approximations, as is sometimes believed to be the case.

Equation (7–19) assumes a convenient and useful form if the system under consideration is "spatially stationary", that is, if the function $K(\mathbf{x}, \boldsymbol{\xi}, \nu)$ is a function of the difference of the spatial coordinates

$$K(\mathbf{x}, \boldsymbol{\xi}, \nu) = K(\mathbf{x} - \boldsymbol{\xi}, \nu) \tag{7–21}$$

---

†The gaussian image plane is always of significance for incoherent illumination. However, the object image relation

$$\frac{1}{s} + \frac{1}{s'} = \frac{1}{f}$$

(s and s' are object and image distances, respectively, and f is focal length) must be applied with caution for coherent light.

This condition is satisfied by scanning systems,† which include most antenna systems, and also by many important (visible) optical systems. For systems which do not scan but form the entire spatial image simultaneously, K will not in general be a function of the difference $(\mathbf{x} - \boldsymbol{\xi})$ only. For most optical systems, however, the form of the diffraction pattern varies slowly across the image plane. Hence, the image space may be divided into "isoplanatic" areas over which K may be assumed to be a function of $(\mathbf{x} - \boldsymbol{\xi})$ to any desired accuracy. This possibility is discussed at length by Fellgett and Linfoot (1955) and by Dumontet (1954).

Throughout the rest of this discussion, we shall be concerned only with systems for which the condition Eq. (7–21) is satisfied.

Using the stationarity condition, Eq. (7–19) may be rewritten as

$$\hat{\Gamma}_i(\mathbf{x}_1, \mathbf{x}_2, \nu) = \iint K(\mathbf{x}_1 - \boldsymbol{\xi}_1, \nu)\, K^*(\mathbf{x}_2 - \boldsymbol{\xi}_2, \nu)\, \hat{\Gamma}_o(\boldsymbol{\xi}_1, \boldsymbol{\xi}_2, \nu)\, d\boldsymbol{\xi}_1\, d\boldsymbol{\xi}_2 \tag{7–22}$$

Taking the "space-type" Fourier transform of both sides of Eq. (7–22) and using the convolution theorem yields

$$\mathring{\Gamma}_i(\boldsymbol{\mu}_1, \boldsymbol{\mu}_2, \nu) = \tilde{K}(\boldsymbol{\mu}_1, \nu)\, \tilde{K}^*(-\boldsymbol{\mu}_2, -\nu)\, \mathring{\Gamma}_o(\boldsymbol{\mu}_1, \boldsymbol{\mu}_2, \nu) \tag{7–23}$$

At this point, we introduce the transfer function, $\mathcal{L}(\boldsymbol{\mu}_1, \boldsymbol{\mu}_2, \nu)$, defined by

$$\mathcal{L}(\boldsymbol{\mu}_1, \boldsymbol{\mu}_2, \nu) = \tilde{K}(\boldsymbol{\mu}_1, \nu)\, \tilde{K}^*(-\boldsymbol{\mu}_2, -\nu) \tag{7–24}$$

In terms of $\mathcal{L}$, Eq. (7–23) becomes simply

$$\mathring{\Gamma}_i(\boldsymbol{\mu}_1, \boldsymbol{\mu}_2, \nu) = \mathcal{L}(\boldsymbol{\mu}_1, \boldsymbol{\mu}_2, \nu)\, \mathring{\Gamma}_o(\boldsymbol{\mu}_1, \boldsymbol{\mu}_2, \nu) \tag{7–25}$$

Equation (7–25) may be regarded as the basic equation in the frequency domain analysis of imaging systems. It is clear from the foregoing discussion that the transfer function analysis is rigorously applicable to any "spatially stationary" system. That is, no approximation need be made concerning the relation between the aperture illumination function, A, and the diffraction pattern, K. In most optical applications, however, and in fact in most antenna applications, the diffraction pattern is characterized by the Fraunhofer approximations (or the formally equivalent far-field approximations); and since, under these conditions, Eq. (7–20) assumes a particularly simple form, we shall introduce these approximations at this point and retain them throughout the subsequent sections.

---

†By this, we mean systems in which the image-forming device (e.g., antenna) scans while the position of the detector (e.g., feed) relative to the aperture remains fixed; i.e., the antenna and feed move together. The preceding consideration is not valid for a system in which the image-forming device remains fixed while the detector scans the aerial image. A camera with a focal plane shutter is a simple example of such a system; the lens creates the entire image simultaneously and the shutter slit then scans the image.

Under the usual approximations which characterize Fraunhofer diffraction, Eq. (7–20) reduces to

$$K(\mathbf{x}, \boldsymbol{\xi}, \nu) = \int A(\boldsymbol{\alpha}, \boldsymbol{\xi}, \nu)\, e^{-2\pi i[(\boldsymbol{\alpha}/\lambda R)\cdot\mathbf{x}]}\, d\boldsymbol{\alpha} \tag{7–26}$$

where λ is the wavelength of the spectral component belonging to frequency ν, and R is the radius of the gaussian reference sphere. $K(\mathbf{x}, \boldsymbol{\xi}, \nu)$ may, however, be expressed as

$$K(\mathbf{x}, \boldsymbol{\xi}, \nu) = \int \tilde{K}(\boldsymbol{\mu}, \boldsymbol{\xi}, \nu)\, e^{-2\pi i(\boldsymbol{\mu}\cdot\mathbf{x})}\, d\boldsymbol{\mu} \tag{7–27}$$

By comparing Eq. (7–26) and Eq. (7–27), we identify the spatial frequency, μ, as the reduced aperture coordinate, that is,

$$\boldsymbol{\mu} = \frac{\boldsymbol{\alpha}}{\lambda R}, \qquad \mu_{1x} = \frac{\alpha}{\lambda R}, \quad \mu_{1y} = \frac{\beta}{\lambda R}$$

Further, we note the important relation

$$\tilde{K}(\boldsymbol{\mu}, \mathbf{x}, \nu) = \tilde{K}\left(\frac{\boldsymbol{\alpha}}{\lambda R}, \mathbf{x}, \nu\right) = A(\boldsymbol{\mu}, \mathbf{x}, \nu) \tag{7–28}$$

Our subsequent analysis will deal solely with K and its transform $\tilde{K}$. From Eqs. (7–24), (7–26), and (7–27) it is clear that under the conditions stated the transfer function, $\mathcal{L}(\boldsymbol{\mu}_1, \boldsymbol{\mu}_2, \nu)$, for a system utilizing partially coherent polychromatic illumination is the product of the frequency-dependent aperture illumination function, considered as a function of spatial frequency and evaluated at $\boldsymbol{\mu}_1 = \boldsymbol{\alpha}_1/\lambda R$, with its complex conjugate evaluated at $\boldsymbol{\mu}_2 = \boldsymbol{\alpha}_2/\lambda R$.

It is clear from the foregoing considerations that the inverse problem, namely, that of determining the object from a knowledge of the image, cannot be solved if the imaging system has a finite aperture. This conclusion can be understood by formally inverting Eq. (7–25). We then obtain

$$\mathring{\Gamma}_o(\boldsymbol{\mu}_1, \boldsymbol{\mu}_2, \nu) = \frac{\mathring{\Gamma}_i(\boldsymbol{\mu}_1, \boldsymbol{\mu}_2, \nu)}{\mathcal{L}(\boldsymbol{\mu}_1, \boldsymbol{\mu}_2, \nu)}; \quad \mathcal{L} \neq 0 \tag{7–29}$$

From Eqs. (7–27) and (7–24), however, it follows that, if the aperture is finite, $\mathcal{L}$ is identically zero beyond some maximum frequency $|\boldsymbol{\mu}|_{\max}$; hence, Eq. (7–28) is indeterminate. Thus the inverse problem is soluble only up to an arbitrary function, f,

$$\mathring{\Gamma}_o(\boldsymbol{\mu}_1, \boldsymbol{\mu}_2, \nu) = \frac{\mathring{\Gamma}_i(\boldsymbol{\mu}_1, \boldsymbol{\mu}_2, \nu)}{\mathcal{L}(\boldsymbol{\mu}_1, \boldsymbol{\mu}_2, \nu)} + f \tag{7–30}$$

where f is any function of frequencies greater than $|\boldsymbol{\mu}|_{\max}$.

Equation (7–25) gives the relation between the total spectral densities of the object and image and is thus the solution sought in this section. In many applications, however, one is interested in a much less general solution, namely, the intensity distribution in the image. Obtaining the intensity distribution, in general, from Eq. (7–22) is somewhat involved and not very helpful. In the limiting cases of coherently and incoherently illuminated objects, however, the problem is tractable, and in the subsequent sections we shall discuss these limits in detail for both polychromatic and quasi-monochromatic illumination.

7.2 THE LIMITING FORMS OF THE TRANSFER FUNCTION

We first examine the limiting forms for polychromatic light and in a later section examine the extremes under the quasi-monochromatic approximation.

We shall show in this section that the transfer function for coherent objects is the frequency-dependent aperture illumination function $\tilde{K}(\boldsymbol{\mu}, \mathbf{x}, \nu) = A[(\boldsymbol{\alpha}/\lambda R), \mathbf{x}, \nu]$ evaluated at ν_o and considered as a function of spatial frequency. (Here ν_o is the frequency of the illumination.)

The analysis of systems imaging incoherent objects is complicated by the fact that the image is partially coherent. Thus, if one seeks a complete solution (i.e., the mutual coherence of the image), the transfer function must operate on the spectral density of the object, $\mathring{I}(\boldsymbol{\mu}, \nu)$ (a function of one point only) to produce the mutual spectral density of the image, $\mathring{\Gamma}_i(\boldsymbol{\mu}_1, \boldsymbol{\mu}_2, \nu)$ —a function of two points. This consideration, often overlooked or omitted in the literature on the imaging problem, is important in the treatment of cascaded systems. The required transfer function will be shown to be the function $\mathcal{L}$ introduced in the previous section.

If, on the other hand, one requires only the intensity distribution in the image, $I(\mathbf{x}, 0)$, the entire analysis of systems using incoherent light may be performed with functions of one point only, the spectral densities of the object and image. For this problem, the transfer function, M, will be shown to be the convolution of the frequency-dependent aperture illumination with its complex conjugate.

The coherent limit

It was shown in Chapter 4 that in a coherent field† the mutual coherence function is of the form

$$\Gamma_o(\boldsymbol{\xi}_1, \boldsymbol{\xi}_2, \tau) = U_o(\boldsymbol{\xi}_1)\, U_o^*(\boldsymbol{\xi}_2)\, e^{-2\pi i \nu_o \tau} \tag{7–31}$$

with a mutual spectral density

†Here the physically unsatisfactory requirement that $|\gamma_{12}(\tau)| = 1$ for all τ is used. The realistic case of quasi-monochromatic light is discussed in a subsequent section.

$$\hat{\Gamma}_o(\xi_1, \xi_2, \nu) = U_o(\xi_1)\, U_o^*(\xi_2)\, \delta(\nu - \nu_o) \tag{7–32}$$

Substituting from Eq. (7–32) into the general solution, Eq. (7–19), and taking the temporal Fourier transform on both sides, we obtain

$$\Gamma_i(\mathbf{x}_1, \mathbf{x}_2, \tau) = U_i(\mathbf{x}_1)\, U_i^*(\mathbf{x}_2)\, e^{-2\pi i \nu_o \tau} \tag{7–33}$$

where

$$U_i(\mathbf{x}) = \int U_o(\xi)\, K(\mathbf{x} - \xi, \nu_0)\, d\xi \tag{7–34}$$

From Eq. (7–33) and the theorems of Chapter 4, it follows immediately that the image of a coherent object is coherent.

Taking the spatial Fourier transform of both sides of Eq. (7–34) and using the convolution theorem, we obtain

$$\tilde{U}_i(\boldsymbol{\mu}) = \tilde{U}_o(\boldsymbol{\mu})\, \tilde{K}(\boldsymbol{\mu}, \nu_o) \tag{7–35}$$

The appropriate transfer function is the frequency-dependent aperture illumination function evaluated at ν_o and considered as a function of spatial frequency, $K(\boldsymbol{\mu}, \nu_o) = A(\boldsymbol{\alpha}/\lambda R, \nu_o)$. The coherent image is completely determined by Eq. (7–35) and the intensity distribution is obtained as a special case of Eq. (7–33) by setting $\mathbf{x}_1 = \mathbf{x}_2$, and $\tau = 0$.

It should be noted that the analysis in this section dealt with an amplitude function $U(\mathbf{x})$. An imaging system dealing with coherent light is nonlinear if the detection of the image is included in the analysis. This point and its consequences are discussed at some length in the next chapter.

The incoherent limit

An incoherent object may be described by a mutual coherence function of the form (see Chapter 4 for limitations of this form),

$$\Gamma_o(\xi_1, \xi_2, \tau) = (\beta) I_o(\xi_2, \tau) \delta(\xi_2 - \xi_1) \tag{7–36}$$

where $I(\xi, \tau)$ is the self-coherence function at ξ defined by the relation

$$I(\xi, \tau) = \langle V(\xi, t + \tau)\, V^*(\xi, t) \rangle \tag{7–37}$$

The mutual spectral density is, therefore,

$$\hat{\Gamma}_o(\xi_1, \xi_2, \nu) = \beta \hat{I}_o(\xi_2, \nu)\, \delta(\xi_2 - \xi_1) \tag{7–38}$$

Substituting from Eq. (7–38) into the general solution, Eq. (7–19), we obtain the image $\hat{\Gamma}_i(\mathbf{x}_1, \mathbf{x}_2, \nu)$, that is,

$$\hat{\Gamma}_i(\mathbf{x}_1, \mathbf{x}_2, \nu) = \beta \iint K(\mathbf{x}_1 - \xi_1, \nu)\, K^*(\mathbf{x}_2 - \xi_2, \nu)\, \hat{I}_o(\xi_2, \nu)\, \delta(\xi_2 - \xi_1)\, d\xi_1\, d\xi_2 \tag{7–39}$$

We may now integrate over $d\xi_2$ and obtain

$$\hat{\Gamma}_i(\mathbf{x}_1, \mathbf{x}_2, \nu) = \beta \int K(\boldsymbol{\xi}_1 - \mathbf{x}_1, \nu)\, K^*(\boldsymbol{\xi}_1 - \mathbf{x}_2, \nu)\, \hat{I}_o(\boldsymbol{\xi}_1, \nu)\, d\boldsymbol{\xi}_1 \tag{7–40}$$

and taking the spatial Fourier transform of both sides and using again the convolution theorem yields

$$\mathring{\Gamma}_i(\boldsymbol{\mu}_1, \boldsymbol{\mu}_2, \nu) = \beta \mathring{I}_o(\boldsymbol{\mu}_1 + \boldsymbol{\mu}_2, \nu)\, \mathcal{L}(\boldsymbol{\mu}_1, \boldsymbol{\mu}_2, \nu) \tag{7–41}$$

where $\mathcal{L}(\boldsymbol{\mu}_1, \boldsymbol{\mu}_2, \nu)$ is the generalized transfer function defined in Section 7.2,

$$\mathcal{L}(\boldsymbol{\mu}_1, \boldsymbol{\mu}_2, \nu) = \tilde{K}(\boldsymbol{\mu}_1, \nu)\, \tilde{K}^*(-\boldsymbol{\mu}_2, -\nu) \tag{7–42}$$

It is sometimes convenient to rewrite Eq. (7–41) in the form

$$\mathring{\Gamma}_i(\boldsymbol{\mu}_1, \boldsymbol{\mu} - \boldsymbol{\mu}_1, \nu) = \beta \mathring{I}_o(\boldsymbol{\mu}, \nu)\, \mathcal{L}(\boldsymbol{\mu}_1, \boldsymbol{\mu} - \boldsymbol{\mu}_1, \nu) \tag{7–43}$$

Equation (7–41) expresses the fact that the correlation between the disturbances associated with the spatial frequencies $\boldsymbol{\mu}_1$ and $\boldsymbol{\mu}_2$ in the image is determined by the intensity associated with the sum frequency $\boldsymbol{\mu}_1 + \boldsymbol{\mu}_2$ in the object plane.

Although Eq. (7–41) is the complete solution (for an incoherent object) for the total mutual spectral density in the image and hence for the mutual coherence function, one is often interested in the more restrictive solution, the intensity in the image. This is obtained at once by setting $\mathbf{x}_1 = \mathbf{x}_2$ in Eq. (7–40), which gives

$$\hat{I}_i(\mathbf{x}, \nu) = \hat{\Gamma}_i(\mathbf{x}_1, \mathbf{x}_1, \nu) = \beta \int |K(\mathbf{x}_1 - \boldsymbol{\xi}_1, \nu)|^2\, I_o(\boldsymbol{\xi}_1, \nu)\, d\boldsymbol{\xi}_1 \tag{7–44}$$

Taking the spatial Fourier transform of both sides of Eq. (7–44), we obtain

$$\mathring{I}_i(\boldsymbol{\mu}, \nu) = \beta \mathcal{M}(\boldsymbol{\mu}, \nu)\, \mathring{I}_o(\boldsymbol{\mu}, \nu) \tag{7–45}$$

where

$$\mathcal{M}(\boldsymbol{\mu}, \nu) = \int |K(\mathbf{x}, \nu)|^2\, e^{2\pi i \boldsymbol{\mu}\cdot\mathbf{x}}\, d\mathbf{x} \tag{7–46}$$

From an interpretation of K, it is clear that $|K|^2$ is the frequency-dependent intensity diffraction pattern of the imaging system. The transfer function for determining the total spectral density of the image of an incoherent object is thus the transform of the "intensity diffraction pattern" of the system. The formula (7–46) is simplified further by again using the convolution theorem and (7–26) which gives

$$\mathcal{M}(\boldsymbol{\mu}, \nu) = \int \tilde{K}(\boldsymbol{\alpha} - \boldsymbol{\mu}, \nu)\, \tilde{K}^*(\boldsymbol{\alpha}, \nu)\, d\boldsymbol{\alpha} \tag{7–47}$$

The spatial spectral density may now be obtained by taking the Fourier transform of both sides of Eq. (7–45) and evaluating at $\tau = 0$; thus

$$\tilde{I}_i(\boldsymbol{\mu}, 0) = \int \beta \mathcal{M}(\boldsymbol{\mu}, \nu)\, \mathring{I}_o(\boldsymbol{\mu}, \nu)\, d\nu \tag{7–48}$$

The formula (7–48) expresses the fact that each temporal spectral component contributes separately and independently to the energy in the spatial frequency component $\boldsymbol{\mu}$. The intensity distribution in the image is then given by the spatial transform of Eq. (7–48).

7.3 IMAGING WITH QUASI-MONOCHROMATIC LIGHT

Although many imaging systems of practical and theoretical interest deal with polychromatic light, only the problem of imaging with quasi-monochromatic or monochromatic illumination has been extensively discussed until recently. The transfer function analysis as usually found in the available literature until the late 1950's is applicable only to quasi-monochromatic light. The quasi-monochromatic approximation is, of course, a special case of the general formulation given here, and we examine in this section the form of the transfer functions under the quasi-monochromatic approximation.

A partially coherent quasi-monochromatic object will be described by a mutual coherence function of the form (see Chapter 4):

$$\Gamma_o(\boldsymbol{\xi}_1, \boldsymbol{\xi}_2, \tau) \approx \Gamma_o(\boldsymbol{\xi}_1, \boldsymbol{\xi}_2, 0)\, e^{-2\pi i\bar{\nu}\tau} \qquad \left(|\tau| \ll \frac{1}{\Delta\nu}\right) \tag{7–49}$$

Its temporal transform is

$$\hat{\Gamma}_o(\boldsymbol{\xi}_1, \boldsymbol{\xi}_{2i}\, \nu) \approx \Gamma_o(\boldsymbol{\xi}_1, \boldsymbol{\xi}_2, 0)\, \delta(\nu - \bar{\nu}) \qquad \left(|\tau| \ll \frac{1}{\Delta\nu}\right) \tag{7–50}$$

Substituting from Eq. (7–50) into the general solution Eq. (7–19) and taking the inverse Fourier transform, we obtain

$$\Gamma_i(\mathbf{x}_1, \mathbf{x}_2, \bar{\nu}) = e^{-2\pi i\bar{\nu}\tau} \int K(\mathbf{x}_1 - \boldsymbol{\xi}_1, \bar{\nu})\, K^*(\mathbf{x}_2 - \boldsymbol{\xi}_2, \bar{\nu})\, \Gamma_o(\boldsymbol{\xi}_1, \boldsymbol{\xi}_2, 0)\, d\boldsymbol{\xi}_1\, d\boldsymbol{\xi}_2\dagger \qquad (|\tau| \ll 1/\Delta\nu) \tag{7–51}$$

Equation (7–51) provides the starting point for the analysis of partially coherent images. Beginning from Eq. (7–51), the entire analysis of the two preceding sections may be taken over *mutatis mutandis* for the quasi-monochromatic imaging problems considered here. Denoting by the suffix q that the functions are applicable to quasi-monochromatic light, the various transfer functions and frequency domain image equations are

Coherent object

transfer function $\qquad \mathcal{K}_q = \tilde{K}(\boldsymbol{\mu}, \bar{\nu})$

imaging equation $\qquad \mathring{U}_i(\boldsymbol{\mu}, \bar{\nu}) = \mathcal{K}_q(\boldsymbol{\mu}, \bar{\nu})\, \mathring{U}_o(\boldsymbol{\mu}, \bar{\nu})$

---

†We also assume here that path length differences (represented in K) are small.

Partially Coherent Object

transfer function $\mathscr{L}_q = \tilde{K}(\boldsymbol{\mu}_1, \bar{\nu})\, \tilde{K}^*(-\boldsymbol{\mu}_2, -\bar{\nu})$

imaging equation $\mathring{\Gamma}_i(\boldsymbol{\mu}_1, \boldsymbol{\mu}_2, \bar{\nu}) = \mathscr{L}_q(\boldsymbol{\mu}_1, \boldsymbol{\mu}_2, \bar{\nu})\, \mathring{\Gamma}_o(\boldsymbol{\mu}_1, \boldsymbol{\mu}_2, \bar{\nu})$

Incoherent Object†

transfer function $\mathscr{L}_q = \tilde{K}(\boldsymbol{\mu}_1, \bar{\nu})\, \tilde{K}^*(-\boldsymbol{\mu}_2, -\bar{\nu})$

imaging equation $\mathring{\Gamma}_1(\boldsymbol{\mu}_1, \boldsymbol{\mu}_2, \bar{\nu}) = \bar{\beta}\mathscr{L}_q(\boldsymbol{\mu}_1, \boldsymbol{\mu}_2, \bar{\nu})\, \mathring{I}_o(\boldsymbol{\mu}_1, \bar{\nu})$

transfer function $\mathscr{M}_q = \int K(\boldsymbol{\alpha} - \boldsymbol{\mu}, \bar{\nu})\, K^*(\boldsymbol{\alpha}, \bar{\nu})\, d\boldsymbol{\alpha}$

imaging equation $\mathring{I}_i(\boldsymbol{\mu}, \bar{\nu}) = \mathscr{M}_q(\boldsymbol{\mu}, \bar{\nu})\, \bar{\beta}\mathring{I}_o(\boldsymbol{\mu}, \bar{\nu}); \quad \bar{\beta} = \beta(\bar{\nu})$

The transfer functions for quasi-monochromatic light are thus seen to be simply the generalized transfer functions evaluated at the mean frequency. This result is to have been expected, since mathematically the quasi-monochromatic approximation is characterized by an approximately monochromatic mutual coherence function. It should be emphasized, however, that whereas the transfer functions obtained in this section may be formally obtained by taking a single spectral component of the general solutions, the inverse procedure (integrating the quasi-monochromatic solution over frequency to obtain the general solutions) is not justifiable.

TABLE 7.1
Summary of Transfer Functions.‡

$\lvert\gamma_{12}(\tau)\rvert$	Transfer Function	Imaging Equation
1	$\tilde{K}(\boldsymbol{\mu}) = \tilde{K}(\boldsymbol{\alpha}/\lambda R)$	$\tilde{U}_i(\boldsymbol{\mu}) = \tilde{K}(\boldsymbol{\mu}, \nu_o)\, \tilde{U}_o(\boldsymbol{\mu})$
$0 < \lvert\gamma_{12}(\tau)\rvert < 1$	$\mathscr{L}(\boldsymbol{\mu}_1, \boldsymbol{\mu}_2, \nu) = \tilde{K}(\boldsymbol{\mu}_1, \nu)\, \tilde{K}^*(-\boldsymbol{\mu}_2, -\nu)$	$\mathring{\Gamma}_i(\boldsymbol{\mu}_1, \boldsymbol{\mu}_2, \nu) = \mathscr{L}(\boldsymbol{\mu}_1, \boldsymbol{\mu}_2, \nu)\, \mathring{\Gamma}_o(\boldsymbol{\mu}_1, \boldsymbol{\mu}_2, \nu)$
0	$\mathscr{L}(\boldsymbol{\mu}_1, \boldsymbol{\mu}_2, \nu) = \tilde{K}(\boldsymbol{\mu}_1, \nu)\, \tilde{K}^*(-\boldsymbol{\mu}_2, -\nu)$	$\mathring{\Gamma}_i(\boldsymbol{\mu}_1, \boldsymbol{\mu} - \boldsymbol{\mu}_1, \nu) = \mathscr{L}(\boldsymbol{\mu}_1, \boldsymbol{\mu} - \boldsymbol{\mu}_1, \nu)\, \beta\mathring{I}_i(\boldsymbol{\mu}, \nu)$
0	$\mathscr{M}(\boldsymbol{\mu}, \nu) = \int \tilde{K}(\boldsymbol{\alpha} - \boldsymbol{\mu}, \nu)\, \tilde{K}^*(\boldsymbol{\alpha}, \nu)\, d\boldsymbol{\alpha}$	$\mathring{I}_i(\boldsymbol{\mu}, \nu) = \mathscr{M}(\boldsymbol{\mu}, \nu)\, \beta\mathring{I}_o(\boldsymbol{\mu}, \nu)$

‡The corresponding equation and transfer functions for quasi-monochromatic light may be obtained formally be setting $\nu = \bar{\nu}$ in these relations.

†Two imaging equations are required for systems involving incoherent objects. $\mathscr{M}_q(\boldsymbol{\mu}, \bar{\nu})$ is used to determine spatial spectral density in the image, whereas the more general problem of determining the mutual spectral density involves the transfer function $\mathscr{L}_q(\boldsymbol{\mu}_1, \boldsymbol{\mu}_2, \bar{\nu})$. Both of these functions, however, operate on the spatial spectral density of the object.

This conclusion is evident from the fact that the solutions obtained in this section are only approximate ($|\tau| \ll 1/\Delta\nu$) and accordingly the transfer functions depend on the mean frequency, $\bar{\nu}$, not on an isolated frequency ν_0. It is thus impossible to obtain the general solutions from the quasi-monochromatic solutions.

7.4 SUMMARY

The transfer functions defined in this chapter are summarized in Table 7–1. (We assume the Fraunhofer approximation used in the latter sections of the chapter.)

chapter

8

Effect of Coherence on Resolution in Optical Images

In this chapter, we examine the effect of coherence on the resolution in optical images. Except for the case of two-point resolution, we shall consider only the two limits of coherent and incoherent illumination. To avoid the pitfalls associated with comparing the transfer functions for coherent and incoherent light directly, we shall keep our discussion at all times closely related to an experiment in which the resolution limits can be measured. As a further protection against such difficulties, we shall always relate the results directly to measurable quantities in the object and image. Although the image distributions will be examined in detail, the resolution limit will be defined in terms of the object.

From this analysis, several factors will emerge which will clarify the effect of coherence on resolution limit. In particular, it will be shown that in terms of Γ_{12} the sine wave resolution limit is independent of the degree of coherence. Because of nonlinearities arising from the consideration of only intensity measurements in the image-forming process, however, the coherence will effect the resolution limit. Moreover, these same nonlinearities make it impossible to give a unique answer for the effect of coherence on resolution even in the case of sine wave objects. For example, it will be shown that if the object is a square wave the coherent and incoherent resolution limits differ by a factor of 2, whereas if the object consists of two points the ratio of the resolution limits is 1.59.

The discussion will be divided into three parts. In the first, Section 8.1, the experimental arrangement for comparing resolution limits will be discussed, the definitions will be set forth and the physical significance of the nonlinearities will be pointed out. In the second part, the mathematical framework will be established and discussed. In the third part, specific problems will be evaluated.

8.1 THE MEASUREMENT OF THE RESOLUTION LIMIT

Throughout this discussion, the resolution will be referred to the object. Thus if a sinusoidal variation of intensity in the object produces a periodic variation of intensity in the image, the object is said to be *resolved.* The choice of words here is purposely vague to allow for the fact that the image intensity variation may bear little similarity to the object intensity distribution. In fact, the nonlinearities arising from the use of coherent or partially coherent radiation will result in images that have the wrong spatial frequency composition in many instances. It is precisely this consideration which makes it necessary to refer the resolution to the object. For example, we shall see that imaging with coherent light a cosinusoidal object of 100 *l*/mm amplitude variation will produce an intensity distribution with spatial frequency components of 200 *l*/mm. In this discussion, such a situation is described by saying 100 *l*/mm were resolved. This interpretation of resolution is necessitated by the consideration that with coherent or partially coherent light nothing would be resolved if resolution implied that only the correct spatial frequency components appeared in the image.

In order for any statement about resolution limit to have meaning, it must be related to a physical measurement. [To avoid confusion, we assume the existence of laboratory devices with resolving power well in excess of the device whose resolution we wish to discuss. (To be specific consider a lens which resolves on the order of 100 *l*/mm; then an adequate laboratory standard is a microscope that can resolve say 1,000 *l*/mm.)] Consider for example the measurement of the sine wave resolution limit. The object (i.e., a sine wave) must be prepared and its spatial frequency measured. This measurement will be an intensity measurement whether coherent or incoherent light is used. Similarly, the intensity will be measured in the image. This is a key point in the entire discussion, i.e., in both object and image space intensity is measured regardless of the coherence of the illumination. It is precisely this consideration that introduces the nonlinearity.

Consider an experiment in which the object is illuminated coherently and by measurement of the intensity distribution of the object plane it is ascertained that the object transmission is cosinusoidal of line frequency ω_o. Here, the amplitude variation may contain line frequency components of $\omega_0/2$ resulting from the fact that for coherent in phase illumination the amplitude is proportional to the square root of the intensity. The lens then operates in a linear fashion on the object amplitude distribution to produce the amplitude distribution in the image plane. To detect this image, however, the intensity is measured, and this involves squaring the amplitude distribution, another nonlinear step.

The same arguments apply to the case where the illumination is reflected rather than transmitted. In summary, the requirement that only intensities can be measured results in the imaging problem being essentially nonlinear for all but incoherent light. As we have seen in Chapter 7, the imaging problem can be formulated in terms of a more general measurable quantity, the mutual coherence function. In this case, the problem is linear, independent of the degree of coherence in object and image space but measurement of the intensity in the image again introduces a nonlinearity except in the incoherent limit. This point is discussed further in the next section.

8.2 MATHEMATICAL FORMULATION OF THE IMAGING PROBLEM

In this section, the equations governing the image formation process will be summarized again. It is convenient to start the discussion with the general solution to the imaging problem and simply particularize the solution as necessary. The most general solution for a spatially stationary system can be written as [see Eq. (7–22)]

$$\hat{\Gamma}_i(\mathbf{x}_1, \mathbf{x}_2, \nu) = \iint_{\text{obj}} \hat{\Gamma}_o(\boldsymbol{\xi}_1, \boldsymbol{\xi}_2, \nu)\, K(\mathbf{x}_1 - \boldsymbol{\xi}_1, \nu)\, K^*(\mathbf{x}_2 - \boldsymbol{\xi}_2, \nu)\, d\boldsymbol{\xi}_1\, d\boldsymbol{\xi}_2 \tag{8–1}$$

Equation (8–1) expresses the relation between the mutual power spectrum of the object and image, $\hat{\Gamma}_o$ and $\hat{\Gamma}_i$ respectively, and K is the amplitude impulse response. The discussion is considerably simplified by introducing the usual quasi-monochromatic approximations, i.e., the spectral width is small compared to the mean frequency and the maximum path differences between interfering beams is small compared to the velocity of light divided by the spectral width. Under these conditions, Eq. (8–1) reduces to

$$\Gamma_i(\mathbf{x}_1, \mathbf{x}_2) = \iint\limits_{\text{obj}} \Gamma_o(\boldsymbol{\xi}_1, \boldsymbol{\xi}_2)\, K(\mathbf{x}_1 - \boldsymbol{\xi}_1)\, K^*(\mathbf{x}_2 - \boldsymbol{\xi}_2)\, d\boldsymbol{\xi}_1\, d\boldsymbol{\xi}_2 \tag{8–2}$$

Here $\Gamma(\mathbf{x}_1, \mathbf{x}_2)$ is the mutual intensity function.† Equation (8–2) demonstrates the linearity of the image-forming process in terms of the mutual intensity. That is, Eq. (8–2) shows that, independent of the degree of coherence, the imaging process is linear in the mutual intensity. Thus if one is content with specifying object and image by the mutual intensity, then there are no nonlinearities in the system. Such a description, however, will provide only a knowledge of the correlation in object and image; it can describe the appearance of the image only when we reduce the solution to the intensity in the image. This is done by setting $\mathbf{x}_1 = \mathbf{x}_2$ in Eq. (8–2). Thus

$$I_i(\mathbf{x}) = \iint\limits_{\text{obj}} \Gamma_o(\boldsymbol{\xi}_1, \boldsymbol{\xi}_2)\, K(\mathbf{x} - \boldsymbol{\xi}_1)\, K^*(\mathbf{x} - \boldsymbol{\xi}_2)\, d\boldsymbol{\xi}_1\, d\boldsymbol{\xi}_2 \tag{8–3}$$

In general, Eq. (8–3) is the description of a nonlinear process. For some relatively simple objects, Eq. (8–3) can be evaluated, e.g., two points; for the most part, however, we shall limit our attention to the limiting forms of Eq. (8–3) for coherent and incoherent illumination. Before introducing these limiting forms, it will prove useful to introduce the spatial frequency representation. Taking the Fourier transform with respect to the spatial coordinates on both sides of Eq. (8–2) yields

$$\tilde{\Gamma}_i(\boldsymbol{\mu}_1, \boldsymbol{\mu}_2) = \tilde{\Gamma}_o(\boldsymbol{\mu}_1, \boldsymbol{\mu}_2)\, \mathcal{L}(\boldsymbol{\mu}_1, \boldsymbol{\mu}_2) \tag{8–4}$$

where

$$\mathcal{L}(\boldsymbol{\mu}_1, \boldsymbol{\mu}_2) = \tilde{K}(\boldsymbol{\mu}_1)\, \tilde{K}^*(-\boldsymbol{\mu}_2) \tag{8–5}$$

is the transfer function.

Like Eq. (8–2), Eqs. (8–4) and (8–5) are valid in general, i.e., regardless of the coherence of the radiation. Since the sine wave resolution limit is simply that spatial frequency for which the transfer function goes to zero, it is clear from Eq. (8–5) that, in terms of the mutual intensity, the sine wave resolution limit is independent of the degree of coherence.

As pointed out earlier, however, in most imaging problems one is concerned with intensity rather than the mutual intensity. To determine the sine wave resolution limit in this case, we must examine Eq. (8–3). Equation (8–3) describes a nonlinear process, however, and thus cannot be described by a transfer function in the customary way. As pointed out by H. H. Hopkins (1956), one can introduce a generalized transfer function for the description of this particular nonlinear process but for imaging anything other than sinusoidal targets, however, this generalized transfer function is not too

†For simplicity of notation we replace $\Gamma(\mathbf{x}_1, \mathbf{x}_2, \nu)$ by the abbreviated notation $\Gamma(\mathbf{x}_1, \mathbf{x}_2)$

useful. Accordingly, we shall use these functions only to describe the imaging of sinusoids. Taking the Fourier transform on both sides of Eq. (8–3) yields

$$\tilde{I}_i(\mu) = \tilde{\Gamma}_0(\mu_1, \mu_2)\, \tilde{K}(\mu_1)\, \tilde{K}^*(\mu_2 - \mu_1) \tag{8–6}$$

Equation (8–6) *is also valid independently of the degree of coherence; and since Eq.* (8–6) *indicates that the "transfer function" for the process of going from mutual intensity to intensity is independent of the coherence, the sine wave resolution limit of such an imaging process is also independent of the degree of coherence.* This point will be examined in detail for the limiting cases of coherent and incoherent illumination in the next section.

In order to obtain the limiting forms of the general solution, Eq. (8–2) we have but to insert the appropriate form of the mutual intensity. We did this in Chapter 7 but shall repeat it with further comments.

The mutual intensity function for coherent radiation has the form

$$\Gamma(\xi_1, \xi_2) = u(\xi_1)\, u^*(\xi_2) \tag{8–7}$$

where $u(\xi_1)$ is a solution to the Helmholtz equation.

The mutual intensity may be written as† (where β has been absorbed into I)

$$\Gamma(\xi_1, \xi_2) = I(\xi_1)\, \delta(\xi_1 - \xi_2) \tag{8–8}$$

For the coherent limit, Eq. (8–3) may thus be rewritten as

$$I_i(x) = \left| \int_{\text{obj}} u_0(\xi_1)\, K(\mathbf{x} - \xi)\, d\xi \right|^2 \tag{8–9}$$

Equation (8–9) can be written as

$$I_i(\mathbf{x}) = u_i(\mathbf{x})\, u_i^*(\mathbf{x}) \tag{8–10}$$

where

$$u_i(\mathbf{x}) = \int_{\text{obj}} u_0(\xi)\, K(\mathbf{x} - \xi)\, d\xi \tag{8–11}$$

Note that this representation of the intensity is not unique. In terms of the measurable quantities in this problem, the complex amplitude is a fictitious construct and one might just as well identify the intensity as cc^*, where $c = ue^{i\phi}$ and ϕ‡ is any function of the coordinates. Continuing the development of the coherent imaging problem, however, we note that Eq. (8–11) describes a system linear in complex amplitude; but Eq. (8–11) *does not describe a coherent imaging system. Equation* (8–9) *is the description of a coherent imaging system; Eq.* (8–11) *is a convenient mathematical construct, but the physics of the imaging system leads to Eq.* (8–9) *not to Eq.* (8–11). As will become clear from the subsequent development, it is precisely this

†See Chapter 4 for a discussion of this equation.

‡The importance of this arbitrary phase term is discussed in Sec. 8.3.

point [erroneously identifying coherent imaging with Eq. (8–11) rather than with Eq. (8–9)] which leads to the mistaken conclusion that the sine wave resolution limit must differ by a factor of 2 in going from coherent to incoherent illumination. A very common experimental error and an unfortunate coincidence have also done much to perpetrate this error. These points, too, are discussed in the next section. The coherent imaging problem may be formulated in the spatial frequency domain by taking the Fourier transform on both sides of Eq. (8–11); thus

$$\tilde{u}_i(\mu) = \tilde{u}(\mu)\,\tilde{K}(\mu) \tag{8–12}$$

The interpretation of $\tilde{K}(\mu)$ as the aperture distribution itself and the consequences of Eq. (8–12) in spatial filtering systems has been discussed by several authors. The reader interested in pursuing this point further is referred to O'Neill (1963).

We complete this section by examining the form of Eq. (8–3) for systems using incoherent light. Equation (8–3) then assumes the form

$$I_i(\mathbf{x}) = \int_{\text{obj}} I_0(\boldsymbol{\xi})\,|K(\mathbf{x} - \boldsymbol{\xi})|^2\,d\boldsymbol{\xi} \tag{8–13}$$

Taking the Fourier transform on both sides of Eq. (8–13) yields

$$\tilde{I}_i(\mu) = \tilde{I}_0(\mu)\,\tau(\mu) \tag{8–14}$$

where

$$\tau(\mu) = \int \tilde{K}(\sigma)\,\tilde{K}^*(\mu - \sigma)\,d\sigma \tag{8–15}$$

Thus with incoherent radiation, the transfer function is given by the convolution of the aperture function with its complex conjugate. The pertinent consequence of Eq. (8–15) for our present discussion is that if $\tilde{K}(\mu)$ goes finally to zero at $\mu = \mu_0$ then $\tau(\mu)$ goes finally to zero for $\mu = 2\mu_0$. Also it should be noted Eqs. (8–14) and (8–15) describe incoherent imaging systems; they are not abstract constructs in the same sense as Eqs. (8–11) and (8–12). The system described by Eqs. (8–14) and (8–15) is linear up to, and including, the detection of the image.

8.3 A DETAILED TREATMENT OF SOME TYPICAL RESOLUTION LIMIT PROBLEMS

In this section, we discuss in detail the sine wave and square wave resolution limits for imaging systems employing coherent and incoherent illumination. The two-point resolution limit will be discussed for partially coherent illumination as well as for the limiting forms.

The sine wave resolution limits

In order to emphasize the effects of the coherence of the radiation we shall deal throughout this section with ideal (diffraction limited) lenses and we shall treat only the one-dimensional problem, i.e., cylindrical lens and line targets and unit magnification. These limitations are by no means essential to the arguments but they keep the mathematical manipulations to a minimum and the physics of the problem in the foreground.

Accordingly, we consider the aperture distribution to be

(8–16) $$\tilde{K}(\mu) = \begin{Bmatrix} 1, |\mu| \leq \mu_o \\ 0, |\mu| > \mu_o \end{Bmatrix}$$

where $$\mu_o = \frac{a}{\lambda f}$$

with a, λ, and f denoting the aperture size, the mean wavelength, and the focal length, respectively. The incoherent transfer function will then be given by

(8–17) $$\tau(\mu) = \begin{Bmatrix} 2\mu_o\left(1 - \frac{|\mu|}{2\mu_o}\right), & |\mu| \leq 2\mu_o \\ 0 & |\mu| > 2\mu_o \end{Bmatrix}$$

We now examine the image of a cosinusoidal target using coherent and incoherent illumination. In order to be specific, we consider the target to be a transparency illuminated from behind. The considerations will, of course, apply for objects viewed in reflected light. Using the laboratory standard, microscope or microdensitometer, etc., we determine then that the transmission of the object varies as $T(x)$ given by

(8–18) $$T(x) = \tfrac{1}{2}(1 + \cos 2\pi 2\mu_1 x)$$

Since the focal setting is the same for coherent or incoherent illumination† and since the resolution limit in both cases is determined by the aperture size of the lens, our experiment requires but one such target. Using either coherent or incoherent light, the lens is focused on the object to provide a one-to-one image, and then the lens is stopped down until the object is just resolved.

Considering first the case of incoherent light, it is clear from Eqs. (8–17) and (8–18) that the target will be resolved as long as the aperture size satisfies the inequality

(8–19) $$a > \lambda f \mu_1$$

The case of coherent light cannot, however, be dismissed so lightly; for whereas the intensity distribution in the object is given by Eq. (8–18), our system using coherent light is nonlinear in intensity and we must de-

†This conclusion is not true in general but can be made so by suitable choice of the parameters.

termine the amplitude distribution in the object before we can determine the limiting aperture size. If the incident coherent illumination is in phase and quasi-monochromatic, it will be represented by a mutual intensity of the form $\Gamma_{12} = v_1 v_2^*$ where v is a constant. Therefore, the field transmitted through the transparency will also be of the form $\Gamma_{12} = u_1 u_2^*$. However, as pointed out in Section 8.2, the measurement of the intensity simply requires that $|u|^2 = I$. That is, we cannot determine the phase of u from the intensity measurement. By means of two simple examples we shall show that this ignorance of the phase of u makes it impossible to determine a unique answer for the ratio of the sine wave resolution limits for coherent and incoherent light. First suppose the object introduces no phase variations on the beam. In this case we may take

$$u(x) = |\cos 2\pi\mu_1 x|. \tag{8–20 a}$$

By Fourier decomposing this object, we see that the lowest frequency component is $2\mu_1$ and then it follows from Eq. (8–11) that we require twice the aperture to resolve the target with coherent light.

Next consider the case where the target does introduce phase variations. In particular, let the phase variations be such that

$$u(x) = \cos 2\pi\mu_1 x. \tag{8–20 b}$$

This can be accomplished either by overlaying the target by a phase grating with phase steps of π and line frequency μ_1 or by using a suitable interference experiment to create the object distribution. If these manipulations with the phase of the object appear subject to question, one should remember that it is just this phase uncertainty that creates the difficulties being illustrated here. By either of the two arrangements just mentioned, a coherent illumination with an amplitude distribution proportional to $\cos 2\pi\mu_1 x$ can be created. The intensity distribution will, of course, remain unchanged. The object will now be resolved by the lens as long as the aperture satisfies the inequality

$$a > \lambda f \mu_1.$$

That is, the sine wave resolution in this case is the same with coherent or incoherent light.

We must conclude, therefore, that it is not possible to compare unambiguously the resolution limits for coherent and incoherent light if we limit our attention to intensity measurements. This is true since the coherent limit depends on the phase of Γ_{12} after the light has passed through (or reflected from) the object. Such difficulties are avoided, of course, by measuring Γ_{12} to characterize the object; and in this case the sine wave resolution is independent of the degree of coherence.

In the subsequent examples of this section we shall consider objects which do not alter the phase of the illumination. It should be borne in mind when reading these sections, however, that altering the phase will change the answer except in the limit of incoherent light.

The square wave resolution limit

In the previous section, the dependence of the sine wave resolution limit on the coherence of the radiation was illustrated. This section will show how the square wave resolution limit depends upon the coherence of the radiation. In particular, in the case of in-phase coherent illumination, the ratio of the incoherent resolution limit to the coherent resolution limit is 2 provided the object introduces no phase variations. It is this unfortunate coincidence that perpetuates the erroneous conclusion that the coherent resolution limit is necessarily half that obtained with incoherent light, since the easiest way of testing this contention is by using square wave targets and illuminating them first with incoherent light and secondly with in-phase (collimated) coherent light.

In the same experimental arrangement as before, a square wave which satisfies the conditions

$$T(x) = T(x - 2\sigma_o) \tag{8–21}$$

and

$$T(x) = \begin{matrix} 1 & 0 < x \leq \sigma_o \\ 0 & \sigma_o < x \leq 1 \end{matrix} \tag{8–22}$$

is used as an object. Using incoherent light, the target is just resolved when only the fundamental space frequency is passed by the lens. That is, the target is resolved if the aperture size satisfies the inequality

$$a > \frac{\lambda f}{\sigma_o} \tag{8–23}$$

If the target is illuminated by a collimated quasi-monochromatic wave front, the amplitude distribution will be proportional to the square root of $T(x)$ which is, of course, $T(x)$ itself. Again, the limiting resolution is obtained when only the fundamental spatial frequency is passed. Using Eqs. (8–21) and (8–16) it is clear that the target will be resolved as long as the aperture satisfies the inequality

$$a > \frac{2\lambda f}{\sigma_o} \tag{8–24}$$

This is just twice the aperture required to resolve the target with incoherent light. So in this special case of square wave targets, the resolution in the coherent and incoherent limits does differ by a factor of 2.

Examination of the image in this case, however, reveals again the danger of the doubled resolution contention even in this case. This is clear since the intensity variation in the incoherent image will contain only a constant (dc background) and a single cosinusoidial component (the fundamental of the object variation $2/\sigma_o$). The coherent image, on the other hand, will consist of an intensity variation containing a constant, the fundamental of its object $1/\sigma_o$, and in addition a component of twice that spatial frequency, $2/\sigma_o$. Thus though the resolution referred to the object plane differs by a factor of 2 in this example, both images will contain an intensity variation of $2/\sigma_o$ lines/mm.

Two-point resolution limit with partially coherent light†

Since we are dealing with only one-dimensional systems here, this discussion could more appropriately be described as the "two-line resolution limit." "Two-point" resolution, however, is a nomenclature more consistent with earlier authors: Barakat (1962). Hence, no confusion should arise over this misnomer. The mutual coherence function describing two equally bright, symmetrically located, partially coherent line sources may be written in the form

$$\Gamma(\xi_1, \xi_2, \tau) = I\gamma(\xi_1, \xi_2, \tau)[\delta(\xi_1 \pm a)\,\delta(\xi_2 \pm a)] \tag{8–25}$$

where the shortened notation

$$\delta(\xi \pm a) = \delta(\xi - a) + \delta(\xi + a) \tag{8–26}$$

has been used; I denotes the intensity appropriately normalized and $\gamma(\xi_1, \xi_2, \tau)$ is the complex degree of coherence. To avoid the complications of integrating over-all frequencies, we will limit the rest of our treatment to quasi-monochromatic illumination and suitably short path differences. Under these conditions, we may replace the mutual coherence function by its zero ordinate, the mutual intensity becomes [see Chapter 4 and Eq. (8–25)]

$$\Gamma(\xi_1, \xi_2) = I\gamma(\xi_1, \xi_2)[\delta(\xi_1 \pm a)\,\delta(\xi_2 \pm a)] \tag{8–27}$$

for quasi-monochromatic light. Substituting from Eq. (8–25) into (8–2) and integrating, we obtain

$$\begin{aligned}\frac{\Gamma_i(x_1, x_2)}{I} &= K(a - x_1)\,K^*(a - x_2)\,\gamma(a, a) \\ &\quad + K(a - x_1)\,K^*(-a - x_2)\,\gamma(a, -a) \\ &\quad + K(-a - x_1)\,K^*(a - x_2)\,\gamma(-a, a) \\ &\quad + K(-a - x_1)\,K^*(-a - x_2)\,\gamma(-a, -a)\end{aligned} \tag{8–28}$$

We obtain the intensity distribution $I(x)$ from Eq. (8–28) by setting $x_1 = x_2$. This procedure may be simplified by noting that, for diffraction-limited systems, we may take K as an even function, that is, $K(x) = K(-x)$. Further simplification of Eq. (8–28) is obtained by arranging the illumination so that the phase of γ is zero. This could be accomplished, for example,

†Much of the material in this section is contained in a Master's thesis of F. Rojak (1961).

by replacing the line sources by slits and illuminating the slits by a single, finite-sized, incoherent source symmetrically located with respect to the slits. Using these simplification, Eq. (8–29) reduces to

(8–29)
$$\frac{I(x)}{I} = |K(x-a)|^2 + |K(x+a)|^2 + 2|\gamma(a,-a)|\,\mathrm{Re}\,\{K(x-a)\,K^*(x+a)\}$$

In Eq. (8–29) $|K(x)|^2$ is the diffraction pattern of a clear nonaberrated slit, that is,

(8–30)
$$K(x) = \int_{-\infty}^{\infty} R(\alpha)\, e^{-2\pi i \alpha x}\, d\alpha$$

where

(8–31)
$$R(\alpha) = \tilde{K}(\alpha) = \begin{cases} 1 & |\alpha| \leq b \\ 0 & |\alpha| > b \end{cases}$$

Thus $I(x)$ depends parametrically on a and b. To determine the resolution limit from the Sparrow criterion,† we form, from Eqs. (8–29), (8–30) and (8–31), the equation

(8–32)
$$\left.\frac{d^2 I(x,a,b)}{dx^2}\right|_{x=0} = 0$$

and solve for a as a function of b. This procedure is somewhat simplified by going into the spatial frequency domain. Thus, the Sparrow criterion becomes

(8–33)
$$\int_{-\infty}^{\infty} (2\pi i \mu)^2\, \tilde{I}(\mu)\, d\mu = 0$$

Introducing the function $\tau_0(\mu)$ defined by

(8–34)
$$\tau_0(\mu) = \mu_0\left(1 - \frac{|\mu|}{\mu_0}\right)$$

and taking the Fourier transform on both sides of Eq. (8–29), we obtain, after rather lengthy algebraic manipulations,

(8–35)
$$\frac{\tilde{I}(\mu)}{I} = 2\tau_0(\mu)[\cos 2\pi\mu a + |\gamma_{12}|\,\mathrm{sinc}\,(2\pi a \tau_0(\mu))]$$

Here $\mathrm{sinc}\, x = (\sin x/x)$ and γ_{12} denotes the degree of coherence between the two sources. Substituting from Eq. (8–35) into Eq. (8–33) and performing

†Fundamentally, of course, there is no such thing as a two-point resolution criterion in the absense of noise limitations. The effect of noise, however, on two-point resolution has been found empirically to correlate well with either of two *ad hoc* criteria: the Rayleigh criterion and the Sparrow criterion. The Sparrow criterion, which states that two-point sources are just resolved if the second derivative of their image intensity vanishes at the point midway between the respective gaussian image points, is more readily amenable to quantitative calculations, and hence is used here.

the integrations, we obtain finally an expression of the form

$$A + B|\gamma| = 0 \tag{8–36}$$

where

$$A = (6 - y^2)(\cos y) + 4y(\sin y) - 6 \tag{8–37}$$

and

$$B = y^2 - 2(1 - \cos y) \tag{8–38}$$

with $y = k(ab) = (2\pi/\lambda)\, ab$.

From Eq. (8–36) the plot of just resolvable separation versus degree of coherence was obtained numerically and is plotted in Fig. 8-1. The just resolvable separation is seen to increase monotonically with the degree of coherence, reaching a value of 1.59 times the initial value when $|\gamma| = 1$. The two end points of this curve are contained in the paper by Barakat (1962). The near linearity of this plot suggests that this effect might provide a useful technique for the measurement of the degree of coherence.

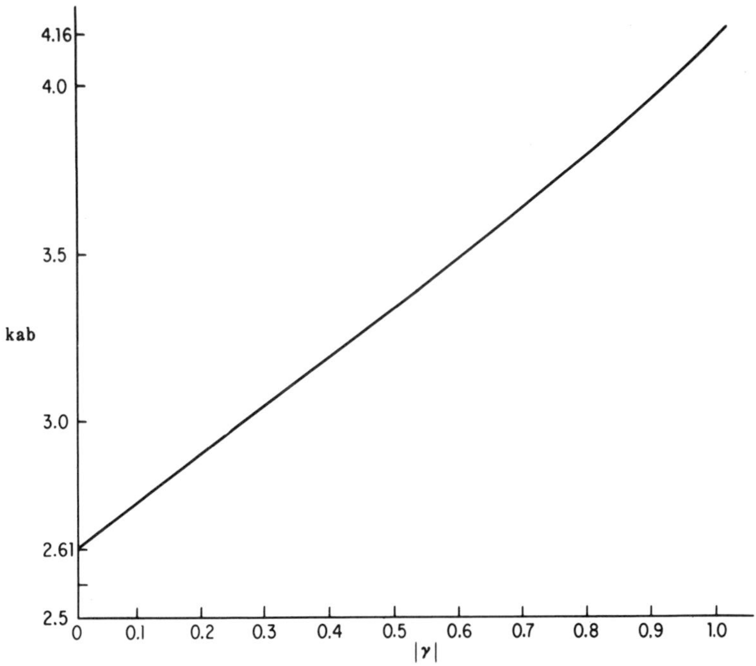

Figure 8-1. Two-point resolution (kab) *vs* modulus of complex degree of coherence.

chapter

9

Applications of the Theory of Partial Coherence

In this chapter, we illustrate a few of the applications in which the theory of partial coherence plays an important role. In this short book, no attempt is made at an exhaustive discussion. Rather we have selected only two examples, and these not as representative but as less obvious applications. In Chapters 7 and 8, we saw the generality which the application of coherence theory lends to the theory of image formation. Other applications to optical problems of this nature, for example, the effect of the character of the illumination on the image-forming properties of the microscope may be found in Born and Wolf (1959). In this chapter, we describe an unusual mapping device (the Covington-Drane antenna), from the viewpoint of coherence theory and discuss the application of the theory to the imaging of radiation that has passed through a real atmosphere.

9.1 THE COVINGTON-DRANE ANTENNA

The Covington-Drane antenna is, as we shall see, an unusual mapping device for the study of extended incoherent objects. This mapping system allows a versatility in the design of systems for imaging self-luminous objects that is equivalent to that available in the design of systems utilizing coherent radiation. This type of system has been constructed for use in radio astronomy and the results of the analyses presented here have been experimentally verified. The device has not yet been built at optical frequencies. Our discussion is closely based on an article by Drane and Parrent (1962) and the reader will find the basic references in this article.

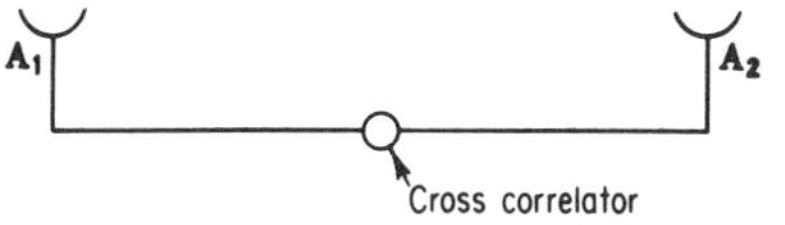

Figure 9-1. Antenna system.

We shall initially describe the necessary concepts in antenna language. We shall consider an antenna system composed of two antennas and a cross-correlating circuit (see Fig. 9-1). The instantaneous output of antenna A_1, is multiplied by the output of antenna A_2 and a long time average of the product is formed. The variation of the output of the correlator as the antenna system scans the object is the image or map of the object distribution. Let $V(\mathbf{x}, t)$ denote the field variation across the source, for example, a cartesian component of the electric vector, and consider $V(\mathbf{x}, t)$ to be a stationary random process.

Since $V(\mathbf{x}, t)$ is to be considered as a stationary random process in time, its temporal Fourier transform does not exist, and we must introduce the truncated function $V(T, \mathbf{x}, t)$ discussed in Chapter 2. We set

$$V(T, \mathbf{x}, t) = V^r(\mathbf{x}, T/t) + i_T V^i(\mathbf{x}, t) \qquad |t| \leq T$$
$$V(T, \mathbf{x}, t) = 0 \qquad |t| > T \tag{9–1}$$

We may then define the Fourier transform $\hat{V}(T, \mathbf{x}, \nu)$ of $V(\mathbf{x}, t)$ as

$$\hat{V}(T, \mathbf{x}, \nu) = \int_{-\infty}^{\infty} V(T, \mathbf{x}, t)\, e^{2\pi i \nu t}\, dt \tag{9–2}$$

With these definitions again in mind, we may now consider the description of the antenna. Letting $G_1(\mathbf{x})$ and $G_2(\mathbf{x})$ be the amplitude diffraction patterns of the two component antennas A_1 and A_2, respectively (where G_1 and G_2 are described relative to a common fixed point in the aperture), then we find that the output, $\hat{V}_1(T, \mathbf{x}, \nu)$, of the first antenna is given by

$$\hat{V}_1(T, \mathbf{x}, \nu) = \int_{-\infty}^{\infty} G_1(\mathbf{x}_1' - \mathbf{x}, \nu)\, \hat{V}(T, \mathbf{x}_1', t)\, d\mathbf{x}_1' \tag{9–3}$$

where $\mathbf{x}_1'$ is a typical point in the extended source distribution. Similarly, the complex conjugate of the output $\hat{V}_2(T, \mathbf{x}, \nu)$ of the second antenna is given by

$$\hat{V}_2^*(T, \mathbf{x}, \nu) = \int_{-\infty}^{\infty} G_2^*(\mathbf{x}_2' - \mathbf{x}, \nu)\, \hat{V}^*(T, \mathbf{x}_2', t)\, d\mathbf{x}_2' \tag{9–4}$$

(Note that the diffraction patterns G_1 and G_2 are frequency-dependent.)

The product of these two functions is clearly:

$$\begin{aligned}\hat{V}_1(T, \mathbf{x}, \nu)\, \hat{V}_2^*(T, \mathbf{x}, \nu) = \int_{-\infty}^{\infty}\int G_1(\mathbf{x}_1' - \mathbf{x}, \nu)\, G_2^*(\mathbf{x}_2' - \mathbf{x}, \nu) \\ \hat{V}(T, \mathbf{x}_1', \nu)\, \hat{V}^*(T, \mathbf{x}_2', \nu)\, d\mathbf{x}_1'\, d\mathbf{x}_2'\end{aligned} \tag{9–5}$$

Let us next divide by $2T$ on both sides of Eq. (9–5) and pass to the limit as T becomes very large. Since G_1 and G_2 do not depend on T, we obtain

$$\hat{P}(\mathbf{x}, \nu) = \int_{-\infty}^{\infty}\int G_1(\mathbf{x}_1' - \mathbf{x}, \nu)\, G_2^*(\mathbf{x}_1' - \mathbf{x}, \nu)\, \hat{\Gamma}(\mathbf{x}_1', \mathbf{x}_2', \nu)\, d\mathbf{x}_1'\, d\mathbf{x}_2' \tag{9–6}$$

In this equation, $\hat{P}(\mathbf{x}, \nu)$ is the complex spectral density of the output and $\Gamma(\mathbf{x}_1', \mathbf{x}_2', \nu)$ is the mutual spectral density of the distribution, that is,

$$\hat{\Gamma}(\mathbf{x}_1', \mathbf{x}_2', \nu) = \lim_{T\to\infty} \frac{\hat{V}(\mathbf{x}_1', \nu)\, \hat{V}^*(\mathbf{x}_2', \nu)}{2T}\,\dagger \tag{9–7}$$

Equation (9–6) represents the general solution for the output spectral density of the system under the condition that the system scans an extended, partially coherent, polychromatic source. Of considerably more interest from a practical point of view, however, is the form of the answer under the quasi-monochromatic approximation.

We remember again that the quasi-monochromatic approximation is usually characterized by the two conditions:

$$\begin{gathered}\Delta\nu \ll \bar{\nu} \\ |\tau| \ll \frac{1}{\Delta\nu} \quad \text{and} \quad l \ll \frac{c}{\Delta\nu}\end{gathered} \tag{9–8}$$

†See Section 2.3 for a note on the existence of this function.

The first of these conditions simply requires that the spectral width, $\Delta\nu$, of the signal be small compared to the mean frequency, $\bar{\nu}$. The second condition requires that all path differences introduced into the system should be small compared to $c/\Delta\nu$. Both of these conditions are easily satisfied in most antenna problems, and we shall accordingly introduce them at this point.

Under the quasi-monochromatic approximation, we may write the mutual coherence function as

$$\Gamma(\mathbf{x}_1, \mathbf{x}_2, \tau) \approx \Gamma(\mathbf{x}_1, \mathbf{x}_2, 0)\, e^{-2\pi i \bar{\nu}\tau} \tag{9–9}$$

Then the mutual power spectral density can be written as

$$\hat{\Gamma}(\mathbf{x}_1, \mathbf{x}_2, \tau) \approx \hat{\Gamma}(\mathbf{x}_1, \mathbf{x}_2, 0)\, \delta(\nu - \bar{\nu}) \tag{9–10}$$

Substituting from Eq. (9–10) into Eq. (9–6) and taking the Fourier transform of both sides of the resulting equation, we obtain, after evaluating at $\tau = 0$,

$$P(\mathbf{x}) = \iint_{-\infty}^{\infty} G_1(\mathbf{x}_1' - \mathbf{x})\, G_2^*(\mathbf{x}_2' - \mathbf{x})\, \Gamma(\mathbf{x}_1', \mathbf{x}_2', 0)\, d\mathbf{x}_1'\, d\mathbf{x}_2' \tag{9–11}$$

where $G_1(\mathbf{x})$ and $G_2(\mathbf{x})$ respectively, are now the radiation patterns of antennas A_1 and A_2 at the frequency $\bar{\nu}$. Equation (9–11) is the general solution for the complex output of an antenna of the type being considered when a partially coherent, quasi-monochromatic, extended distribution is scanned. (As indicated earlier, the actual output signal is proportional to the real part of $P(\mathbf{x})$.)

For most applications, the limiting cases of coherent and incoherent sources are of particular interest and we shall discuss these limits in some detail. It has been shown (see Chapter 4) that, for a coherent source, the mutual intensity may be uniquely represented in the form,

$$\Gamma(\mathbf{x}_1', \mathbf{x}_2', 0) = V(\mathbf{x}_1')\, V^*(\mathbf{x}_2') \tag{9–12}$$

With this theorem, Eq. (9–11) becomes

$$P(\mathbf{x}) = \int_{-\infty}^{\infty} G_1(\mathbf{x}_1' - \mathbf{x})\, V(\mathbf{x}_1)\, d\mathbf{x}_1' \int_{-\infty}^{\infty} G_2^*(\mathbf{x}_2' - \mathbf{x})\, V^*(\mathbf{x}_2')\, d\mathbf{x}_2' \tag{9–13}$$

We see that, for mapping extended objects which are coherently illuminated, the system is essentially nonlinear, and interpretation of the map would be extremely difficult at best. In the limit where $V(\mathbf{x}')$ is of the form $c\delta(\mathbf{x}' - \mathbf{x})$, Eq. (9–13) reduces to

$$P(\mathbf{x}) = c^2 G_1(\mathbf{x})\, G_2^*(\mathbf{x}) \tag{9–14}$$

as might have been expected from earlier analyses. Thus, for point sources, the system behaves as though we had a power diffraction pattern of the form given in Eq. (9–14).

Incoherent limit

In radio-astronomy applications, the sources are self-luminous and essentially incoherent. In this case, an extremely interesting form of the solution is obtained. For incoherent sources, the mutual intensity is often of the form†

$$\Gamma_o(\mathbf{x}_1, \mathbf{x}_2, 0) = \bar{\beta} P_o(\mathbf{x}_1)\, \delta(\mathbf{x}_1 - \mathbf{x}_2) \tag{9–15}$$

In this equation, the subscript o denotes the distribution at the source. If we substitute from Eq. (9–15) into the general solution Eq. (9–11) and integrate over the source, we obtain

$$P(\mathbf{x}) = \int_{\text{source}} \bar{\beta} P_o(\mathbf{x}')\, G_1(\mathbf{x}' - \mathbf{x})\, G_2^*(\mathbf{x}' - \mathbf{x})\, d\mathbf{x}' \tag{9–16}$$

where $P_o(\mathbf{x}')$ is the distribution of power in the source. Eq. (9–16) describes a system which is linear in power and which has a complex impulse response $\tilde{K}(\mathbf{x})$ given by

$$\tilde{K}(\mathbf{x}) = G_1(\mathbf{x})\, G_2^*(\mathbf{x}) \tag{9–17}$$

We have thus shown that the system under consideration, although nonlinear for mapping extended coherent sources, is certainly linear for mapping extended incoherent sources. In other words, if this antenna system were used, for example, in a typical radio-astronomical application, it would be linear in power. Recalling that G_1 and G_2 are defined relative to a common fixed point, we realize that we can establish the phase center of antenna A_1 at this point. For example, for a one-dimensional source, G_2 can be shown to be of the form

$$G_2(x) = e^{i\xi x}\, G_2'(x) \tag{9–18}$$

where $G_2'(x)$ is the radiation pattern of A_2 relative to its own phase center, and ξ is the physical separation of these two phase centers. If $A_2(\eta)$, η being the aperture coordinate, is real and symmetric, then $G_2'(x)$ will likewise be real and symmetric. The real part $K(x)$ of $\tilde{K}(x)$ corresponding to a real symmetric $A_1(\eta)$ is

$$K(x) = G_1(x)\, G_2'(x) \cos \xi x \tag{9–19}$$

Therefore, the appropriate impulse response or power pattern is simply the product of the two amplitude patterns and the interference term resulting from the phase center separation; i.e., it is the pattern which guided the design of the system. For example, if antenna A_1 is uniformly illuminated,

---

†See Chapter 4 for the limitations of this assumption. This form is appropriate for the applications we consider here.

giving rise to a pattern of the form $G_1(x) = \sin x/x$, and antenna A_2 is an interferometer of the same length as antenna A_1, giving a pattern of the form $G_2'(x) = \cos x$, then, if the two antennas are aligned end to end, the pattern of the system when used to scan incoherent sources is

$$K(x) = \left[\frac{\sin x}{x}\right][\cos x][\cos 2x] = \frac{\sin 4x}{4x} \tag{9–20}$$

If a single continuous aperture antenna of the length of both the interferometer and the continuous aperture were used, the corresponding pattern would be

$$K(x) = \left(\frac{\sin 2x}{2x}\right)^2 \tag{9–21}$$

Thus, the resolution of this system is increased. More promising, however, is the fact to be shown in the next section: this system provides complete control of the transfer function.

Frequency domain analysis

An extremely important consideration now becomes evident with respect to spatial frequency domain analysis. It has been pointed out many times in the past that, although systems utilizing incoherent illumination could be analyzed in the spatial frequency domain, the synthesis of a system with a desired transfer function is, in general, prohibitive. It will be shown that this is not the case for the correlation-type antennas considered in this example. We will see in fact that we have great control over the system response (transfer function).

If we look again at Eq. (9–16), the expression for the response of this single-multiplicative system to a distributed incoherent source, it is clear that this response is the convolution of the intensity function of the source and the system's impulse response. Application of the convolution theorem of Fourier theory yields

$$\hat{P}(\mu) = \hat{P}_o(\mu)\,\tau(\mu) \tag{9–22}$$

where μ designates spatial frequency, and $P(\mu)$, $P_o(\mu)$, and $\tau(\mu)$ represent Fourier transforms of $P(x)$, $P_o(x)$, and $G_1(x)\,G_1^*(x)$, respectively. By application of this same theorem, it is also clear that

$$\tau(\mu) = \int_{-\infty}^{\infty} A_1(x)\,A_2^*(x-\mu)\,dx \tag{9–23}$$

where $A_1(x)$ and $A_2(x)$ are the two antenna aperture distributions of our system.

In the usual linear, additive antenna, $\tau(\mu)$ is an autocorrelation function providing, therefore, much less flexibility in the synthesis of a desired response function than the cross-correlation techniques just given. In the foregoing example, $A_1(x')$ is a non-zero constant over a finite range, zero elsewhere (uniformly illuminated array), whereas $A_2(x')$ consists of two Dirac delta functions separated by a distance equal to the cited range of A_1 (simple interferometer). It must be remembered that both functions A_1 and A_2 are described relative to the same fixed coordinate system. It then follows that $\tau(\mu)$ is constant over a range in μ four times that of the corresponding range of A_1 and is zero otherwise. The corresponding radiation pattern is of the form

$$\text{Re}[G_1(x)\, G_2^*(x)] = \left[\frac{\sin x}{x}\right][\cos x][\cos 2x] = \frac{\sin 4x}{4x} \tag{9–24}$$

as noted before. Such a transfer function is physically unrealizable when $\tau(\mu)$ is an autocorrelation function.

It should be noted that the system cited, being linear in intensity, has nevertheless an impulse response of the form $(\sin 4x)/4x$, which should be compared with the power pattern $[(\sin 2x)/(2x)]^2$ of a linear, additive array. The main advantage of the former is a flat spectral system response (transfer function) rather than the triangularly shaped response of the latter, although both have the same cut-off spatial frequency. This statement, of course, implies that the object is an unweighted reception of the source frequency content falling within the bandwidth of the system.

It is quite conceivable, however, that one might be interested in a transfer function which particularly emphasizes high-frequency content. Here again, the precise shape desired for the transfer function is much more easily achieved by the convolution of two independent functions, rather than the very restrictive characteristic of the autoconvolution of a single aperture function tapered downward from the edges to the center of the array. We may illustrate this point by considering a particular application. Suppose we wish to map an object distribution in such a way as to enhance the edges, i.e., sudden changes in brightness. One way to accomplish this is to build an antenna array which acts as a differentiator with respect to the spatial coordinates. Recall that if

$$f(x) = \int_{-\infty}^{\infty} \tilde{f}(\mu)\, e^{2\pi i \mu x}\, d\mu \tag{9–25}$$

then

$$f''(x) = \int_{-\infty}^{\infty} (2\pi i \mu)^2 \tilde{f}(\mu)\, e^{2\pi i \mu x}\, d\mu \tag{9–26}$$

Thus, if our antenna system is to find the second derivative we require a transfer function of the form

$$\tau(\mu) = (2\pi i \mu)^2 \tag{9–27}$$

From Eq. (9–23) it is immediately clear that this could be accomplished by taking

$$A_1(\nu) = 4\pi^2 \nu^2 \quad \text{and} \quad A_2(\nu) = c_1\, \delta(\nu) \tag{9–28}$$

9.2 ATMOSPHERIC LIMITATIONS ON IMAGE-FORMING SYSTEMS

Many current applications of both visible and microwave optics require image-forming systems to "look" through the earth's atmosphere and the ever-increasing demand for higher resolution leads to the development of larger and larger lenses or antennas. As a result, a large class of problems for which the theory of partial coherence is particularly well suited have arisen. Some of these problems and the necessary coherence theory techniques for their solution are treated in this section. We shall begin with a more or less standard discussion of a class of atmospheric effects. Since our objective in this chapter is the applications of coherence theory and not an exhaustive discussion of atmospheric phenomena, we make no attempt at completeness. We simply discuss problems and techniques related to our subject.

Of the wealth of subject matter to choose from, the example best suited for our purpose is the atmospheric limitation on image quality. A simple illustration of this limitation may be seen by simply viewing the stars—they

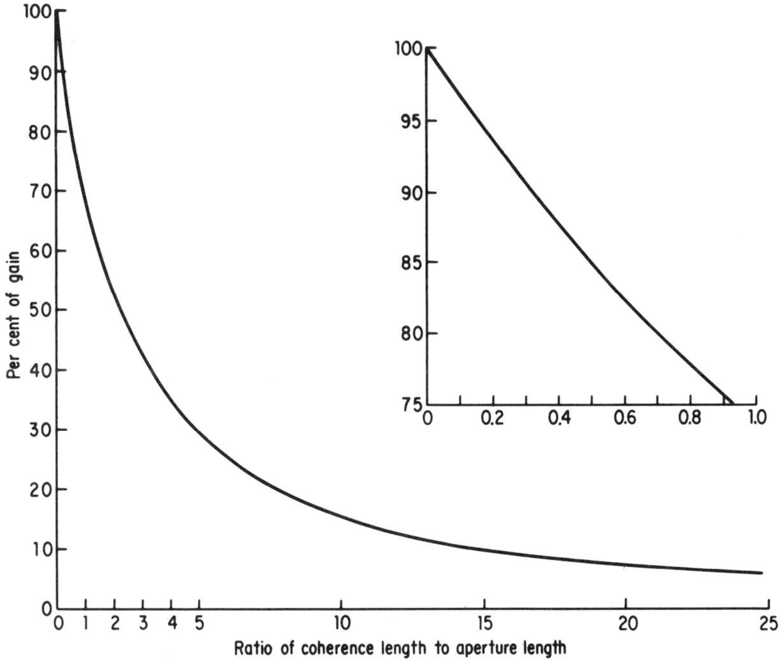

Figure 9-2. Example of gain *vs* coherence.

twinkle. This twinkle may be explained by saying that, at any instant, the atmosphere has a random variation in its refractive index; and that the pattern of variation moves in times of the order of the resolution time of the eye. To get a model more useful for the purpose of calculation, we need to take a somewhat closer look at the phenomenon.

We find that, if we build increasingly larger apertures for looking through the atmosphere, the antenna gain increases as the area of the aperture, as predicted by vacuum calculations, only for small lenses. As we continue to increase the aperture size, the gain eventually begins to increase only with the linear dimension of the aperture itself (see Fig. 9-2). Furthermore, we note that, for very large lenses, the resolution of the lens is equal to the vacuum resolution only a small part of the time; and the larger the lens, the smaller is the percentage of the time that the "theoretical" resolution is realized. Also we note that, if very short time exposures are made of the diffraction pattern of the lens, by starlight, say, the diffraction pattern looks very much like a photograph of Rayleigh noise, provided that the lens is large enough; a longer time exposure yields a diffraction pattern very similar to that obtained by using partially coherent light.

From the point of view of coherence theory, the explanation of these phenomena is straightforward and the method of studying the atmospheric limitations is clear. In order to be as specific as possible in our example consider an imaging system as schematically illustrated in Fig. 9-3. Here $\boldsymbol{\xi}$ is the position vector of a typical point on an incoherently illuminated object, $\boldsymbol{\alpha}$ is the position vector of a typical point in the pupil A of an image-forming device, and $\mathbf{x}$ is the position vector of a point in the image plane. The atmosphere fills the intervening space (or part of it) between the lens and the object. We shall consider the problems of determining the intensity distribution in the image plane under the condition that the exposure time is large compared to the period of oscillations in the atmosphere or the

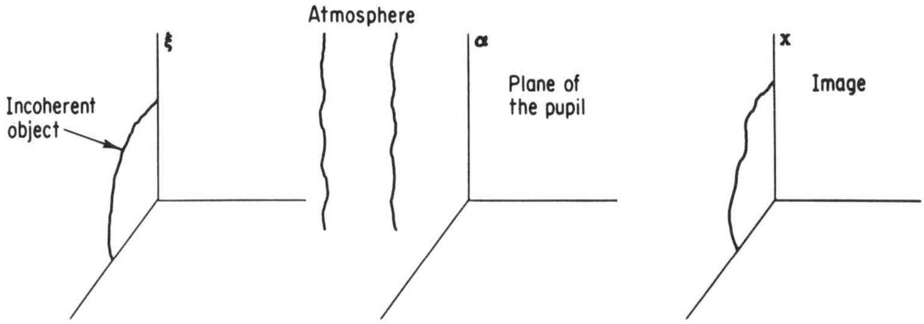

Figure 9-3. Coordinate systems used in analysis of imaging through a turbulent atmosphere.

equivalent problem of determining the ensemble averaged distribution for relatively short exposures. Note that, short of specifying the atmosphere at every point at every instant, this is the most complete solution that is possible.

Assuming the quasi-monochromatic approximations apply, we may express (see Chapter 4) the mutual intensity of the incident field in the nth experiment as

$$\Gamma_n(\boldsymbol{\alpha}_1, \boldsymbol{\alpha}_2) = \int_{\text{obj}} I(\boldsymbol{\xi})\, K_n(\boldsymbol{\xi}, \boldsymbol{\alpha}_1, \boldsymbol{\alpha}_2)\, d\boldsymbol{\xi}\ \dagger \tag{9–29}$$

Here, K_n is a two-point Green's function characterizing the atmosphere for that experiment. β_n is included in K_n. Note K_n is expressed as a general function of its argument and not as a function of the difference only. We now consider an ensemble of experiments. Denoting the ensemble average by a bar and now terming the coherence function $\Gamma^E(\boldsymbol{\alpha}_1, \boldsymbol{\alpha}_2)$ we may write

$$\Gamma^E(\boldsymbol{\alpha}_1, \boldsymbol{\alpha}_2) = \int_{\text{obj}} I(\boldsymbol{\xi})\, \bar{K}(\boldsymbol{\xi}, \boldsymbol{\alpha}_1, \boldsymbol{\alpha}_2)\, d\boldsymbol{\xi} \tag{9–30}$$

If we assume that, whereas instantaneously the atmosphere may not in general be assumed to be characterized by a function of the separation only, that is, $K_n(\boldsymbol{\xi}, \boldsymbol{\alpha}_1, \boldsymbol{\alpha}_2) \neq K_n(\boldsymbol{\xi} - \boldsymbol{\alpha}_1, \boldsymbol{\xi} - \boldsymbol{\alpha}_2)$, we can with prudence assume that the statistics are stationary with respect to the spatial coordinates, that is, $\bar{K} \equiv f(\boldsymbol{\xi} - \boldsymbol{\alpha}_1, \boldsymbol{\xi} - \boldsymbol{\alpha}_2)$. Thus Eq. (9–30) becomes

$$\Gamma^E(\boldsymbol{\alpha}_1, \boldsymbol{\alpha}_2) = \int_{\text{obj}} I(\boldsymbol{\xi})\, \bar{K}(\boldsymbol{\xi} - \boldsymbol{\alpha}_1, \boldsymbol{\xi} - \boldsymbol{\alpha}_2)\, d\boldsymbol{\xi} \tag{9–31}$$

$\Gamma^E(\boldsymbol{\alpha}_1, \boldsymbol{\alpha}_2)$ is the mutual intensity distribution in the aperture plane of our imaging system. We may now obtain the distribution in the image plane by again solving the wave equations taking account of the lens. This result is an expression of the form (see Chapter 7)

$$\begin{aligned} \Gamma^E(\mathbf{x}_1, \mathbf{x}_2) &= \int_{\text{apert}} \Gamma^E(\boldsymbol{\alpha}_1, \boldsymbol{\alpha}_2) \frac{\partial G_1(\boldsymbol{\alpha}_1 - \mathbf{x}_1)}{\partial n} \frac{\partial G_2(\boldsymbol{\alpha}_2 - \mathbf{x}_2)}{\partial n}\, d\boldsymbol{\alpha}_1\, d\boldsymbol{\alpha}_2 \\ &= \int_{\text{apert}} \Gamma^E(\boldsymbol{\alpha}_1, \boldsymbol{\alpha}_2)\, F(\boldsymbol{\alpha}_1 - \mathbf{x}_1, \boldsymbol{\alpha}_2 - \mathbf{x}_2)\, d\boldsymbol{\alpha}_1\, d\boldsymbol{\alpha}_2 \end{aligned} \tag{9–32}$$

Here G_1 and G_2 are the appropriate Green's functions for going through the optical system. Their exact form is not an important consideration at this point. Substituting Eq. (9–31) into Eq. (9–32), we obtain

---

†This equation is a special case of Eq. (6–9). The form in Eq. (9–29) thus apparently obviates the need for the perturbation procedures given in Chapter 6, but unfortunately, of course, the ensemble average of K cannot be calculated. The point of this development, however, as we shall show, is that the ensemble average of K may be measured and the measured function may easily be used.

$$\Gamma^E(\mathbf{x}_1, \mathbf{x}_2) = \int_{\text{apert}} \int_{\text{obj}} I(\boldsymbol{\xi})\, \bar{K}(\boldsymbol{\xi} - \boldsymbol{\alpha}_1, \boldsymbol{\xi} - \boldsymbol{a}_2) \, F(\boldsymbol{a}_1 - \mathbf{x}_1, \boldsymbol{\alpha}_2 - x_2)\, d\boldsymbol{\xi}\, d\boldsymbol{\alpha}_1\, d\boldsymbol{\alpha}_2 \tag{9–33}$$

We obtain the intensity distribution in the image by setting $\mathbf{x}_1 = \mathbf{x}_2$ in Eq. (9–33). After introducing the change of variable $\boldsymbol{\xi} - \boldsymbol{\alpha}^1 = \boldsymbol{\rho}_1$ and $\boldsymbol{\xi} - \boldsymbol{\alpha}_2 = \boldsymbol{\rho}_2$ and setting $\mathbf{x}_1 = \mathbf{x}_2$, we have

$$\bar{I}(\mathbf{x}) = \int I(\boldsymbol{\xi}) \int \bar{K}(\boldsymbol{\rho}_1, \boldsymbol{\rho}_2)\, F[(\boldsymbol{\xi} - \mathbf{x}) - \boldsymbol{\rho}_1, (\boldsymbol{\xi} - \mathbf{x}) - \boldsymbol{\rho}_2]\, d\boldsymbol{\rho}_1\, d\boldsymbol{\rho}_2\, d\boldsymbol{\xi} \tag{9–34}$$

Defining the symbol $\bar{A}(\boldsymbol{\xi} - \mathbf{x})$ by the equation

$$\bar{A}(\boldsymbol{\xi} - \mathbf{x}) = \int \bar{K}(\boldsymbol{\rho}_1, \boldsymbol{\rho}_2)\, F[(\boldsymbol{\xi} - \mathbf{x}) - \boldsymbol{\rho}_1, (\boldsymbol{\xi} - \mathbf{x}) - \boldsymbol{\rho}_2]\, d\boldsymbol{\rho}_1\, d\boldsymbol{\rho}_2 \tag{9–35}$$

we may rewrite Eq. (9–35) as

$$\bar{I}(\mathbf{x}) = \int I(\boldsymbol{\xi})\, \bar{A}(\boldsymbol{\xi} - \mathbf{x})\, d\boldsymbol{\xi} \tag{9–36}$$

The implication here is clear. Under the conditions stated, we may regard the atmosphere and the lens as cascaded image-forming devices with the effective impulse response $\bar{A}(\mathbf{x})$. Although this result is not too surprising after some reflection, we can gain some insight into the usefulness of the coherence theory point of view for the discussion of this problem by carrying our development a step further. In particular let us consider the problem of determining the optimum-sized aperture for imaging through the atmosphere. We assume aberration-free systems in order to keep the atmospheric problem tantamount. We wish to determine then the impulse response of a diffraction-limited system and in particular to observe the manner in which this impulse response varies with aperture size. Our first question is what atmospheric parameters must be determined?

This question may be answered by examining Eq. (9–31). It is clear that, by considering a point source as our object (that is, replacing $I(\boldsymbol{\xi})$ by a delta function) and measuring $\Gamma^E(\boldsymbol{\alpha}_1, \boldsymbol{\alpha}_2)$, we will have completely determined the problem. That is, the significant experiment is to put a point source in the object space and determine the ensemble averaged mutual intensity resulting from passage of the light through the atmosphere. Thus a conceptually simple interference experiment determines the atmospheric effects.†

Having determined $\Gamma^E(\boldsymbol{\alpha}_1, \boldsymbol{\alpha}_2)$, we may then determine the intensity diffraction pattern for an arbitrary aperture size. The solution of this problem is indicated in Chpater 3. The calculation simply involves solving the two wave equations for Γ_{12}, and although the calculation usually involves a

†Of course, this must be done under different weather conditions, different hours of the day, different seasons, etc.

computer, the solution is straightforward. Of course, having once obtained the impulse response, our problem must then be solved for the particular parameter in which we are most interested, e.g., two-point resolution. This may be accomplished however by the methods outlined in Chapter 8. A similar development can also be given for imaging through any diffuse or scattering medium. Thus, the problem of determining the atmospheric effect on image quality is reduced to determining the effect of the atmosphere on the ensemble coherence of the radiation.

chapter

10

Partial Polarization

In the next chapter, we shall formulate the concept of partial coherence for the entire electromagnetic field. Here, however, we wish to treat a somewhat simpler problem: the propagation of plane parallel radiation. In this case, the electric vector (the magnetic vector may be treated similarly) is perpendicular to the direction of propagation, and we need only study its orientation or polarization in this perpendicular plane.

When the radiation is strictly monochromatic, the polarization direction is fixed, and the problem is of little interest. (Superimposing a number of monochromatic waves of the same frequency with different orientation simply yields a single wave with some fixed polarization.) If we consider a superposition of plane waves of differing frequency and different orientation, however, the problem is of considerable interest. As before, we shall be mainly concerned with radiation that may be treated from a statistical point of view.

We shall begin by defining a matrix, which allows us to treat the statistical nature of the polarization. We shall then show how the statistical properties of the polarization may be calculated after passage of the radiation through compensators, rotators, absorbers, and polarizers. These elements, which we shall carefully define, represent the elements found in many optical systems (and, indeed, other electromagnetic systems) and thus this treatment will allow the solution of a great many practical problems.

We shall treat the problem only of quasi-monochromatic radiation and consider the partial polarization at a single point. For the problem of radiation of finite spectral width the reader is referred to Barakat (1963). The question of the coherence of the polarization between two points is a problem of current research.

10.1 DEFINITIONS

We consider the radiation to propagate in the z direction and thus the electric field to be defined by the components $E_x^r(\mathbf{x}_1, t)$ and $E_y^r(\mathbf{x}_1, t)$. As in the scalar case, we use an analytic signal representation and thus treat the complex quantities $E_x(\mathbf{x}_1, t)$ and $E_y(\mathbf{x}_1, t)$. These quantities may be used to form a column matrix:

$$C(\mathbf{x}_1, t) = \begin{pmatrix} E_x(\mathbf{x}_1, t) \\ E_y(\mathbf{x}_1, t) \end{pmatrix} \tag{10–1}$$

The hermitian conjugate of $C(\mathbf{x}_1, t)$ is the row matrix:

$$C^\dagger(\mathbf{x}_1, t) = (E_x^*(\mathbf{x}_1, t)\ E_y^*(\mathbf{x}_1, t)) \tag{10–2}$$

From C and $C^\dagger$, we define by matrix multiplication and time averaging the coherency matrix $\mathcal{J} = \langle CC^\dagger \rangle$.† Written explicitly, this is

$$\mathcal{J} = \begin{pmatrix} \langle E_x E_x^* \rangle & \langle E_x E_y^* \rangle \\ \langle E_x^* E_y \rangle & \langle E_y E_y^* \rangle \end{pmatrix} = \begin{pmatrix} J_{xx} & J_{xy} \\ J_{yx} & J_{yy} \end{pmatrix} \tag{10–3}$$

and we notice that $\mathcal{J}$ is hermitian.

The coherency matrix $\mathcal{J}$ tells us all we wish to know about second-order statistical propagation of the radiation. We note that the trace of $\mathcal{J}$ is the intensity.‡ That is,

---

†We are using a dyadic notation here.

‡We remember that because of the complex notation we commonly call quantities like Tr $\mathcal{J}$ the *intensity* whereas actually it is twice the true intensity.

$$I = \mathrm{Tr}\,\mathcal{J} = \langle E_x E_x^* \rangle + \langle E_y E_y^* \rangle \tag{10–4}$$

Further, $\langle E_x E_x^* \rangle$ and $\langle E_y E_y^* \rangle$ are the partial intensities in the x and y directions respectively, and as we shall soon show, we can, from the matrix, find the partial intensities in any direction.

To define the degree of polarization we shall use here a definition given by Parrent and Roman (1960). An earlier definition given by Wolf (1959) yields similar information.

In order to formulate the definition of partial coherence properly, it is useful first to introduce the concepts of polarizers and rotators. We shall thus postpone the definition of degree of polarization, to Section 10.5. Our development will follow that given by Parrent and Roman (1960).

10.2 ELEMENTS

It is at this point that the introduction of the quasi-monochromatic approximation greatly simplifies the discussion. The operations of elements that affect the polarization are in general frequency-dependent. In considering radiation of narrow spectral width, we assume all frequency components of the radiation are affected similarly by the element and we do not need to decompose the radiation spectrally, send each frequency component through the element, and then reconstruct the result. Care must be taken, however, when invoking this approximation to make sure that path lengths of the radiations are not so large that the finite though small spectral width of the radiation will become important. With this approximation in mind then, we define the following elements:

Compensator

When the radiation passes through this device, the E_x and E_y components of the electric field experience phase changes, ϵ_x and ϵ_y respectively. It is convenient to represent this as a net phase change of $\delta = \epsilon_x - \epsilon_y$, and we may represent the effect of a compensator on C and $\mathcal{J}$ by defining the following matrix ζ:

$$\zeta = \begin{pmatrix} e^{i\delta/2} & 0 \\ 0 & e^{-i\delta/2} \end{pmatrix} \tag{10–5}$$

The emergent electric field is then

$$C_c = \zeta C = \begin{pmatrix} E_x\, e^{i\delta/2} \\ E_y\, e^{-i\delta/2} \end{pmatrix} \tag{10–6}$$

$\mathcal{J}_c$ may then be calculated as follows:

$$\mathcal{J}_c = \langle C_c C_c^\dagger \rangle = \langle \zeta C C^\dagger \zeta^\dagger \rangle$$
$$= \zeta \langle C C^\dagger \rangle \zeta^\dagger \qquad (10\text{–}7)$$
$$= \zeta \mathcal{J} \zeta^\dagger$$

Or, since ζ is unitary,

$$\mathcal{J}_c = \zeta \mathcal{J} \zeta^{-1} \qquad (10\text{–}8)$$

We may easily show that $I_c = I$ since there is no absorption or reflection.

Absorption

An element which decreases the field strength may be represented by the matrix $\mathcal{A}$:

$$\mathcal{A} = \begin{pmatrix} e^{-1/2\eta_x} & 0 \\ 0 & e^{-1/2\eta_x} \end{pmatrix} \qquad (10\text{–}9)$$

This yields as before:

$$\mathcal{J}_A = \mathcal{A} \mathcal{J} \mathcal{A}^\dagger \qquad (10\text{–}10)$$

The intensity is now reduced, and we may calculate

$$I_A = \mathrm{Tr}\,[\mathcal{A}^2 \mathcal{J}] \qquad (10\text{–}11)$$

Rotator

An element which rotates the electric vector through an angle of α may be represented by the matrix:

$$\mathcal{R}(\alpha) = \begin{pmatrix} \cos\alpha & \sin\alpha \\ -\sin\alpha & \cos\alpha \end{pmatrix} \qquad (10\text{–}12)$$

Then $\quad \mathcal{J}_{\mathcal{R}} = \mathcal{R}(\alpha)\,\mathcal{J}\mathcal{R}^\dagger(\alpha) = \mathcal{R}(\alpha)\,\mathcal{J}\mathcal{R}^{-1}(\alpha) = \mathcal{R}(\alpha)\,\mathcal{J}\mathcal{R}(-\alpha)$

Here $I_{\mathcal{R}} = I$.

Polarizer

A polarizer is an element which passes only one component of the field, say at an angle θ with the x direction. Thus the polarizer which we represent by $\mathcal{P}_+(\theta)$ is a projection operator, and satisfies the idempotency condition.

$$\mathcal{P}_+(\theta)\,\mathcal{P}_+(\theta) = \mathcal{P}_+(\theta) \qquad (10\text{–}13)$$

If we now define a second projection operator $\mathcal{P}_-(\theta)$, as a polarizer which passes only the component of the field perpendicular to θ, we have the following relations:

$$\begin{aligned} &\mathcal{P}_-(\theta)\,\mathcal{P}_-(\theta) = \mathcal{P}_-(\theta) \\ &\mathcal{P}_-(\theta)\,\mathcal{P}_+(\theta) = \mathcal{P}_+(\theta)\,\mathcal{P}_-(\theta) = 0 \\ &\mathcal{P}_+(\theta) + \mathcal{P}_-(\theta) = I \end{aligned} \tag{10–14}$$

$\mathcal{P}_+(\theta)$ and $\mathcal{P}_-(\theta)$ have the following explicit forms:

$$\mathcal{P}_+(\theta) = \begin{pmatrix} \cos^2\theta & \sin\theta\cos\theta \\ \sin\theta\cos\theta & \sin^2\theta \end{pmatrix}$$

$$\mathcal{P}_-(\theta) = \begin{pmatrix} \sin^2\theta & -\sin\theta\cos\theta \\ -\sin\theta\cos\theta & \cos^2\theta \end{pmatrix}$$

As before, we have

$$\mathcal{J}_P = \mathcal{P}_+\mathcal{J}\mathcal{P}_+^\dagger = \mathcal{P}_+\mathcal{J}\mathcal{P}_+ \tag{10–15}$$

noting P_+ is hermitian.

A polarizer decreases the intensity according to the relation:

$$I_P = \mathrm{Tr}\,[\mathcal{P}_+\mathcal{J}]$$

10.3 CASCADED SYSTEMS

To determine the effect of a cascade of elements we just apply the operations one after another. Thus the effect of an absorption and a polarization is

$$\mathcal{J}_K(\theta, \eta) = \mathcal{P}_+\mathcal{A}\mathcal{J}\mathcal{A}^\dagger\mathcal{P}_+ \tag{10–16}$$

with similar expressions for other combinations.

10.4 DEFINITION OF DEGREE OF COHERENCE AND DEGREE OF POLARIZATION

In analogy to the definition of $\gamma_{12}(\tau)$, we define the degree of coherence between the x and y components of the field as

$$\mu_{xy} = \frac{\langle E_x E_y^* \rangle}{\sqrt{\langle E_x E_x^* \rangle \langle E_y E_y^* \rangle}} \tag{10–17}$$

To see how this function is directly measurable, it may be written in terms of polarizers and rotators as follows:

$$\mu_{xy} = \frac{\mathrm{Tr}\,\langle[\mathcal{P}_+(0)\,C][\mathcal{P}_+(0)\,\mathcal{R}(-\pi/2)\,C)]\rangle^\dagger}{\{\mathrm{Tr}\,\langle[\mathcal{P}_+(0)C][\mathcal{P}_+(0)C]\rangle^\dagger\}^{1/2} \cdot \{\mathrm{Tr}\,\langle[\mathcal{P}_+(0)\,\mathcal{R}(-\pi/2)C][\mathcal{P}_+(0)\,\mathcal{R}(-\pi/2)C]\rangle^\dagger\}^{1/2}} \tag{10–18}$$

By using the Schwarz inequality, we can show that the modulus of μ_{xy} lies between 1 and 0. We should like to show that the limit 1 corresponds to completely polarized light, and the limit 0 to completely unpolarized light. First, however, we note that μ_{xy} depends upon the coordinates x and y chosen, and is thus unsatisfactory as a measure of the state of polarization. Rather we shall consider the maximum value of $|\mu_{xy}|^2$ which can be proved always to exist.

If θ is the angle made with the original xy coordinate axes, we can show from Eq. (10–18) that

$$|\mu_{xy}(\theta)|^2 = \frac{\mathrm{Tr}\,[\mathcal{R}(\pi/2)\,\mathcal{P}_+(\theta)\,\mathcal{J}]\,\mathrm{Tr}\,[\mathcal{R}(\pi/2)\,\mathcal{P}_+(\theta)\,\mathcal{J}^*]}{\mathrm{Tr}\,[\mathcal{P}_+(\theta)\,\mathcal{J}]\,\mathrm{Tr}\,[\mathcal{P}_-(\theta)\,\mathcal{J}]} \tag{10–19}$$

Maximation of this quantity yields

$$\tan 2\,\theta_{\max} = \frac{J_{yy} - J_{xx}}{J_{xy} + J_{yx}} \tag{10–20}$$

and

$$P = |\mu_{xy}(\theta)| = \sqrt{1 - \frac{4\det\mathcal{J}}{(\mathrm{Tr}\,\mathcal{J})^2}} \tag{10–21}$$

where P is termed the *degree of polarization.*

If $P = 1$, we now say the radiation is *completely polarized*, and if $P = 0$ we call the radiation *completely unpolarized.* The case $P = 1$ yields

$$\det\mathcal{J} = 0 \tag{10–22}$$

If all the radiation is polarized in some direction, it can be shown by direct calculation that indeed $\det\mathcal{J} = 0$.

If $P = 0$,

$$(\mathrm{Tr}\,\mathcal{J})^2 = 4\det\mathcal{J} \tag{10–23}$$

This yields as the only solution:

$$J_{xx} = J_{yy} \quad \text{and} \quad J_{xy} = J_{yx} = 0 \tag{10–24}$$

which corresponds to our concept of unpolarized radiation.

When P is neither 1 or 0, we consider the radiation to be partially polarized. Now it turns out that the radiation field can be uniquely written as a weighted sum of a completely polarized and a completely unpolarized field. Following Wolf (1959) we may write

$$\begin{aligned} \mathcal{J} &= \mathcal{J}^{UP} + \mathcal{J}^{P} \\ \mathcal{J}^{UP} &= \begin{pmatrix} A & O \\ O & A \end{pmatrix} \\ \mathcal{J}^{P} &= \begin{pmatrix} B & D \\ D^* & C \end{pmatrix} \end{aligned} \tag{10–25}$$

where A, B, and C are chosen real and positive and $BC - DD^* = 0$.

Remembering that the elements of $\mathcal{J}$ are denoted by J_{xx}, etc., we have the following relations:

$$\begin{aligned} A + B &= J_{xx} \\ D &= J_{xy} \\ D^* &= J_{yx} \\ A + C &= J_{yy} \end{aligned} \tag{10–26}$$

Using the condition $BC - DD^* = 0$ and Eq. (10–26), we find

$$A = \frac{1}{2}(J_{xx} + J_{yy}) \pm \frac{1}{2}\sqrt{(J_{xx} + J_{yy})^2 - 4 \det \mathcal{J}} \tag{10–27}$$

Only the negative sign satisfies the nonnegativity conditions on A, B, and C. Using this sign only, we may, from Eq. (10–26), find expressions for B, C, and D in terms of J_{xx}, J_{yy}, J_{xy}, and J_{yx}.

If we call I_P, the intensity of the polarized part of the radiation, then $I_P = \text{Tr}\,\mathcal{J}^P$, and we find after some calculation that

$$\frac{I_P}{I_{TOT}} = \sqrt{1 - \frac{4 \det \mathcal{J}}{(\text{Tr}\,\mathcal{J})^2}} \tag{10–28}$$

where $I_{TOT} = \text{Tr}\,\mathcal{J}$

Comparing Eq. (10–21) and Eq. (10–28) we see that

$$P = \frac{I_P}{I_{TOT}} \tag{10–29}$$

and we have perhaps a more physical notion of partial polarization than we can get from the square root definition.

10.5 MEASUREMENT OF $\mathcal{J}$

The utility of using $\mathcal{J}$ stems from the fact that it is measurable. We shall now show a sequence of measurements which will allow us to measure J_{xx} and J_{yy} and the real and complex parts of J_{xy}. [For a fuller discussion, see Born and Wolf (1959).]

Let us put a compensator in front of the radiation which introduces a phase delay of ϵ for the y component of the radiation relative to the x component. Then we put in a polarizer at an angle θ with respect to the x axis. The intensity of the radiation which emerges from these two elements, which we will represent as $I(\theta, \epsilon)$, may be shown to equal

$$\begin{aligned} I(\theta, \epsilon) = {} & J_{xx} \cos^2\theta + J_{yy} \sin^2\theta + J_{xy}\, e^{-\epsilon i} \cos\theta \sin\theta \\ & + J_{yx}\, e^{i\epsilon} \sin\theta \cos\theta \end{aligned} \tag{10–30}$$

Then we find that

$$J_{xx} = I(0, 0)$$

$$J_{yy} = I\left(\frac{\pi}{2}, 0\right)$$

(10–31)
$$J_{xy} = \frac{1}{2}\left\{I\left(\frac{\pi}{4}, 0\right) - I\left(\frac{3\pi}{4}, 0\right)\right\} + \frac{i}{2}\left\{I\left(\frac{\pi}{4}, \frac{\pi}{2}\right) - I\left(\frac{3\pi}{4}, \frac{\pi}{2}\right)\right\}$$

$$J_{yx} = \frac{1}{2}\left\{I\left(\frac{\pi}{4}, 0\right) - I\left(\frac{3\pi}{4}, 0\right)\right\} - \frac{i}{2}\left\{I\left(\frac{\pi}{4}, \frac{\pi}{2}\right) - I\left(\frac{3\pi}{4}, \frac{\pi}{2}\right)\right\}$$

We may note from the preceding expressions that J_{xx}, J_{yy}, and $\operatorname{Re} J_{xy}$ may be measured using only a polarizer, but that the measurement of $\operatorname{Im} J_{xy}$ requires use of a compensator.

10.6 STOKES PARAMETERS

We note here that the Stokes parameters may be defined by the relations:

(10–32)
$$S_0 = J_{xx} + J_{yy}$$
$$S_1 = J_{xx} - J_{yy}$$
$$S_2 = J_{xy} + J_{yx}$$
$$S_3 = i(J_{yx} - J_{xy})$$

chapter

11

Vector Formulation

Except in Chapter 10, we have previously considered problems where a scalar formulation of electromagnetic theory was applicable. Although the scalar theory we have presented serves a wide scope of problems, it is, of course, in general not appropriate, and it is the purpose of this chapter to generalize the concept of the scalar coherence function. We shall consider the propagation of the generalized coherence function in free space and, as in the scalar case, derive the wave equations which govern its propagation. Some conservation laws will also be given.

Very little work has been done toward solving these equations in the treatment of boundary value problems. Bourret (1960), however, has solved these equations to obtain the coherence within a blackbody cavity and his work will be outlined here.

11.1 DEFINITIONS

In this section, we generalize the scalar definition of the mutual coherence function. As before, we shall present a time-averaged and an ensemble definition.

An electromagnetic field is defined by its electric and magnetic fields which we denote by $E_i(\mathbf{x}, t)$ and $H_i(\mathbf{x}, t)$ respectively. The subscript i signifies the ith component of $\mathbf{E}$ or $\mathbf{H}$, and for a complete description, we let $i = 1,2$, and 3. E_i and H_i satisfy Maxwell's equations, which may be written as

$$\epsilon_{jkl}\partial_k^{(1)} E_l(\mathbf{x}_1, t_1) = -\frac{\partial}{\partial t_1} H_j(\mathbf{x}_1, t_1) \tag{11–1}$$

$$\epsilon_{jkl}\partial_k^{(1)} H_l(\mathbf{x}_1, t) - \frac{\partial E_j}{\partial t_1}(\mathbf{x}_1, t_1) = j_j(\mathbf{x}_1, t_1) \tag{11–2}$$

where $\partial_k^{(1)} = \partial/\partial x_1^k$ and ϵ_{jkl} is the antisymmetric unit tensor of Levi-Civita; $j_j(\mathbf{x}_1, t)$ is the current density. We have let $c = 1$ and included 4π into the definitions of current and charge density.

To generalize the concept of coherence we follow (by analogy) Roman and Wolf (1960), and define the following functions:

$$\begin{aligned}
\mathscr{E}_{jk}^{E}(\mathbf{x}_1, t_1; \mathbf{x}_2, t_2) &= \{E_j(\mathbf{x}_1, t_1)\, E_k(\mathbf{x}_2, t_2)\} \\
\mathscr{H}_{jk}^{E}(\mathbf{x}_1, t_1; \mathbf{x}_2, t_2) &= \{H_j(\mathbf{x}_1, t_1)\, H_k(\mathbf{x}_2, t_2)\} \\
\mathscr{G}_{jk}^{E}(\mathbf{x}_1, t_1; \mathbf{x}_2, t_2) &= \{E_j(\mathbf{x}_1, t_1)\, H_k(\mathbf{x}_2, t_2)\} \\
\mathscr{J}_{jk}^{E}(\mathbf{x}_1, t_1; \mathbf{x}_2, t_2) &= \{j_j(\mathbf{x}_1, t_1) j_k(\mathbf{x}_2, t_2)\} \\
\mathscr{P}^{E}(\mathbf{x}_1, t_1; \mathbf{x}_2, t_2) &= \{\rho(\mathbf{x}_1, t_1)\, \rho(\mathbf{x}_2, t_2)\}
\end{aligned} \tag{11–3}$$

where the brackets, { }, indicate average over an ensemble. The functions **E** and **H** are real, and ρ is the charge density.

We also define

$$\begin{aligned}
\mathscr{E}_{jk}(\mathbf{x}_1, \mathbf{x}_2\, \tau) &= \langle E_j(\mathbf{x}_1, t + \tau)\, E_k^*(\mathbf{x}_2, t)\rangle \\
\mathscr{H}_{jk}(\mathbf{x}_1, \mathbf{x}_2, \tau) &= \langle H_j(\mathbf{x}_1, t + \tau)\, H_k^*(\mathbf{x}_2, t)\rangle \\
\mathscr{G}_{jk}(\mathbf{x}_1, \mathbf{x}_2, \tau) &= \langle E_j(\mathbf{x}_1, t + \tau)\, H_k^*(\mathbf{x}_2, t)\rangle \\
\tilde{\mathscr{G}}_{jk}(\mathbf{x}_1, \mathbf{x}_2, \tau) &= \langle H_j(\mathbf{x}_1, t + \tau)\, E_k^*(\mathbf{x}_2, t)\rangle \\
\mathscr{J}_{jk}(\mathbf{x}_1, \mathbf{x}_2, \tau) &= \langle j_j(\mathbf{x}_1, t + \tau) j_k^*(\mathbf{x}_2, t)\rangle \\
\mathscr{P}(\mathbf{x}_1, \mathbf{x}_2, \tau) &= \langle \rho(\mathbf{x}_1, t + \tau)\, \rho^*(\mathbf{x}_2, t)\rangle
\end{aligned} \tag{11–4}$$

where the angular brackets indicate time averages. Here the functions **E** and **H**, **j** and ρ are complex analytic signals (see Chapter 2).

11.2 ENSEMBLE AVERAGES

In this section, we formulate the equations governing $\mathcal{E}_{jk}^E$ and $\mathcal{H}_{jk}^E$. Ensemble averaging is necessary to treat nonstationary problems. After the general formulation, however, we shall derive the equations for the special case of stationary statistics.

We shall derive the equations governing $\mathcal{E}_{jk}^E$ and $\mathcal{H}_{jk}^E$ in the presence of sources. To derive the equations [see Beran and Parrent (1962)] we first multiply Eq. (11–1) by itself, replacing $(\mathbf{x}_1, t_1)$ by $(\mathbf{x}_2, t_2)$ in one of the terms. After the ensemble average of both sides (assuming one can interchange differentiation and ensemble averaging) are taken,

$$\epsilon_{jkl}\epsilon_{mnp}\,\partial_k^{(1)}\partial_n^{(2)}\mathcal{E}_{lp}^E(\mathbf{x}_1, t_1; \mathbf{x}_2, t_2) = \frac{\partial}{\partial t_1}\frac{\partial}{\partial t_2}\mathcal{H}_{jm}^E(\mathbf{x}_1, t_1; \mathbf{x}_2, t_2) \tag{11–5}$$

A second equation obtained by performing a similar operation on Eq. (11–2) yields

$$\begin{aligned}&\epsilon_{jkl}\epsilon_{mnp}\,\partial_k^{(1)}\partial_n^{(2)}\mathcal{H}_{lp}^E(\mathbf{x}_1, t_1; \mathbf{x}_2, t_2) + \frac{\partial}{\partial t_1}\frac{\partial}{\partial t_2}\mathcal{E}_{jm}^E(\mathbf{x}_1, t_1; \mathbf{x}_2, t_2)\\ &\quad -\epsilon_{jkl}\,\partial_k^{(1)}\frac{\partial}{\partial t_2}\mathcal{G}_{ml}^E(\mathbf{x}_2, t_2; \mathbf{x}_1, t_1) - \epsilon_{mnp}\,\partial_n^{(2)}\frac{\partial}{\partial t_1}\mathcal{G}_{jp}^E(\mathbf{x}_1, t_1; \mathbf{x}_2, t_2)\\ &= \mathcal{J}_{jm}^E(\mathbf{x}_1, t_1; \mathbf{x}_2, t_2)\end{aligned} \tag{11–6}$$

The $\mathcal{G}_{ij}^E$ tensors may be eliminated by differentiating Eq. (11–6) with respect to t_1 and t_2 and expressing terms like $\partial/\partial t_1\,\mathcal{G}_{ml}^E(\mathbf{x}_2, t_2, \mathbf{x}_1, t_1)$ in terms of derivatives of the $\mathcal{E}_{ij}^E$, $\mathcal{H}_{ij}^E$ tensors. These latter expressions may be obtained from Eq. (11–1) by multiplying the equation by either

$$E_m(\mathbf{x}_2, t_2) \quad \text{or} \quad E_j(\mathbf{x}_1, t_1)$$

and then taking an ensemble average. In this manner, utilizing Eq. (11–5), a single equation is obtained for $\mathcal{E}_{jk}(\mathbf{x}_1, t_1; \mathbf{x}_2, t_2)$

$$\begin{aligned}&\epsilon_{jkl}\epsilon_{mnp}\epsilon_{lab}\epsilon_{pcd}\,\partial_a^{(1)}\partial_k^{(1)}\partial_c^{(2)}\partial_n^{(2)}\mathcal{E}_{bd}^E(\mathbf{x}_1, t_1; \mathbf{x}_2, t_2)\\ &\quad + \frac{\partial^2}{\partial t_1^2}\frac{\partial^2}{\partial t_2^2}\mathcal{E}_{jm}^E(\mathbf{x}_1, t_1; \mathbf{x}_2, t_2) + \epsilon_{jkl}\epsilon_{lrs}\,\partial_k^{(1)}\partial_r^{(1)}\frac{\partial^2}{\partial t_2^2}\mathcal{E}_{sm}^E(\mathbf{x}_1, t_1; \mathbf{x}_2, t_2)\\ &\quad + \epsilon_{mnp}\epsilon_{puv}\,\partial_n^{(2)}\partial_u^{(2)}\frac{\partial^2}{\partial t_1^2}\mathcal{E}_{vj}^E(\mathbf{x}_1, t_1; \mathbf{x}_2, t_2)\\ &= \frac{\partial}{\partial t_1}\frac{\partial}{\partial t_2}\mathcal{J}_{jm}^E(\mathbf{x}_1, t_1; \mathbf{x}_2, t_2)\end{aligned} \tag{11–7}$$

A similar equation is derived for $\mathcal{H}_{ij}^E$

(11–8)
$$\begin{aligned}
&\epsilon_{usj}\epsilon_{jkl}\epsilon_{mnp}\epsilon_{rqm}\,\partial_k^{(1)}\,\partial_s^{(1)}\,\partial_q^{(2)}\,\partial_n^{(2)}\,\mathcal{H}_{lp}^E(\mathbf{x}_1, t_1; \mathbf{x}_2, t_2)\\
&\quad+\frac{\partial^2}{\partial t_1^2}\frac{\partial^2}{\partial t_2^2}\mathcal{H}_{ur}^E(\mathbf{x}_1, t_1; \mathbf{x}_2, t_2)\\
&\quad+\epsilon_{jkl}\epsilon_{usj}\frac{\partial^2}{\partial t_2^2}\partial_k^{(1)}\partial_s^{(2)}\mathcal{H}_{rl}^E(\mathbf{x}_1, t_1; \mathbf{x}_2, t_2)\\
&\quad+\epsilon_{mnp}\epsilon_{rqm}\frac{\partial^2}{\partial t_1^2}\partial_n^{(2)}\,\partial_q^{(2)}\,\mathcal{H}_{up}^E(\mathbf{x}_1, t_1; \mathbf{x}_2, t_2)\\
&\quad=\epsilon_{rqm}\epsilon_{usj}\,\partial_s^{(1)}\,\partial_q^{(2)}\,\mathcal{J}_{jm}(\mathbf{x}_1, t_1; \mathbf{x}_2, t_2)
\end{aligned}$$

From the divergence condition,

(11–9)
$$\partial_j^{(1)}E_j(\mathbf{x}_1, t_1) = \rho(\mathbf{x}_1, t_1)$$

and the continuity equation,

(11–10)
$$\frac{\partial}{\partial t_1}\rho(\mathbf{x}_1, t_1) = -\partial_k^{(1)}j_k(\mathbf{x}_1, t_1)$$

the following relations may be similarly derived

(11–11)
$$\partial_j^{(1)}\,\partial_l^{(2)}\mathcal{E}_{jl}^E(\mathbf{x}_1, t_1; \mathbf{x}_2, t_2) = \mathcal{P}^E(\mathbf{x}_1, t_1; \mathbf{x}_2, t_2)$$

(11–12)
$$\frac{\partial}{\partial t_1}\frac{\partial}{\partial t_2}\mathcal{P}^E(\mathbf{x}_1, t_1; \mathbf{x}_2, t_2) = \partial_k^{(1)}\,\partial_l^{(2)}\,\mathcal{J}_{kl}^E(\mathbf{x}_1, t_1; \mathbf{x}_2, t_2)$$

Stationary processes

If the processes considered are stationary, the correlation tensors depend only upon $t_2 - t_1 = \tau$. In this case,

$$\frac{\partial}{\partial(t_2 - t_1)} = \frac{\partial}{\partial t_2} = -\frac{\partial}{\partial t_1}$$

and Eq. (11–7), for example, assumes the form

(11–13)
$$\begin{aligned}
&\epsilon_{jkl}\epsilon_{mnp}\epsilon_{lab}\epsilon_{pcd}\,\partial_a^{(1)}\,\partial_k^{(1)}\,\partial_c^{(2)}\,\partial_n^{(2)}\,\mathcal{E}_{bd}^E(\mathbf{x}_1, \mathbf{x}_2, \tau)\\
&\quad+\frac{\partial^4}{\partial\tau^4}\mathcal{E}_{jm}^E(\mathbf{x}_1, \mathbf{x}_2, \tau)+\epsilon_{jkl}\,\epsilon_{lrs}\,\partial_k^{(1)}\,\partial_r^{(1)}\,\frac{\partial^2}{\partial\tau^2}\,\mathcal{E}_{sm}^E(\mathbf{x}_1, \mathbf{x}_2, \tau)\\
&\quad+\epsilon_{mnp}\epsilon_{puv}\,\partial_n^{(2)}\,\partial_u^{(2)}\,\frac{\partial^2}{\partial\tau^2}\mathcal{E}_{vj}^E(\mathbf{x}_1, \mathbf{x}_2, \tau) = -\frac{\partial}{\partial\tau^2}\mathcal{J}_{jm}^E(\mathbf{x}_1, \mathbf{x}_2, \tau)
\end{aligned}$$

We also note that in the case of stationary processes, the terms like $\mathcal{G}_{ml}^E$ in Eq. (11–6) can be eliminated without differentiation of Eq. (11–6), and we can obtain a set of equations that contain no higher than second derivatives in τ. They are

(11–14)
$$\epsilon_{jkl}\epsilon_{mnp}\,\partial_k^{(1)}\,\partial_n^{(2)}\mathcal{E}_{lp}^E(\mathbf{x}_1, \mathbf{x}_2, \tau) = -\frac{\partial^2}{\partial\tau^2}\mathcal{H}_{jm}^E(\mathbf{x}_1, \mathbf{x}_2, \tau)$$

$$\epsilon_{jkl}\epsilon_{mnp}\,\partial_k^{(1)}\,\partial_n^{(2)}\,\mathcal{H}_{lp}^E(\mathbf{x}_1,\mathbf{x}_2,\tau) - \frac{\partial^2}{\partial\tau^2}\mathcal{E}_{jm}^E(\mathbf{x}_1,\mathbf{x}_2,\tau)$$

(11–15)
$$- \epsilon_{jkl}\epsilon_{lqr}\,\partial_k^{(1)}\partial_q^{(1)}\mathcal{E}_{rm}^E(\mathbf{x}_1,\mathbf{x}_2,\tau)$$

$$- \epsilon_{mnp}\epsilon_{prs}\,\partial_n^{(2)}\,\partial_r^{(2)}\mathcal{E}_{sj}^E(\mathbf{x}_1,\mathbf{x}_2,\tau) = \mathcal{J}_{jm}^E(\mathbf{x}_1,\mathbf{x}_2,\tau)$$

11.3 TIME AVERAGES

When time averages are used, we assume the statistics are stationary. We further assume that an ergodic-type hypothesis is true and that, in this case, time and ensemble averages are equal. Then Eq. (11–14) may be written with $\mathcal{E}_{lp}(\mathbf{x}_1, \mathbf{x}_2, \tau)$ and $\mathcal{H}_{lp}(\mathbf{x}_1, \mathbf{x}_2, \tau)$ replacing $\mathcal{E}_{lp}^E(\mathbf{x}_1, \mathbf{x}_2, \tau)$ and $\mathcal{H}_{lp}^E(\mathbf{x}_1, \mathbf{x}_2, \tau)$. The fact that $\mathcal{E}_{lp}$ and $\mathcal{H}_{lp}$ are now complex quantities must be remembered, but it can be shown that the substitution is still valid.

11.4 SOURCE TERMS IN EQUATIONS

Eqs. (11–7),(11–8) are useful only if $\mathcal{J}_{jm}$ is independent of $\mathcal{E}_{jm}$ and $\mathcal{H}_{jm}$, or may be simply expressible in terms of them. The writers originally derived these equations in order to study the properties of optically thin gases; i.e., radiating gases in which it is assumed that the $\mathcal{J}_{jm}$ are not affected by the radiation they produce. It was hoped to gain some information about the charge and current correlations by studying the radiation pattern. Other projects, however, prevented the writers from doing further work on this problem, and to their knowledge, nothing more has been done in this direction. It should be noted though, that the foregoing equations are most useful for macroscopic current variations, such as in a turbulent plasma, but are not particularly useful for radiation due to atomic transitions. In this latter case, the variation of atomic density and temperature is most important and the fourth-order correlation function should be used [see Beran and Parrent (1962)].

Roman (1961a), subsequent to his derivation of the stationary equations, pointed out that if we take $\mathbf{j} = \sigma\mathbf{E}$, ($\mathcal{J}_{jm} = \sigma^2\mathcal{E}_{jm}$), then Eqs. (11–11) and (11–12) yield

(11–16)
$$\frac{\partial^2}{\partial\tau^2}\mathcal{P}(\mathbf{x}_1,\mathbf{x}_2,\tau) + \sigma^2\mathcal{P}(\mathbf{x}_1,\mathbf{x}_2,\tau) = 0$$

or

(11–17)
$$\mathcal{P}(\mathbf{x}_1,\mathbf{x}_2,\tau) = A(\mathbf{x}_1,\mathbf{x}_2)e^{i\sigma\tau}$$

In this case, we note that if σ is real, $\mathcal{P}$ is oscillating rather than decaying as we might expect. This occurs because the assumption of stationarity demands that there be no decay. If the nonstationary formulation is used, a decay is possible.

It is impossible, however, to set $\mathbf{j} = \sigma(\mathbf{E} + \mathbf{v} \times \mathbf{H})$ (as we might desire in studying plasmas) and derive equations having only $\mathcal{E}$, $\mathcal{H}$ and $\mathcal{J}$ tensors in them. Higher-order correlations appear and destroy the simplicity of the formulation.

11.5 SOURCE-FREE REGIONS

In a source-free region, $\rho = 0$, $\mathbf{j} = 0$, and we have $\mathcal{P} = 0$, $\mathcal{J}_{jk} = 0$. In this case, it is possible, for the stationary case, to derive a set of four equations for $\mathcal{E}$, $\mathcal{H}$, $\mathcal{G}$, and $\tilde{\mathcal{G}}$ which have no higher than first derivatives in τ. They were derived by Roman and Wolf (1960a) and are†

$$\epsilon_{jkl}\, \partial_k^{(2)} \mathcal{E}_{ml}(\mathbf{x}_1, \mathbf{x}_2, \tau) - \frac{\partial}{\partial \tau} \mathcal{G}_{mj}(\mathbf{x}_1, \mathbf{x}_2, \tau) = 0$$

$$\epsilon_{jkl}\, \partial_k^{(2)} \tilde{\mathcal{G}}_{ml}(\mathbf{x}_1, \mathbf{x}_2, \tau) - \frac{\partial}{\partial \tau} \mathcal{H}_{mj}(\mathbf{x}_1, \mathbf{x}_2, \tau) = 0$$

$$\epsilon_{jkl}\, \partial_k^{(2)} \mathcal{G}_{ml}(\mathbf{x}_1, \mathbf{x}_2, \tau) + \frac{\partial}{\partial \tau} \mathcal{E}_{mj}(\mathbf{x}_1, \mathbf{x}_2, \tau) = 0 \tag{11–18}$$

$$\epsilon_{jkl}\, \partial_k^{(2)} \mathcal{H}_{ml}(\mathbf{x}_1, \mathbf{x}_2, \tau) + \frac{\partial}{\partial \tau} \tilde{\mathcal{G}}_{mj}(\mathbf{x}_1, \mathbf{x}_2, \tau) = 0$$

$$\partial_j^{(2)} \mathcal{E}_{ij}(\mathbf{x}_1, \mathbf{x}_2, \tau) = \partial_j^{(2)} \mathcal{H}_{ij}(\mathbf{x}_1, \mathbf{x}_2, \tau) = \partial_j^{(2)} \mathcal{G}_{ij}(\mathbf{x}_1, \mathbf{x}_2, \tau)$$
$$= \partial_j^{(2)} \tilde{\mathcal{G}}_{ij}(\mathbf{x}_1, \mathbf{x}_2, \tau) = 0$$

All solutions of Eq. (11–18) are solutions of Eqs. (11–14) and (11–15) with $\mathcal{J}_{jm} = 0$. The converse has not been proved, however, though as Roman (1961a) points out, for fixed boundary conditions we do not expect an extraneous solution.

From Eq. (11–18), one can, by differention, derive wave equations for $\mathcal{E}$, $\mathcal{H}$, $\mathcal{G}$, and $\tilde{\mathcal{G}}$. The equations for $\mathcal{E}_{jm}$ are

$$\nabla_{(i)}^2 \mathcal{E}_{jm}(\mathbf{x}_1, \mathbf{x}_2, \tau) = \frac{\partial^2}{\partial \tau^2} \mathcal{E}_{jm}(\mathbf{x}_1, \mathbf{x}_2, \tau) \qquad (i = 1, 2) \tag{11–19}$$

The laplacian term is obtained above by using the divergence condition $\partial_j \mathcal{E}_{pj} = 0$ just as one does in deriving a wave equation for E_j.

11.6 CONSERVATION LAWS

Roman and Wolf (1960b) and Roman (1961b) have derived a number of conservation laws associated with the second-order coherence function for source-free regions. They considered the tensors:

---

†Equations with $\partial_k^{(2)}$ relaced by $\partial_k^{(1)}$ may be obtained from these equations from consideration of the definitions of the coherence tensors. The two sets are equivalent.

(11–20) $$\mathcal{W}_{jk}(\mathbf{x}_1, \mathbf{x}_2, \tau) = \mathcal{E}_{jk}(\mathbf{x}_1, \mathbf{x}_2, \tau) + \mathcal{H}_{jk}(\mathbf{x}_1, \mathbf{x}_2, \tau)$$

and

$$\mathcal{S}_{jk}(\mathbf{x}_1, \mathbf{x}_2, \tau) = \mathcal{G}_{jk}(\mathbf{x}_1, \mathbf{x}_2, \tau) - \tilde{\mathcal{G}}_{jk}(\mathbf{x}_1, \mathbf{x}_2, \tau)$$

and termed $\mathcal{W}_{jk}$ the *energy coherence tensor* and $\mathcal{S}_{jk}$ the *flow coherence tensor.*

The time-averaged energy density $\langle W \rangle$ and the time averaged energy flow $\langle S_l \rangle$ may be shown to have the following form:

(11–21)
$$\langle W \rangle = \frac{1}{16\pi} \mathrm{Tr} \{\mathcal{E}_{jk}(\mathbf{x}, \mathbf{x}, 0) + \mathcal{H}_{jk}(\mathbf{x}, \mathbf{x}, 0)\}$$
$$\langle S_l \rangle = \frac{1}{16\pi} \mathrm{Re} \{\mathcal{G}_{jk}(\mathbf{x}, \mathbf{x}, 0) - \tilde{\mathcal{G}}_{jk}(\mathbf{x}, \mathbf{x}, 0)\}$$

where Tr is the trace and $(j, k, l) = (1, 2, 3)$ or a cyclic variation thereof.

It is easily shown by reference to Eqs. (11–20) that

(11–22 a–d)
$$\epsilon_{jkl}\, \partial_k \mathcal{W}_{lm} = \frac{\partial}{\partial \tau} \mathcal{S}_{jm}$$
$$\epsilon_{jkl}\, \partial_k \mathcal{S}_{lm} = -\frac{\partial}{\partial \tau} \mathcal{W}_{jm}$$
$$\partial_j \mathcal{W}_{jk} = 0$$
$$\partial_j \mathcal{S}_{jk} = 0$$

From Eq. (11–22) we may find

(11–23)
$$\nabla^2 \mathcal{W}_{jk} = \frac{\partial^2}{\partial \tau^2} \mathcal{W}_{jk}$$
$$\nabla^2 \mathcal{S}_{jk} = \frac{\partial^2}{\partial \tau^2} \mathcal{S}_{jk}$$

Taking the trace of Eqs. (11–22a, 11–22b), we find two scalar conservation laws:

(11–24)
$$\partial_k \epsilon_{klj} \mathcal{W}_{lj} = \frac{\partial}{\partial \tau} \mathrm{Tr}\, \mathcal{S}_{ij}$$
$$\partial_k \epsilon_{klj} \mathcal{S}_{lj} = \frac{\partial}{\partial \tau} \mathrm{Tr}\, \mathcal{W}_{ij}$$

Roman and Wolf then show that the second of these equations may be put into the following form when $\mathbf{x}_1 = \mathbf{x}_2 = \mathbf{x}$ and $\tau = 0$:

(11–25) $$\langle \mathrm{div}\, S(x, t) \rangle = -\left\langle \frac{\partial}{\partial t} W(x, t) \right\rangle$$

where

$$S(x, t) = \frac{1}{4\pi} (\mathbf{E}^{(r)} \times \mathbf{H}^{(r)}), \quad W(x, t) = \frac{1}{8\pi} (|\mathbf{E}^{(r)}|^2 + |\mathbf{H}^{(r)}|^2)$$

As they point out, this is the time average of the common energy conservation law for an electromagnetic field. The first equation reduces to an identity upon similar manipulations and thus in a sense the law with $\mathbf{x}_1 \neq \mathbf{x}_2$ has no analog to the ordinary **E** and **H** field conservation laws.

From Eq. (11–22), one may also derive two vector conservation laws:

$$\partial_k(\delta_{sk}\,\mathrm{Tr}\,\mathcal{W}_{ij} - \mathcal{W}_{sk}) = -\frac{\partial}{\partial\tau}\epsilon_{sjm}\mathcal{S}_{jm} \tag{11–26 a}$$

$$\partial_k(-\delta_{sk}\,\mathrm{Tr}\,\mathcal{S}_{ij} + \mathcal{S}_{sk}) = -\frac{\partial}{\partial\tau}\epsilon_{sjm}\mathcal{W}_{jm} \tag{11–26 b}$$

Equation (11–26a) may be manipulated into the form

$$\left\langle -\partial_k T_{ks}(\mathbf{x}, t) + \frac{\partial}{\partial t}P_s(\mathbf{x}, t)\right\rangle = 0 \tag{11–27}$$

where T_{ks} is the electromagnetic stress tensor, and P_s is the momentum density. We note again that we have let $\mathbf{x}_1 = \mathbf{x}_2$ and $\tau = 0$ to arrive at Eq. (11–27). Hence Eq. (11–26a) reduces to the time average of the law of conservation of momentum for an electromagnetic field. Equation (11–26b) reduces to an identity upon similar manipulations and as above is again a law which has no analog to the ordinary **E** and **H** field conservation laws.

Roman (1961b) has derived some further conservation laws of a somewhat different nature. The laws are obtained by multiplying Eqs. (11–18)† by the tensors $\mathfrak{E}_{ij}$, $\mathcal{H}_{ij}$, $\mathcal{G}_{ij}$, or $\tilde{\mathcal{G}}_{ij}$, appropriately choosing the indices and combining the resultant equations. He obtains the following relations:

$$\partial_j^{(1)}(\epsilon_{jkl}\mathfrak{E}_{km}\tilde{\mathcal{G}}_{lm}) + \frac{\partial}{\partial\tau}\left(\frac{\mathfrak{E}^2 + \mathcal{G}^2}{2}\right) = 0 \tag{11–28}$$

$$\partial_j^{(1)}(\epsilon_{jkl}\mathcal{G}_{km}\mathcal{H}_{lm}) + \frac{\partial}{\partial\tau}\left(\frac{\mathcal{G}^2 + \mathcal{H}^2}{2}\right) = 0 \tag{11–29}$$

$$\partial_j^{(1)}[\epsilon_{jkl}(\mathfrak{E}_{km}\mathcal{H}_{lm} + \tilde{\mathcal{G}}_{km}\mathcal{G}_{lm})] + \frac{\partial}{\partial\tau}(\mathcal{G}\mathfrak{E} + \tilde{\mathcal{G}}\mathcal{H}) = 0 \tag{11–30}$$

$$\partial_j^{(1)}[\epsilon_{jlk}(\mathcal{H}_{lm}\mathcal{G}_{km} + \tilde{\mathcal{G}}_{lm}\mathfrak{E}_{km})] + \frac{\partial}{\partial\tau}(\mathfrak{E}\mathcal{H} + \mathcal{G}\tilde{\mathcal{G}}) = 0 \tag{11–31}$$

where $\mathfrak{E}^2 = \mathfrak{E}_{jm}\mathfrak{E}_{jm}$ with similar expressions for $\mathcal{H}$, $\mathcal{G}$, and $\tilde{\mathcal{G}}$.

Further laws along these lines are obtained by multiplying by the complex conjugates of the tensors rather than the tensors themselves and also by performing similar manipulations with the tensors $\mathcal{W}_{jk}$ and $\mathcal{S}_{jk}$.

As of the writing of this book, little direct physical significance beyond that indicated in this section has been given to the conservation laws just cited. Research is proceeding along these lines, however.

†Actually these equations in terms of $\partial_k^{(1)}$ instead of $\partial_k^{(2)}$

11.7 COHERENCE PROPERTIES OF BLACKBODY RADIATION

Bourret (1960) determined the function $\mathcal{G}_{jm}(\mathbf{x}_1, \mathbf{x}_2, \tau)$† for blackbody radiation in a very large cavity from the wave equation (11–18), and consideration of the symmetry properties of the radiation.

For blackbody radiation, we assume spatial homogeneity and isotropy. Thus only one equation of Eq. (11–19) is needed, and for convenience we set $\mathbf{x}_1 = 0$ and term $\mathbf{x}_2 = \mathbf{r}$. (The components of $\mathbf{r}$ are x, y, z.) The governing equation is thus

$$\nabla^2 \mathcal{G}_{ij} = \frac{1}{c^2}\frac{\partial^2 \mathcal{G}_{ij}}{\partial \tau^2} \tag{11–32}$$

where we now explicitly reintroduce c into our equation for clarity.‡

The conditions of isotropy and homogeneity yield

$$\begin{aligned} \text{Trace } \mathcal{G}_{ij}(r = 0, \tau = 0) &= \text{Trace } \mathcal{H}_{ij}(r = 0, \tau = 0) \\ \mathcal{G}_{ij}(r = 0, \tau = 0) &= \mathcal{G}_{11}(r = 0, \tau = 0)\,\delta_{ij} \end{aligned} \tag{11–33}$$

The solution of Eq. (11–32) may be written as a Fourier transform in space:

$$\mathcal{G}_{ij}(\mathbf{r}, \tau) = \iiint_{-\infty}^{\infty} e^{i(\mathbf{k}\cdot\mathbf{r} - ck\tau)} f_{ij}(\mathbf{k})\, dk_1\, dk_2\, dk_3 \tag{11–34}$$

where $f_{ij}(\mathbf{k})$ is a function of k_1, k_2, k_3, and $k_1^2 + k_2^2 + k_3^2 = k^2$.

Since there is no preferred direction in wave number space, f_{ij} must be an isotropic tensor and hence have the form [see Batchelor (1953)]:

$$f_{ij}(\mathbf{k}) = A'(k) k_i k_j + B(k)\,\delta_{ij} \tag{11–35}$$

where A' and B are even functions of k.

However, $\partial_j \mathcal{G}_{ij} = 0$ so that $k_j f_{ij}(\mathbf{k}) = 0$. This requires that $B(k) = -k^2 A'(k)$ and thus

$$f_{ij}(\mathbf{k}) = A(k)\,(k^2\,\delta_{ij} - k_i k_j) \tag{11–36}$$

where $A(k) = -A'(k)$.

To determine $A(k)$, we calculate the quantity,

$$\mathcal{G}_{ij}(0, \tau) = \iiint_{-\infty}^{\infty} e^{-ick\tau} A(k)\,(k^2\,\delta_{ij} - k_i k_j)\, dk_1\, dk_2\, dk_3 \tag{11–37}$$

The integral may be simplified by transforming to spherical coordinates in k space. We let

$$\begin{aligned} k_1 &= k \sin\theta \sin\Phi \\ k_2 &= k \cos\theta \sin\Phi \\ k_3 &= k \cos\Phi \end{aligned} \tag{11–38}$$

---

†Bourret in his article used——the real part of $\mathcal{G}_{jm}(\mathbf{x}_1, \mathbf{x}_2, \tau)$ but in this development we shall consider the analytic signal.

‡We use gaussian units throughout the remainder of this chapter.

which yields upon integration:

$$\mathcal{E}_{ij}(0, \tau) = \frac{8\pi}{3} \delta_{ij} \int_0^\infty k^4 A(k) e^{-ick\tau} \, dk \tag{11–39}$$

Since $\mathcal{E}_{ij}(0, \tau)$ is an analytic signal, we may represent it as

$$\mathcal{E}_{ij}(0, \tau) = \int_0^\infty \hat{\mathcal{E}}_{ij}(k) e^{-ikc\tau} \, dk \frac{c}{2\pi} \tag{11–40}$$

and therefore,

$$\frac{c}{2\pi} \hat{\mathcal{E}}_{ij}(k) = k^4 A(k) \frac{8\pi}{3} \delta_{ij} \tag{11–41}$$

Now for blackbody radiation, the total energy density has the form

$$\mathcal{U} = \frac{\hbar c}{\pi^2} \int_0^\infty \frac{k^3 \, dk}{e^{\alpha k} - 1} \tag{11–42}$$

where $\alpha = \hbar c / KT$, $h = 2\pi\hbar$ is Planck's constant and K is Boltzmann's constant.

Further, we remember that

$$\mathcal{U} = \frac{1}{2} \frac{1}{8\pi} [(\mathrm{Tr}\, \mathcal{E}_{ij}(0, 0) + \mathrm{Tr}\, \mathcal{H}_{ij}(0, 0)]^\dagger \tag{11–43}$$

and since

$$\mathcal{E}_{ij}(0, 0) = \frac{1}{3} [\mathrm{Tr}\, \mathcal{E}_{mn}(0, 0)] \delta_{ij} \quad \text{and} \quad \mathrm{Tr}\, \mathcal{E}_{ij}(0, 0) = \mathrm{Tr}\, \mathcal{H}_{ij}(0, 0)$$

we find

$$\begin{aligned} \mathcal{E}_{ij}(0, 0) &= \int_0^\infty \frac{c}{2\pi} \mathcal{E}_{ij}(k) \, dk \\ &= \int_0^\infty k^4 A(k) \frac{8\pi}{3} \delta_{ij} \, dk = \delta_{ij} \frac{8\pi}{3} \mathcal{U} \end{aligned} \tag{11–44}$$

and finally,

$$k^4 A(k) \frac{8\pi}{3} = \frac{8}{3} \frac{1}{\pi} \hbar c \frac{k^3}{e^{\alpha k} - 1} \tag{11–45}$$

or

$$A(k) = \frac{1}{\pi^2} \frac{\hbar c}{k} \frac{1}{e^{\alpha k} - 1} \tag{11–46}$$

The final expression for $\mathcal{E}_{ij}(\mathbf{r}, \tau)$ is therefore,

$$\mathcal{E}_{ij}(\mathbf{r}, \tau) = \beta \iiint_{-\infty}^{\infty} e^{i(\mathbf{k}\cdot\mathbf{r} - ck\tau)} \left(k\, \delta_{ij} - \frac{k_i k_j}{k} \right) \frac{1}{e^{\alpha k} - 1} \, dk_1 \, dk_2 \, dk_3 \tag{11–47}$$

where $\beta = (1/\pi^2)\hbar c$

†The extra factor of $\frac{1}{2}$ comes from the use of the complex notation.

When $\mathbf{r} = 0$, one finds

$$\frac{1}{2}\mathrm{Re}\mathfrak{S}_{ij}(0, \tau) = -\delta_{ij}\frac{2}{3\pi}\hbar c\left(\frac{\pi}{\alpha}\right)^4 \frac{\partial^3}{\partial s^3}\left(ctghs - \frac{1}{s}\right) \tag{11–48}$$

where $s = \pi c\tau/\alpha$.

The function $\mathfrak{S}_{ii}(0, \tau)$ has a zero value when s is approximately unity and a minimum value between 2 and 3. Thus a typical characteristic time of coherence is $\tau_c = \gamma\hbar/(\pi KT)$ where γ is of the order of unity. The frequency half-width for blackbody radiation at temperature T is $\Delta\nu \approx (h/KT)^{-1}$ Thus $\tau_c\Delta\nu = O(1)$ as we would expect.

Space coherence effects are most easily studied when the **E** or **H** vectors considered are either parallel or perpendicular to the spatial separation **r**. Thus we consider determination of the functions $\mathfrak{S}_{ii}^{\text{long}}$ and $\mathfrak{S}_{ii}^{\text{lat}}$. (Here the ii subscript does not indicate summation.) For example,

$$\mathfrak{S}_{11}^{\text{long}} = \langle E_1(\mathbf{x}, \tau)\, E_1(\mathbf{x} + \Delta\mathbf{x}, 0)\rangle$$

where $\Delta\mathbf{x} = (x_1, 0, 0)$

and
$$\mathfrak{S}_{11}^{\text{lat}} = \langle E_1(\mathbf{x}, \tau) E_1(\mathbf{x} + \Delta\mathbf{x}, 0)\rangle$$

where $\Delta\mathbf{x} = (0, x_2, 0)$. We first consider the case of $\tau = 0$. Then,

$$\mathfrak{S}_{33}^{\text{long}} = \beta\int_0^\infty \frac{dk}{e^{\alpha k} - 1}\int_0^{2\pi}\int_0^\pi e^{i(k\cos\Phi)r} \tag{11–49}$$
$$(k - k\cos^2\Phi)\, k^2 \sin\Phi\, d\Phi\, d\theta\dagger$$

Integrating over Φ and θ, we obtain

$$\mathfrak{S}_{33}^{\text{long}}(\mathbf{r}, 0) = \frac{8\pi}{r^2}\int_0^\infty k^2 A(k)\left[\frac{\sin kr}{kr} - \cos kr\right] dk \tag{11–50}$$

or, more conveniently,

$$\mathfrak{S}_{33}^{\text{long}}(\mathbf{r}, 0) = \frac{8\pi}{r^3}\left(1 - r\frac{d}{dr}\right)\int_0^\infty kA(k)\sin kr\, dk \tag{11–51}$$

This expression may be integrated to give

$$\frac{1}{2}\mathrm{Re}\mathfrak{S}_{33}^{\text{long}}(\mathbf{r}, 0) = \frac{2\hbar c}{\alpha}\frac{1}{r^3}\left(1 - r\frac{\partial}{\partial r}\right)\left[\text{cotgh}\left(\frac{\pi}{\alpha}r\right) - \frac{1}{(r\pi/\alpha)}\right] \tag{11–52}$$

$\mathfrak{S}_{33}^{\text{lat}}(\mathbf{r}, 0)$ has the form,

$$\mathfrak{S}_{33}^{\text{lat}}(\mathbf{r}, 0) = \beta\int_0^\infty \frac{dk}{e^{\alpha k} - 1}\int_0^{2\pi}\int_0^\pi e^{i(k\cos\Phi)r} \tag{11–53}$$
$$(k - k\sin^2\theta\sin^2\Phi)\, k^2\sin\Phi\, d\Phi\, d\theta$$

Equation (11–53) may be integrated in a manner similar to Eq. (11–49), or by noting the relationship between lateral and longitudinal coherence

†We remember $\mathfrak{S}_{33}^{\text{long}} = \mathfrak{S}_{22}^{\text{long}} = \mathfrak{S}_{11}^{\text{long}}$

functions in an isotropic field. Both expressions are difficult to survey in analytic form, but Bourret (1960) has plotted the normalized functions of $\mathcal{E}^{\text{long}}$ and $\mathcal{E}^{\text{lat}}$ against the nondimensional variable $\eta = \pi KTr/hc$, and we refer the reader to his paper. Both functions go sensibly to zero somewhere between 4 and 9. Thus r_c, a characteristic coherence length, is of the order of a number of mean wavelengths. These functions differ little in basic character from the coherence functions derived for incoherent sources in Chapter 4. r_c is principally determined by the fact that the waves are uncorrelated and isotropically distributed.

From Eq. (11–47), we may determine the expression for $\mathcal{E}_{ij}(\mathbf{r}, \tau)$ when both $\mathbf{r}$ and τ vary. This expression was evaluated incorrectly by Bourret. We present the correct expression [Molyneux (1962)]:

$$\frac{1}{2}\text{Re}\,\mathcal{E}_{33}^{\text{long}}(\mathbf{r}, \tau) = \frac{4\pi}{r^3}\left(1 - r\frac{\partial}{\partial r}\right) \frac{1}{2}\left\{\int_0^\infty (kA(k)\sin[k(r + c\tau)] + kA(k)\sin[k(r - c\tau)])\,dk\right\} \tag{11–54}$$

and thus

$$\frac{1}{2}\text{Re}\,\mathcal{E}_{33}^{\text{long}}(\mathbf{r}, \tau) = \frac{\hbar c}{\alpha}\frac{1}{r^3}\left[1 - \frac{\partial}{\partial r}\right] \left(\left\{\text{cotgh}\,\frac{\pi}{\alpha}(r + c\tau) - \frac{1}{\frac{(r + c\tau)\pi}{\alpha}}\right\} + \left\{\text{cotgh}\,\frac{\pi}{\alpha}(r - c\tau) - \frac{1}{\frac{(r - c\tau)\pi}{\alpha}}\right\}\right) \tag{11–55}$$

Again, a similar expression may be generated for $\mathcal{E}_{33}^{\text{lat}}(\mathbf{r}, \tau)$.

It would be desirable to extend Bourret's manner of solution to higher-order moments of blackbody radiation. This type of approach has not yet been used. It may be perhaps necessary to use the methods of J. Sarfatt (1963) or Glauber (1963b), who used the formalism of quantum field theory for calculating all moments. Calculating the second-order moments with this formalism, Sarfatt arrived at the same results as Bourret. Neglecting vacuum fluctuations as does Sarfatt, Glauber shows that the probability distribution of $\mathbf{E}(\mathbf{x}, t)$ is gaussian, and hence all moments are determined from the second moments. Since this method of solution may be the only appropriate one for higher order moments,† we give in Appendix A a very brief outline of the method used to obtain the second-order moments. (A knowledge of elementary quantum field theory is needed in order to follow the discussion.)

---

†Certainly if one wishes to include vacuum fluctuations by taking local time and space averages.

APPENDIX A: Quantum Field Theory Approach for Calculating the Coherence Functions of Blackbody Radiation

Sarfatt (1963) defines the correlation function, $\mathfrak{G}^E_{ij}(\mathbf{r}_1, t_1; \mathbf{r}_2, t_2)$ as

$$\mathfrak{G}^E_{ij}(\mathbf{r}_1, t_1; \mathbf{r}_2, t_2) = \frac{1}{2}\mathrm{Tr}\,[\{\hat{E}_i(\mathbf{r}_1, t_1)\,\hat{E}_j(\mathbf{r}_2, t_2) + \hat{E}_j(\mathbf{r}_2, t_2)\,\hat{E}_i(\mathbf{r}_1, t_1)\}\hat{\rho}]\dagger \tag{11-56}$$

where $\hat{E}_i(\mathbf{r}, t)$ is the time-varying operator associated with the ith component of the electric field. $\hat{\rho}$ is the density matrix associated with blackbody radiation:

$$\hat{\rho} = \frac{e^{-\hat{H}/kT}}{\mathrm{Tr}\,[e^{-\hat{H}/kT}]} \tag{11-57}$$

where $\hat{H}$ is the Hamiltonian operator of the radiation.

He first decomposes the electric field operator into its Fourier components. He sets

$$\hat{\mathbf{E}}(\mathbf{r}, t) = \frac{i}{c}\sum_{\omega}[\omega\hat{q}_\omega e^{-i\omega t}\,\mathbf{A}_\omega(\mathbf{r}) - \omega\hat{q}^*_\omega e^{i\omega t}\mathbf{A}^*_\omega(\mathbf{r})] \tag{11-58}$$

where $\mathbf{A}_\omega(\mathbf{r})$ is the spatial part of the vector potential. Each component of $\mathbf{A}_\omega(\mathbf{r})$ satisfies the Helmholtz equation. $\hat{\mathbf{q}}_\omega$ and $\hat{\mathbf{q}}^*_\omega$ are the usual creation and destruction operators and satisfy the commutation relations:

$$\hat{q}_\omega\hat{q}^*_{\omega'} - \hat{q}^*_{\omega'}\hat{q}_\omega = \frac{\hbar}{2\omega}\,\delta_{\omega\omega'} \tag{11-59}$$

$$\hat{q}^*_\omega\hat{q}_\omega = \frac{\hbar}{2\omega}\,\hat{n}_\omega,$$

where $\hat{n}_\omega$ is the number operator associated with the Fourier component ω.

The states he uses for calculation of his matrix elements are the states of fixed number of photons in each frequency band.

These definitions allow him to calculate the second-order moments, in terms of $\mathbf{A}_\omega(\mathbf{r})$. In the course of these calculations, he subtracts out a divergent vacuum contribution. It then remains for him to choose a form for $\mathbf{A}_\omega(\mathbf{r})$. He chooses a plane-wave representation and is able to complete his calculations by assuming that the radiation field is isotropic.

†In this Appendix, we use the hook symbol to denote an operator.

chapter

12

Intensity Interferometry

In this book, we have principally studied the coherence function $\Gamma_{12}(\tau)$, which is a second-order moment. Because of its theoretical simplicity and the ease with which it may be measured, this moment has received the most attention in the literature. Higher-order moments, however, may, of course, also be treated and in 1954 Hanbury Brown and Twiss (1954) showed that it is possible and often convenient to obtain information about the moment,

$$R_{ij}(\mathbf{x}_1, \mathbf{x}_2, 0) = \langle I_i(\mathbf{x}_1, t)\, I_j(\mathbf{x}_2, t)\rangle$$

where $I_i(\mathbf{x}_p)$ is the instantaneous radiation intensity resulting from the electric field with polarization in the ith direction at $\mathbf{x}_p$. Determination of information about R_{ij} is called *intensity interferometry.*

The moment $\langle I_i(\mathbf{x}_1, t)\, I_j(\mathbf{x}_2, t)\rangle$ is a contracted form of the more general stationary fourth-order moment:†

$$(12\text{–}1)\quad \begin{aligned} &L_{ijkl}(\mathbf{x}_1, t; \mathbf{x}_2, t+\tau_2; \mathbf{x}_3, t+\tau_3; \mathbf{x}_4, t+\tau_4) \\ &\qquad = \langle E_i(\mathbf{x}_1, t)\, E_j(\mathbf{x}_2, t+\tau_2)\, E_k(\mathbf{x}_3, t+\tau_3)\, E_l(\mathbf{x}_4, t+\tau_4)\rangle \end{aligned}$$

It is obtained by setting $\mathbf{x}_1 = \mathbf{x}_2, \mathbf{x}_3 = \mathbf{x}_4, \tau_2 = \tau_3 = \tau_4 = 0, i = j, k = l$. In general L_{ijkl} and $\langle E_p(\mathbf{x}_m, t)\, E_q(\mathbf{x}_n, t+\tau)\rangle$ are not related. When the basic statistics are gaussian, however, there is a simple relationship between the two functions.

Treating the problem classically, the function L_{ijkl} may be shown to satisfy differential equations similar to those given for the second-order moment (see Chapter 13). To find L_{ijkj} external to a surface radiator, it is necessary to know L_{ijkl} for all combinations of four points on the surface of the radiator and to impose the Sommerfeld radiation condition at infinity. Thus to predict $R_{ij}(\mathbf{x}_1, \mathbf{x}_2, 0)$ one must know in general $L_{ijkl}(\mathbf{x}_{1S}, t; \mathbf{x}_{2S}, t+\tau_2; \mathbf{x}_{3S}, t+\tau_3; \mathbf{x}_{4S}, t+\tau_4)$, where the subscripts indicate points on the surface of the radiator.

When the source is incoherent (in the sense discussed in Chapter 4), the fourth-order moment is essentially replaced by a number of second-order moments, since

$$L_{ijkl}(\mathbf{x}_1, t; \mathbf{x}_2, t+\tau_2; \mathbf{x}_3, t+\tau_3; \mathbf{x}_4, t+\tau_4)$$

is essentially zero unless

$$\mathbf{x}_1 = \mathbf{x}_2, \mathbf{x}_3 = \mathbf{x}_4 \quad \text{or} \quad \mathbf{x}_1 = \mathbf{x}_3, \mathbf{x}_2 = \mathbf{x}_4 \quad \text{or} \quad \mathbf{x}_1 = \mathbf{x}_4, \mathbf{x}_2 = \mathbf{x}_3$$

If one further assumes that the radiation is quasi-monochromatic, then for small path differences, one may set $\tau_2 = \tau_2 = \tau_4 = 0$ and determine a linear relationship between $R_{ij}(\mathbf{x}_{1S}, \mathbf{x}_{2S}, 0)$ and $R_{ij}(\mathbf{x}_1, \mathbf{x}_2, 0)$.

If the statistics of the radiation are gaussian, this function contains no more information about the source than does the second-order moment. If the statistics of the radiation are nongaussian (as they would be for example if turbulent fluctuations were present), however, then this relationship gives new informatiton. Most of the work concerning the measurement of $R_{ij}(\mathbf{x}_{1S}, \mathbf{x}_{2S}, 0)$ has been done assuming the radiation statistics are gaussian and we shall make this assumption in the remainder of the chapter. We shall briefly discuss nongaussian statistics in Chapter 13.

Classically, the concept of both second- and fourth-order moments presents no difficulty, since we assume that $\mathbf{E}(\mathbf{x}, t)$ is a measurable function of $\mathbf{x}$ and t and that thus averages are taken for convenience or because of the lack of technological success in developing fast response detectors.

†In most of this chapter we take $E_i(\mathbf{x}, t)$ to be real. We do this initially, since a complete analytic signal formulation has not yet been given for fourth-order moments. Note added in proof. See, however, M. Beran and P. Corson, "Use of Analytic Signals in Third and Fourth Order Coherence Functions," (to be published).

In the case of the second-order moment, the measurement procedure itself (as outlined in Chapter 2) does not force one to consider the validity of the classical approach directly since we perform a classical interference experiment to measure† $\mathfrak{G}'_{ij}(\mathbf{x}_1, \mathbf{x}_2, \tau)$.‡ To be sure, if the radiation intensity is low our averaging procedure must extend over very long periods of time but rarely so long as to be impractical.

When measuring the moment $R_{ij}(\mathbf{x}_1, \mathbf{x}_2, 0)$ no such direct averaging approach has been developed§ and we are forced to consider the intermediate averages and also look into the nature of radiation-measuring device interaction more closely. One measuring procedure, for example, is to use two photomultipliers to determine average functions of $I_i(\mathbf{x}_1, t)$ and $I_j(\mathbf{x}_2, t)$ and then subsequently average these two already averaged functions to find information about $R_{ij}(\mathbf{x}_1, \mathbf{x}_2, 0)$. The nature of the radiation-measuring device interaction enters when one attempts to relate the photomultiplier currents to the average functions of $I_i(\mathbf{x}_1, t)$ and $I_j(\mathbf{x}_2, t)$ since the relation between the discrete photoelectrons ejected and the instantaneous radiation intensity is a statistical one.

In this chapter, we explore the use of photomultipliers to obtain information about $R_{ij}(\mathbf{x}_1, \mathbf{x}_2, 0)$ from both a classical and semiclassical viewpoint. We then discuss the utility of using $R_{ij}(\mathbf{x}_1, \mathbf{x}_2, 0)$ for determining the dimensions of both visible and radio stars. We conclude the chapter with a section on the manner in which index of refraction changes affects an intensity interferometer.

12.1 MEASUREMENT OF $R_{ij}(\mathbf{x}_1, \mathbf{x}_2, 0) = \langle I_i(\mathbf{x}_1, t)\, I_j(\mathbf{x}_2, t)\rangle$

Introduction

As mentioned previously, the measurement of $\mathfrak{G}'_{ij}(\mathbf{x}_1, \mathbf{x}_2, \tau)$ may be accomplished by interference experiments. No knowledge of the instan-

---

†We will use a prime here to indicate

$$\mathfrak{G}'_{ij}(x_1, x_2, \tau) = \langle E_i(\mathbf{x}_1, t + \tau)\, E_j(\mathbf{x}_2, t)\rangle$$

where the E_i's are real, not analytic signals. For simplicity of notation, we shall not put a prime on $I(\mathbf{x}_1, t)$.

‡Actually, we have given only procedures for measuring $\Gamma(\mathbf{x}_1, \mathbf{x}_2, \tau)$, but if we measure $\mathfrak{G}'_{ij}(\mathbf{x}_1, \mathbf{x}_2, \tau)$ far from the radiating source, so that only the components of $E(\mathbf{x}_1, t)$ essentially perpendicular to the direction of propagation are important, then a simple extension of the procedure give in Chapter 2 may be developed to consider two-dimensional polarization effects.

§Though nonlinear dielectrics may provide such a procedure, to our knowledge, this possibility has not yet been seriously considered.

taneous function $\mathbf{E}(\mathbf{x}\, t)$ is needed. To measure $R_{ij}(\mathbf{x}_1, \mathbf{x}_2, 0)$ on the other hand, knowledge of the instantaneous values of $I_i(\mathbf{x}, t)$ is needed, since no way is known to obtain the average of the product of instantaneous intensities without having explicit knowledge of the instantaneous quantitites themselves.

Now measurement of $I_i(\mathbf{x}, t)$ is not possible unless the radiation intensity is extremely intense; i.e., unless there are very many photons per wavelength. We, however, wish a procedure that is not dependent upon the magnitude of the intensity for its applicability. Just as in the measurement of $\mathfrak{G}'_{ij}(x_1, x_2, \tau)$, where our experiment worked for all intensity levels, we wish a general procedure.

Viewing the problem classically, such a procedure must, of necessity, consider the correlation of average functions of $I_i(\mathbf{x}, t)$. We shall thus obtain in our measurements not R_{ij} but some average over R_{ij}. The average will contain all the information available to us, and from this average, we must obtain as much information about R_{ij} as is possible. As we shall show under "Classical Approach," in that approach, the spatial coherence of R_{ij} may often be determined to within a constant from the averaged measured function if we assume gaussian statistics and a quasi-monochromatic approximation.

In the classical approach, we assume we have a detector with a resolving time T and that many photons impinge upon the detector in this time. We treat the detector output as continuous and ignore the discrete nature of the detector output. Such a procedure is quite suitable for many purposes, since it illustrates the assumptions necessary to determine the shape of R_{ij}. This method does not, however, tell us whether or not the measurement is practical. For although we always theoretically consider our time averages to be infinite, as a practical matter we usually preclude averages that exceed many hours.

To determine realistic averaging times, the discrete aspects of the photoelectric current must be discussed. The results given in the sub-section "Formulation-Classical Approach" show only the order of magnitude of the signal; they give no indication of the magnitude of any noise. In general, we have not considered noise problems in this book, but the practical possibility of measuring $R_{ij}(\mathbf{x}_1, \mathbf{x}_2, 0)$ when considering optical sources has played so great a part in the history of intensity interferometry [see the discussion in Hanbury Brown and Twiss (1957 a,b)] that after our classical discussion we shall consider this question.

The noise problem may be treated semiclassically; i.e., we do not need to quantize the electromagnetic field but may consider that the probability of a photoelectron being ejected in a photomultiplier is proportional to the classical electromagnetic field intensity. A treatment by Mandel (1958) considers this problem very clearly and we shall summarize his development before considering the noise problem.

Classical approach

Formulation: Since we cannot measure $I_i(\mathbf{x}_1, t)$ and $I_j(\mathbf{x}_2, t)$ to obtain $R_{ij}(\mathbf{x}_1, \mathbf{x}_2, 0)$ we must determine $R_{ij}(\mathbf{x}_1, \mathbf{x}_2, 0)$ from some average functions of $I_i(\mathbf{x}_1, t)$ and $I_j(\mathbf{x}_2, t)$. To begin let us proceed classically and assume as do Mandel and Wolf (1961) that we have a detector which has a resolving time T and thus measures a function of the form:†

$$S_i(\mathbf{x}, t) = \frac{\beta}{T} \int_t^{t+T} I_i(\mathbf{x}, t')\, dt' \tag{12–2}$$

where β is a factor which reflects the efficiency of the detector. We will implicitly assume here that T is chosen so that it is probable that there are many photons impinging upon the detector in time T.

Next form the average $\mathcal{S}_{ij}(\mathbf{x}_1, \mathbf{x}_2, \tau)$, defined as

$$\begin{aligned} \mathcal{S}_{ij}(\mathbf{x}_1, \mathbf{x}_2, \tau) &= \langle S_i(\mathbf{x}_1, t + \tau)\, S_j(\mathbf{x}_2, t)\rangle \\ &= \left\langle \frac{\beta^2}{T^2} \int_t^{t+T} \int_t^{t+T} I_i(\mathbf{x}_1, t' + \tau)\, I_j(\mathbf{x}_2, t'')\, dt'\, dt'' \right\rangle \end{aligned} \tag{12–3}$$

A single integral relation between $\mathcal{S}_{ij}(\mathbf{x}_1, \mathbf{x}_2, \tau)$ and $R_{ij}(\mathbf{x}_1, \mathbf{x}_2, \tau)$ can be established by changing to the variables:

$$\begin{aligned} u &= t' - t \\ v &= t'' - t \end{aligned} \tag{12–4}$$

Then we have

$$\mathcal{S}_{ij}(\mathbf{x}_1, \mathbf{x}_2, \tau) = \left\langle \frac{\beta^2}{T^2} \int_0^T \int_0^T I_i(\mathbf{x}_1, u + t + \tau)\, I_j(\mathbf{x}_2, v + t)\, du\, dv \right\rangle \tag{12–5}$$

Interchanging integration and averaging and using the stationary property of $R_{ij}(\mathbf{x}_1, \mathbf{x}_2, \tau)$, we find

$$\mathcal{S}_{ij}(\mathbf{x}_1, \mathbf{x}_2, \tau) = \frac{\beta^2}{T^2} \int_0^T \int_0^T R_{ij}(\mathbf{x}_1, \mathbf{x}_2, u - v + \tau)\, du\, dv \tag{12–6}$$

A final change of variables to

$$\begin{aligned} \tau' &= u - v \\ q &= u \end{aligned}$$

†Actually Mandel and Wolf (1961) replace $I_i(x, t)$ in Eq. (12–27) by an average of $I_i(\mathbf{x}, t)$ over a few periods of the average wavelength. They use the analytic signal which may conveniently be used at this point if this averaging is desired. Although, from a quantum-mechanical viewpoint, such an average is demanded, classically it is not and it is felt that it is of some interest to see the consequences of an average over a time short compared to $1/\bar{\nu}$. In the future development, we shall be mainly concerned with difference frequency terms generated when a quantity is squared, but considering very short time averages shows what happens to the sum frequency terms which are also produced. For time averages long compared to $1/\bar{\nu}$ our method yields the same results as that of Mandel and Wolf.

yields

$$\mathscr{S}_{ij}(\mathbf{x}_1, \mathbf{x}_2, \tau) = \frac{\beta^2}{T^2}\int_T^T (T - |\tau'|)\, R_{ij}(\mathbf{x}_1, \mathbf{x}_2, \tau' + \tau)\, d\tau' \tag{12–7}$$

Since $I_p(\mathbf{x}_q, t + s)$ is always positive, it is convenient to write

$$I_p(\mathbf{x}_q, t + s) = \bar{I}_p(\mathbf{x}_q) + I'(\mathbf{x}_q, t + s)$$

where $\langle I'(\mathbf{x}_q, t + s)\rangle = 0$.
Then we have

$$\mathscr{S}_{ij}(\mathbf{x}_1, \mathbf{x}_2, \tau) = \frac{\beta^2}{T^2}\int_{-T}^T (T - |\tau'|) \cdot [\bar{I}_i(\mathbf{x}_1)\, \bar{I}_j(\mathbf{x}_2) + R'_{ij}(\mathbf{x}_1, \mathbf{x}_2, \tau + \tau')]\, d\tau \tag{12–8}$$

where $R'_{ij}(\mathbf{x}_1, \mathbf{x}_2, \tau + \tau') = \langle I'_i(\mathbf{x}_1, t + \tau + \tau')\, I'_j(\mathbf{x}_2, t)\rangle$

This gives

$$\mathscr{S}_{ij}(\mathbf{x}_1, \mathbf{x}_2, \tau) = \beta^2 \bar{I}_i(\mathbf{x}_1)\, \bar{I}_j(\mathbf{x}_2) + \frac{\beta^2}{T^2}\int_{-T}^T (T - |\tau'|) \cdot R'_{ij}(\mathbf{x}_1, \mathbf{x}_2, \tau + \tau')\, d\tau' \tag{12–9}$$

If nothing further is known about R_{ij}, this is our final answer. If, however, $R'_{ij}(\mathbf{x}_1, \mathbf{x}_2, \tau + \tau')$ splits into the product of a spatial and a temporal part, say,

$$R'_{ij}(\mathbf{x}_1, \mathbf{x}_2, \tau + \tau') = M_{ij}(\mathbf{x}_1, \mathbf{x}_2)\, G(\tau + \tau') \tag{12–10}$$

then $R'_{ij}(\mathbf{x}_1, \mathbf{x}_2, 0) = M_{ij}(\mathbf{x}_1, \mathbf{x}_2)\, G(0)$ would be measurable (to within a constant factor), since

$$\mathscr{S}_{ij}(\mathbf{x}_1, \mathbf{x}_2, 0) = \beta^2 \bar{I}_i(\mathbf{x}_1)\, \bar{I}_j(\mathbf{x}_2) + \frac{\beta^2}{T^2} F(0)\, M_{ij}(\mathbf{x}_1, \mathbf{x}_2) \tag{12–11}$$

where $$F(0) = \int_{-T}^T (T - |\tau'|)\, G(\tau')\, d\tau'$$

An assumption like that given by Eq. (12–10) is at the heart of all practical measuring systems, and we now turn to a brief discussion of its plausibility. In subsequent sections, we shall consider only situations in which Eq. (12–10) is valid.

Plausibility of form given in Eq. (12–10):† For the case of gaussian statistics, this product division is indeed possible for quasi-monochromatic light from incoherent sources when small path differences are involved. We now show this.

If the statistics are gaussian,

$$R'_{ij}(\mathbf{x}_1, \mathbf{x}_2, \tau) = 2[\mathfrak{S}'_{ij}(\mathbf{x}_1, \mathbf{x}_2, \tau)]^2 \tag{12–12}$$

†Or of its analog if a complex representation is used.

Thus we need consider only the second-order correlation function to determine whether the splitting given in Eq. (12–10) is indeed possible.

The possible splitting of the coherence function may be seen most easily by considering a problem treated in Chapter 5. There we considered radiation from a plane finite incoherent source. We treated the problem there using a scalar theory; hence the results are correct near an axis perpendicular to and crossing the radiating source surface. Near this axis, the solution $\Gamma^{rr}(\mathbf{x}_1, \mathbf{x}_2, \tau)$ yields the same information as $\mathfrak{E}'_{ij}(\mathbf{x}_1, \mathbf{x}_2, \tau)$ if the radiation is polarized. Study of the scalar function $\Gamma(\mathbf{x}_1, \mathbf{x}_2, \tau)$ will thus be adequate to show the nature of the calculation.

For distances much greater than a characteristic source dimension, we found, for a source of constant intensity—see Eq. (5–15):

$$\Gamma(P_1, P_2, \tau) = \frac{1}{\pi}\frac{z^2}{R_1^4}\int_0^\infty e^{-2\pi i\nu[\tau-(R_1-R_2)/c]}\,\bar{I}(\nu)\,d\nu \left(\int_S e^{-i(k/R_1)(x_{1s}x_{12}+y_{1s}y_{12})}\,dS_1\right) \tag{12–13}$$

If the radiation is quasi-monochromatic $\Delta\nu/\nu \ll 1$ and if $\Delta\nu[(R_1 - R_2)/c] \ll 1$, then we have shown for a number of source shapes that the surface integral is insensitive to ν over the range $\bar{\nu} - \Delta\nu$ to $\bar{\nu} + \Delta\nu$. Calling this integral $L(P_1, P_2, \bar{\nu})$, we have

$$\Gamma(P_1, P_2, \tau) = \frac{1}{\pi}\frac{z^2}{R^4}L(P_1, P_2, \bar{\nu})\int_0^\infty e^{-2\pi i\nu[\tau-(R_1-R_2)/c]}\,\hat{I}(\nu)\,d\nu \tag{12–14}$$

If $\hat{I}(\nu)$ is essentially zero when $\Delta\nu[(R_1 - R_2)/c] \ll 1$, then we find

$$\Gamma(P_1, P_2, \tau) = \frac{1}{\pi}\frac{z^2}{R^4}L(P_1, P_2, \bar{\nu})\,e^{[2\pi i\bar{\nu}(R_1-R_2)]/c}\int_0^\infty e^{-2\pi i\nu\tau}\,\hat{I}(\nu)\,d\nu \tag{12–15}$$

If the source is symmetric and $\hat{I}(\nu)$ is symmetric about $\bar{\nu}$, then $\Gamma(P_1, P_2, \tau)$ is equal to a real function multiplied by the phase factor

$$\exp\left[2\pi i\bar{\nu}\left[\frac{(R_1 - R_2)}{c} - \tau\right]\right.$$

When $T \gg 1/\bar{\nu}$, the phase factor may be discarded, since its effect is averaged out in the integration subsequent to squaring. For this case then, $\Gamma^{rr}(P_1, P_2, \tau)$ splits into the desired product form. No such simplification results if $T < 1/\bar{\nu}$, and we must make use of the fact that for the geometrical configuration given,

$$\bar{\nu}\frac{(R_1 - R_2)}{c} \ll 1.$$

This requires, however, that the measurements be performed with wavelength accuracy.

When neither the source nor $\hat{I}(\nu)$ have symmetry properties, an effective splitting occurs only when $T \gg 1/\bar{\nu}$. Here, however, as Mandel and Wolf

(1961) show, we measure $|L(P_1, P_2, \bar{\nu})|^2$ rather than $[L^{rr}(P_1, P_2, \bar{\nu})]^2$. This again is the result of squaring $\Gamma^{rr}(P_1, P_2, \tau)$ and then integrating. $M(\mathbf{x}_1, \mathbf{x}_2)$ (dropping the ij subscript) may be identified here with $|L(\mathbf{x}_1, \mathbf{x}_2, \bar{\nu})|^2$.

Equation (12–15) justifies, for at least the configuration given above, the form Eq. (12–10). For every new configuration, this form of the solution must be justified anew, but this example indicates that this type of solution is to be expected for a wide class of similar problems. For a further discussion of this problem, see Mandel (1961).

Magnitude of correlation term: Assuming the validity of Eq. (12–10), we may determine const $R_{ij}(\mathbf{x}_1, \mathbf{x}_2, 0)$ from $\mathcal{S}_{ij}(\mathbf{x}_1, \mathbf{x}_2, 0)$. As a practical matter, the order of magnitude of the factor $[\beta^2 F(0)]/T$ is important in determining the feasibility of a measurement. We will discuss the order of magnitude of this term in this section. As stated previously, the signal-to-noise problem will be treated after a discussion of the discrete aspects of the photoelectric current.

The function $[\beta^2 F(0)]/T^2$ indicates the magnitude of the term involving correlation between $I_i(\mathbf{x}_1, t)$ and $I_j(\mathbf{x}_2, t)$. Consider

$$F(0) = \int_{-T}^{T} (T - |\tau'|)\, G(\tau')\, d\tau' \tag{12–16}$$

The magnitude of this term depends upon the characteristic coherence time, τ_c, of $G(\tau')$; $\bar{\nu}$; and T. τ_c is a characteristic decay time of $G(\tau)$; $1/\tau_c$ is a rough measure of $\Delta\nu$†, and for order-of-magnitude calculations, we may set $1/\tau_c = \Delta\nu$.

There are three cases to consider:

$$\frac{T}{\tau_c} \gg 1, \quad \tau_c \gg T \gg \frac{1}{\bar{\nu}}, \quad \text{and} \quad T \ll \frac{1}{\bar{\nu}}$$

Remember that we have assumed that $\Delta\nu/\bar{\nu} \ll 1$ and for illustration, we suppose that we can find a time T such that $\tau_c \ll T \ll 1/\bar{\nu}$.

In the first case, $T \gg \tau_c$. Since

$$\int_{-\infty}^{\infty} G(\tau')\, d\tau'$$

is a measure of τ_c, we have

$$F(0) \approx C_1 \tau_c T \tag{12–17}$$

where C_1 is of the order of 1.

The case $T \ll 1/\bar{\nu}$ is also simple.‡ For such times T, $G(\tau')$ is essentially a constant (which we assume normalized to 1) and hence,

---

†$G(\tau)$ now represents the square of the autocorrelation function; hence its characterstic time is not so simply related to $\Delta\nu$. For order-of-magnitude calculations, however, it is still adequate here to assume $1/\tau_c = \Delta\nu$.

‡We remember that we have considered the radiation to be classical so that it is defined for $T \ll 1/\bar{\nu}$.

(12–18) $$F(0) \approx T^2$$

The intermediate case is somewhat more difficult to evaluate. For illustration, suppose that the frequency spectrum of the incident radiation, $\hat{\Gamma}(P_1, P_2, \nu)$ may be represented by a function such that

(12–19) $$\hat{\Gamma}(P_1, P_1, \nu) = \text{const}; \quad \bar{\nu} - \frac{\Delta\nu}{2} < \nu < \bar{\nu} + \frac{\Delta\nu}{2}; \quad \frac{\Delta\nu}{\bar{\nu}} \ll 1$$

$$= 0 \qquad \nu > \bar{\nu} + \frac{\Delta\nu}{2}$$

$$\nu < \bar{\nu} - \frac{\Delta\nu}{2}$$

Then the autocorrelation $\Gamma(P_1, P_2, \tau)$ is

(12–20) $$\Gamma(P_1, P_1, \tau) = \text{const} \quad \cos 2\pi\bar{\nu}\tau\, [\text{sinc}\, 2\pi\, \Delta\nu\tau]$$

Assuming gaussian statistics, normalizing, and neglecting the constant term, we have

(12–21) $$G(\tau) = \cos^2 2\pi\bar{\nu}\tau[\text{sinc}^2\, 2\pi\, \Delta\nu\tau]$$

If, as cited, $T \ll 1/\bar{\nu}$, $F(0) = T^2$. Now, when $1/\bar{\nu} \ll T \ll 1/\Delta\bar{\nu}$ the integral $F(0)$ has the value

(12–22) $$\int_{-T}^{T} G(\tau')\, d\tau' = 2\frac{T^2}{2^2} = \frac{T^2}{2}$$

This result is general for any narrow-band signal. This can be seen by using the formulation given in Chapter 4 for representing a quasi-monochromatic term.
Thus

(12–23) $$F(0) \approx \frac{T^2}{2} \quad \text{when} \quad \frac{1}{\bar{\nu}} \ll T \ll \frac{1}{\Delta\nu}$$

Summary: We may summarize our discussion to this point by stating that we have shown that $R_{ij}(\mathbf{x}_1, \mathbf{x}_2, 0)$ is theoretically measurable up to a constant from measurement of $\mathscr{S}_{ij}(\mathbf{x}_1, \mathbf{x}_2, 0)$ if one assumes gaussian statistics, an incoherent source, and the applicability of a quasi-monochromatic approximation. The magnitude of the term $F(0)$ depends upon the magnitude of T [see Eqs. (12–17), (12–18), (12–23)].

We now turn to a discussion of some particle aspects of the measurement of $R_{ij}(\mathbf{x}_1, \mathbf{x}_2, 0)$.

Semiclassical treatment of the measurement of $R_{ij}(\mathbf{x}_1, \mathbf{x}_2, 0)$

The nature of the radiation-measuring device interaction is considered in intensity correlation measurements, since photomultiplier measurements result from the emission of photoelectrons by the impinging photons. This effect can be avoided by an analysis such as that previously given, but the foregoing discussion requires some further analysis to justify it. The results we obtain from a less classical argument, however, will be essentially the same as those just presented.

Here, we make the basic assumption [see Mandel (1958)] that the probability of a photoelectron being emitted in a time interval t to $t + dt$ is proportional to the classical intensity at time t. We take the local time average over a few cycles at the average frequency $\bar{\nu}$ (we will consider only quasi-monochromatic radiation) since we cannot localize photons to within a wavelength of the radiation. This local time averaging prohibits the possibility $T \ll 1/\bar{\nu}$ that we considered in the previous section and has the effect of eliminating the influence of sum frequencies on the intensity correlation function. Let us denote this local time average of $I_i(\mathbf{x}, t)$ as $\bar{\bar{I}}_i(\mathbf{x}, t)$. Thus $P(t, dt)$, the probability of ejecting a photoelectron in the time interval t to $t + dt$, is

$$P(t, dt) = \alpha \bar{\bar{I}}_i(\mathbf{x}_1, t)\, dt \tag{12–24}$$

where α reflects the efficiency of the process. For convenience, we assume that there is a polarizer in front of the detector so that the radiation is polarized in the i direction.

We cannot overemphasize how significant is the assumption represented by Eq. (12–24). It allows us to dispense with the quantum aspects of the radiation field itself. Since a proper quantum formulation would demand a discussion of the photon-photoelectron interaction, in effect we are saying here that the probability of a photon being present is proportional to the classical electromagnetic field intensity (to within a wavelength or so) and that if, indeed, a photon is present a photoelectron is emitted with some efficiency represented in α. The reason that the photoelectric current reflects the variations in the classical intensity and that two photoelectric currents reflect the effect of a classical wave interference follows directly from these assumptions. So, too, with some qualifications, does the statement that photons obey Bose-Einstein rather than classical statistics.

Equation (12–24) leads to the following distribution for $P_n(t, T)$, the probability that n photoelectrons will be emitted in the interval t to $t + T$:

$$P_n(t, T) = \frac{1}{n!}\left[\alpha \int_t^{t+T} \bar{\bar{I}}_i(\mathbf{x}_1, t')\, dt'\right]^n e^{-\alpha \int_t^{t+T} \bar{\bar{I}}_i(\mathbf{x}_1, t')dt'} \tag{12–25}$$

This is an extension of the usual Poisson distribution.

Since $\bar{\bar{I}}_i(\mathbf{x}_1, t')$ is a random function of time, any average functions like

$$\begin{aligned} \langle n_T \rangle &= \sum_{n=0}^{\infty} n P_n(t, T) \\ \langle n_T^2 \rangle &= \sum_{n=0}^{\infty} n^2 P_n(t, T) \end{aligned} \tag{12–26}$$

must be averaged over all time intervals t to $t + T$.†

Direct calculations show then that

$$\text{(12–27)} \qquad \begin{aligned} \langle n_T \rangle &= \sum_{n=0}^{\infty} \langle n P_n(t, T) \rangle \\ \langle n_T \rangle &= \alpha \left\langle \int_t^{t+T} \bar{\bar{I}}_i(\mathbf{x}_1, t')\, dt' \right\rangle \end{aligned}$$

The integrals may be interchanged by changing to the variable $t'' = t' - t$ and using the stationarity property of the radiation. This yields then, as under "Classical approach,"

$$\text{(12–28)} \qquad \langle n_T \rangle = \alpha T \langle \bar{\bar{I}}_i(\mathbf{x}_1, t) \rangle$$

Similarly, we find that

$$\text{(12–29)} \qquad \langle n_T^2 \rangle = \langle n_T \rangle + \alpha^2 \int_0^T \int_0^T \langle \bar{\bar{I}}_i(\mathbf{x}_1, t + u)\, \bar{\bar{I}}_i(\mathbf{x}_1, t + v) \rangle \, du\, dv$$

Calling

$$\bar{R}_{ii}(\mathbf{x}_1, \mathbf{x}_1, u + v) = \langle \bar{\bar{I}}_i(\mathbf{x}_1, t + u)\, \bar{\bar{I}}_i(\mathbf{x}_1, t + v) \rangle$$

this gives

$$\text{(12–30)} \qquad \langle n_T^2 \rangle = \langle n_T \rangle + \alpha^2 \int_0^T \int_0^T R_{ii}(\mathbf{x}_1, \mathbf{x}_2, u - v)\, du\, dv$$

or, transforming to the variables,

$$\tau' = u - v$$

$$q = u$$

$$\text{(12–31)} \qquad \langle n_T^2 \rangle = \langle n_T \rangle + \alpha^2 \int_{-T}^{T} (T - |\tau'|)\, R_{ii}(\mathbf{x}_1, \mathbf{x}_1, \tau')\, d\tau'$$

Further, we find that

$$\text{(12–32)} \qquad \begin{aligned} \langle n_1 n_2 \rangle &= \sum_{n_1=0}^{\infty} \sum_{n_2=0}^{\infty} \langle n_1 n_2\, P_{n_1}(t, T)\, P_{n_2}(t, T) \rangle \\ &= \alpha^2 \int_{-T}^{T} (T - |\tau'|)\, R_{ij}(\mathbf{x}_1, \mathbf{x}_2, \tau')\, d\tau' \end{aligned}$$

where n_1 and n_2 are the number of photoelectrons ejected in time T in detector

---

†Note that

$$\sum_{n=0}^{\infty} \frac{n}{n!} (z)^n e^{-z} = \left[z \frac{d}{dz} \left(\sum_{n=0}^{\infty} \frac{z^n}{n!} \right) \right] e^{-z} = z$$

$$\sum_{n=0}^{\infty} \frac{n^2}{n!} z^n e^{-z} = \left[z \frac{d}{dz} z \frac{d}{dz} \left(\sum_{n=0}^{\infty} \frac{z^n}{n!} \right) \right] e^{-z} = z + z^2$$

These formulas aid in actual calculation of the expressions in Eq. (12–26) if we let

$$z = \alpha \int_t^{t+T} \bar{\bar{I}}_i(\mathbf{x}_1, t')\, dt'$$

1 and 2 respectively. This expression is analogous to Eq. (12–7). [The term $\langle n_T \rangle$ in Eq. (12–31) is considered in the next section.]

Thus we find from Eq. (12–32) that this approach leads to essentially the same results as the classical approach. We now turn to a discussion of the signal-to-noise problem.

Signal-to-noise aspects in the measurement of $R_{ij}(x_1, x_2, 0)$

The term $\langle n_T \rangle$ in Eq. (12–31) is a result of the discreteness of the photoelectrons. If the discrete nature of the photoelectrons were unimportant, the *fluctuating part* of the second term on the right-hand side of Eq. (12–31) would be large compared to $\langle n_T \rangle$. Unfortunately, for ordinary (non-laser) optical sources this is not so. From Eq. (12–17) we find that

(12–33) $$\langle n_T^2 \rangle - \langle n_T \rangle^2 = \langle n_T \rangle + O(\alpha^2 T \tau_c \bar{\bar{I}}^2)$$

In terms of particles/unit bandwidth n_B, the ratio of the signal, S, (the second term) to the noise, N, (the first term) is

(12–34) $$\frac{S}{N} \approx \gamma n_B$$

where γ is the quantum efficiency. For a bright optical labortary source or for star radiation measured on earth, this quantity is $\ll 1$.

A term analogous to $\langle n_T \rangle$ does not appear in cross-correlation calculations as $T \to \infty$ [see Eq. (12–33)]. If T is not infinite, however, the effect of the discrete nature of the photoelectrons is the dominant noise effect in a photomultiplier tube and hence must be considered. We note that the mean square noise, N^2, is

(12–35) $$N^2 = \left[\sum_{n_1=0}^{\infty} \sum_{n_2=0}^{\infty} (n_1 - \langle n_T \rangle)(n_2 - \langle n_T \rangle) P_{n_1}(t, T) P_{n_2}(t, T) \right]^2$$

where we assume $\langle n_T(\mathbf{x}_1, t) \rangle = \langle n_T(\mathbf{x}_2, t) \rangle = \langle n_T \rangle$

Since shot noise dominates Eq. (12–33), the principal contribution to the right-hand side of Eq. (12–35) will come from the uncorrelated portions of the signal, for the shot noise at point $\mathbf{x}_1$ is uncorrelated to the shot noise at point $\mathbf{x}_2$. This term may be written

(12–36) $$N^2 = \langle [n'_T(\mathbf{x}_1, t)\, n'_T(\mathbf{x}_2, t)]^2 \rangle$$

where

$$n'_T(\mathbf{x}_i, t) = n_T(\mathbf{x}_i, t) - \langle n_T \rangle$$

Assuming the photoelectrons at $\mathbf{x}_1$ and $\mathbf{x}_2$ are uncorrelated, this gives

(12–37) $$\langle n_T'^2(\mathbf{x}_1, t) \rangle \langle n_T'^2(\mathbf{x}_2, t) \rangle \approx \langle n_T \rangle^2$$

and finally

(12–38) $$N \approx \langle n_T \rangle$$

If now the root mean square value of noise, N, is $\langle n_T \rangle$ and the signal is S, then

$$\lim_{t\to\infty} \frac{1}{t} \int_0^t (S + N)\, dt = S + c\langle n_T \rangle \left(\frac{\tau_N}{t}\right)^{1/2} \tag{12–39}$$

where c is a constant of order 1 and τ_N is the reciprocal of the noise bandwidth.

Since in our problem $S \approx (\alpha^2 T/\tau_c)\, n_B^2$ for very small separations,

$$\begin{aligned} \frac{S}{N} &\approx \left[\frac{\alpha T}{\tau_c}\right] \frac{[n_B^2]}{\left[\left\{\dfrac{n_B T}{\tau_c}\right\}\left\{\dfrac{\tau_N}{t}\right\}^{1/2}\right]} \\ &\approx \alpha n_B \left(\frac{t}{\tau_N}\right)^{1/2} \end{aligned} \tag{12–40}$$

For $\alpha = 0.10$, $n_B = 10^{-3}$, $\tau_N = 10^{-7}$ (numbers obtainable in the laboratory) $t = 1{,}000$ sec for $S/N = 10$. Thus very long averaging times are needed to secure reliable results. When $\mathbf{x}_1$ and $\mathbf{x}_2$ are separated by large distances so that the spatial coherence is low, the problem is much more demanding. It follows directly that t is proportional to the reciprocal of the square of the spatial coherence.

We suggest that any reader who desires to do intensity interferometry experiments or calculations first read Hanbury Brown and Twiss (1956a, 1957a, b) where the problem is discussed in detail. In the preceding treatment, we have simplified the problem to bring out only the very basic aspects.

12.2 MEASUREMENT OF RADIO AND VISIBLE STAR DIAMETERS

Conceptually speaking, the measurement of the diameters of stars is the same for intensity interferometry as for ordinary interferometry. The principal advantage of intensity interferometry is that the signals from two measuring points may be transmitted as low-frequency signals. The actual visible radio radiation reaching the two points need not be transmitted directly to a central point for examination (as in an ordinary interferometer). A further advantage, which we shall discuss in Section 12.4, is the relative insensitivity of intensity interferometry to atmospheric scintillations.

Examination of Eqs. (12–11) and (12–12) and the example given in the section on the plausibility of Eq. (12–10) shows that measurement of $\mathscr{I}_{ij}(\mathbf{x}_1, \mathbf{x}_2, 0) - \beta^2\, \bar{I}_i(\mathbf{x}_1)\, \bar{I}_j(\mathbf{x}_2)$ will yield the shape of the square of the two-point space coherence function resulting form distant incoherent sources. Since the square root of the magnitude of a function is nonunique, we could not, in principle, find the intensity distribution across a source by inverting an equation, such as Eq. (5–29). [The inversion is actually between $\Gamma(P_1, P_2, 0)$ and $\hat{L}(P_1, P_2, \bar{\nu})$.] If, however, we make certain assumptions about the intensity distributions, as in Chapter 5 for visible stars, the angular size of objects may be roughly determined.

Radio sources

Hanbury Brown, Jennison, and Das Gupta (1952) first made measurements of radio stars using the principle of intensity interferometry. They studied the Cygnus radio source, and by studying essentially $|\hat{L}(P_1, P_2, \bar{\nu})|^2$ at $\bar{\nu} = 125$ megacycles, they determined the source to be asymmetric and to have characteristic dimensions between about $\frac{1}{2}$ min. and 2 min of arc. They used a maximum separation of 4 km. They thus established that radio sources may have much larger angular diameters than visible stars.

In practice, this type of device is most successful for very intense sources, and unless the source is very small so that the separation of receivers is very large, it compares unfavorably with the ordinary interferometer in over-all performance.

The experimental details of the device are carefully considered in articles by Handbury Brown and Twiss (1954) and Jennison and Das Gupta (1956) and we refer the reader to these articles.

Visible stars

Hanbury Brown and Twiss (1956 b, c) first measured the angular diameter of the star Sirius using intensity interferometry. Its use is especially important in the visible range because of the difficulty of building large interferometers of the Michelson type. Using photoelectric receivers, the two receivers (equivalent to the two ends of an ordinary interferometer) may be very far apart. Hence stars of small angular diameter may be measured. Hanbury Brown and Twiss obtained an angular diameter for Sirius of 0.0068 seconds assuming the intensity was uniform over an osculating flat disk. This agrees reasonably well with the prediction that would be made on the basis of the spectrum and intensity of the radiation from Sirius.

Hanbury Brown and Twiss point out that the collecting apertures may be made crudely by optical standards and that the measurement is relatively insensitive to atmospheric scintillation. Both these effects follow from the fact that only the difference frequencies are being recorded. In the next section, we discuss this effect in more detail.

Again we refer readers to the articles of the workers in the field if they are interested in the very nontrivial difficulties of performing this experiment. Hanbury Brown and Twiss (1957 a, b) give a very good discussion of intensity interferometry at optical frequencies. Particularly noteworthy is a laboratory experiment that they performed to check the theory.

12.3 EFFECT OF PHASE CHANGES ON THE MEASUREMENT OF $R_{ij}(\mathbf{x}_1, \mathbf{x}_2, 0)$

As mentioned previously, Hanbury Brown and Twiss (1956 b, c) have stated that an intensity interferometer would be much less affected by atmospheric scintillation than an ordinary Michelson interferometer. In this section, we discuss the validity of this statement by considering a simple example: We suppose that a polarized quasi-monochromatic radiation field described by an analytic signal, $V(t)$†, impinges on two columns AA' and BB' (Refer to Fig. 12–1). The two columns, each of a dimension b which is large compared to a wavelength, are separated by a distance d which is large compared to b. The axis of both columns is perpendicular to the mean direction of propagation. In column AA', all Fourier components of the field experience a phase change ϕ_A; and in column BB', a phase change ϕ_B. To simulate the atmosphere, we suppose we have an ensemble of such columns such that ϕ_A and ϕ_B are statistical variables where $\overline{\phi_A} = \overline{\phi_B} = \overline{\phi_A \phi_B} = 0$ (the bar denoting ensemble averaging) and ϕ_A and ϕ_B have equal probability of having any value between $-\pi$ and π.

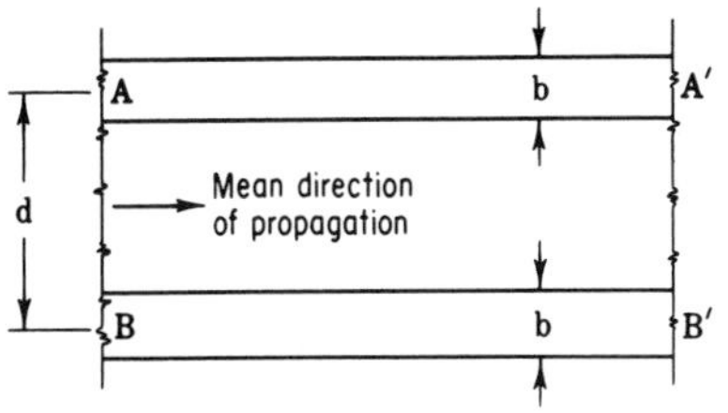

Figure 12-1. Effect of random phase changes on coherence.

Denote $R_{AB}(\tau)$ as

(12–41)‡ $$R_{AB}(\tau) = \langle V_A(t+\tau)\, V_A^*(t+\tau)\, V_B(t)\, V_B^*(t) \rangle$$

We now wish to show that, assuming $\Gamma_{AB}(\tau)$ is not zero, $\overline{\Gamma_{A'B'}(\tau)}$ is equal to zero, whereas $\overline{R_{A'B'}(\tau)} = R_{AB}(\tau)$.

---

†We return to a complex representation here, since it is too inconvenient to use real functions when considering phase changes.

‡We note that $V_A(t)\, V_A^*(t)$ implies an average over a few cycles of the mean radiation frequency for a quasi-monochromatic signal. For this example, this local averaging is not improtant, and as we stated previously, it is appropriate from a physical point of view.

Letting

$$V_i(T, t) = \int_0^\infty \hat{V}_i(T, \nu)\, e^{-2\pi i\nu t}\, d\nu \qquad (i = A, B) \tag{12–42}$$

we have assumed

$$V_i'(T, t) = e^{-i\phi_i} \int_0^\infty \hat{V}_i(T, \nu)\, e^{-2\pi i\nu t}\, d\nu \qquad (i' = A', B') \tag{12–43}$$

Direct calculation then yields

$$\overline{\Gamma_{A'B'}(\tau)} = \Gamma_{AB}(\tau)\, e^{\overline{i(\phi_B - \phi_A)}} = 0 \tag{12–44}$$

since $e^{\overline{i(\phi_B - \phi_A)}} = 0$

On the other hand, calculation of $V_A'(t)\, V_A'^*(t)$ and $V_B'(t)\, V_B'^*(t)$ shows they are independent of ϕ_A and ϕ_B, respectively, and thus

$$\overline{R_{A'B'}(\tau)} = R_{AB}(\tau) \tag{12–45}$$

In other words, the intensity coherence is insensitive to phase changes that radically change the two-point coherence function. If ϕ_A and ϕ_B were functions of ν, this result would not have been obtained, and for success, it is necessary that ϕ_A and ϕ_B be insensitive to ν over the range $\Delta\nu$ of the quasi-monochromatic signal.

It is very interesting to note that the joint statistics of the radiation at A' and B' are not gaussian, even assuming the joint statistics of the radiation at A and B were gaussian; the simple relationship between $\Gamma_{AB}(\tau)$ and $R_{AB}(\tau)$ does not hold between $\overline{\Gamma_{A'B'}(\tau)}$, and $\overline{R_{A'B'}(\tau)}$. (The expression $\overline{\Gamma_{A'B'}(\tau)}$ is now zero).

chapter

13

Locally Stationary Fields, Spatial Averaging, and Higher-order Correlation Functions

13.1 LOCALLY STATIONARY FIELDS

Through use of ensemble averaging we have indicated how we can treat nonstationary fields that have statistical properties. An important subclass of nonstationary fields may, however, be treated by time-averaging techniques if we introduce the concept of a local stationarity field. We define this as follows: A locally stationary field is one in which the statistics are essentially stationary over times long compared to a characteristic time variation of the field (say $1/\Delta\nu$), but vary and may be nonstationary over the long times of interest in a particular physical problem.†

†See Tatarski (1961) for an alternate definition.

We have previously introduced this concept briefly when considering propagation through media with variable index of refraction but shall now consider it in more detail. Consider a source whose radiation characteristics may be described statistically. Let us break up the time interval $-T$ to T (where in the past we have let $T \to \infty$) into smaller time intervals t_{-n}, $t_{-n+1}, t_{-n+2}, \ldots, t_{-1}, 0, t_1, t_2, \ldots, t_{n-1}, t_n$, where $t_j - t_{j-1} = \eta$ and $n\eta = T$. We choose $\eta \gg \tau_c$ where τ_c is a characteristic time of the radiation. The introduction of the concept of local stationarity is based on the assumption that the statistics of the radiation are essentially constant over a time η but change significantly over time intervals many, many times η.

For locally stationary processes, we introduce the time-averaged coherence function $\Gamma_{12}^j(\tau)$ defined as

$$\Gamma_{12}^j(\tau) = \frac{1}{\eta}\int_{t_j}^{t_j+1} V_1(t+\tau)\, V_2(t)\, dt \tag{13–1}$$

where now V_1 and V_2 are real functions. This definition requires one further assumption in order to be meaningful. We require that $\Gamma_{12}^j(\tau) \to 0$ when $\tau \ll \eta$. If this were not so, the integral would depend upon just how we broke up the time interval $-T$ to T, and this would be unacceptable.

At this point, we note that, for the concept of local stationarity to have operational meaning, we must have measuring apparatus that can perform time integrations in times of the order of η. If the instrument can average only over times long compared to η, the resultant measurement will not be meaningful, for, in the large, the process may be nonstationary and time averages over nonstationary processes are undefined since no definite limit is approached as $T \to \infty$.

Within each interval $t_j - t_{j+1}$, the same theory we have used for averaging over infinite intervals may be used. The same differential equations that governed $\Gamma_{12}(\tau)$ now govern $\Gamma_{12}^j(\tau)$. Now, however, we must be careful when the time it takes for the radiation to travel from the source to the point of measurement is long compared to η. For then the local stationarity of the field is a property of only a portion of the field and if measurements are made for radiation from two radiation paths† l_1 and l_2 such that

$$\frac{|l_1 - l_2|}{c} \geq \eta$$

the concept of local stationarity is invalid. If all measurements are made such that

$$\frac{|l_1 - l_2|}{c} \ll \eta$$

†By paths we can take here the rough estimate of propagation path obtained from a geometric optics-type analysis. This statement can be made precise by analyses similar to those given in Chapters 4 and 5.

the problem may be treated by solving the propagation equation governing $\Gamma_{12}^{j}(\tau)$ with $\Gamma_{1S,\,1S}^{j}(\tau)$ as a boundary condition. We note, however, that $\Gamma_{1S,\,1S}^{j}(\tau)$ corresponds really to the boundary condition

$$\Gamma_{1S,\,1S}^{t_j - l/c}(\tau)$$

(where we have used the superscript t_j rather than j for clarity). That is, the field at time t_j depends upon the boundary condition at time $t_j - l/c$ where l/c is the time it takes for the radiation to travel from the vicintity of the boundary to the vicinity of the observation point.

Fields that are locally stationary and stationary in the large

An interesting situation arises if the statistics of the radiation are locally stationary and also stationary for time intervals $\ggg \eta$. For example suppose that we had a series of M ($M \gg 1$) transparent containers filled with materials that have spatially varying indices of refraction which depend upon the state of the material. Assuming that the indices of refraction in each container may be described by stationary statistics (in a spatial or ensemble sense) suppose that every time interval η another container is placed in front of the source, the particular container M used, being chosen in a random manner. Let us suppose the radiation impinging upon any container has stationary statistics. Then for time intervals η, the statistics of the radiation may be considered locally stationary. For time intervals $\ggg \eta$, the statitics of the radiation are again stationary since the use of many containers will average out the particular effects of any single container.

In such a case, one may measure either $\Gamma_{12}^{j}(\tau)$ or $\Gamma_{12}(\tau)$, depending upon one's interest and the time constants of one's measuring instruments.

As indicated in Chapter 6, this type of problem is not academic if one wishes to measure the coherence of visible star radiation passing through the atmosphere. For then one may think of the containers being replaced by the atmosphere; the varying index of refraction being due to turbulent fluctuations. Since the time scale of sensible turbulent fluctuations is greater than, say, a millisecond, whereas the time scale of the visible radiation is much less than that, the star radiation "sees" a succession of different media. Of course there is no sudden change of containers as just proposed, but this does not change the essential aspect of the problem.

In a problem such as this, we have two choices in making our measurements. We may choose to study $\Gamma_{12}^{j}(\tau)$ where $t_{j+1} - t_j$ is of the order of say a millisecond or we may study $\Gamma_{12}(\tau)$. If we use film to make our measurements it must be very high-speed if we choose to measure $\Gamma_{12}^{j}(\tau)$, and the film must be changed every millisecond. On the other hand, to measure $\Gamma_{12}(\tau)$, we need only a single slow film that we expose for times long compared to the scale of turbulent fluctuations. By taking measurements of $\Gamma_{12}^{j}(\tau)$ and studying them in succession, we essentially follow the twinkling of the star. $\Gamma_{12}(\tau)$, on the other hand, gives us a smeared average effect.

Which function one chooses to deal with depends upon the application in mind or the limitations of one's measuring equipment. The important point, however, is to realize the difference between $\Gamma_{12}^{j}(\tau)$ and $\Gamma_{12}(\tau)$ and interpret your measurements appropriately.

13.2 SPATIAL AVERAGING

This book has been principally concerned with the time-averaged coherence function $\Gamma_{12}(\tau)$, since most electromagnetic radiation measuring devices measure time averages. One could, however, consider spatial averaging devices and derive a spatial coherence function if one assumes either good time resolution of the radiation-measuring device or if one is not particularly concerned with the time resolution of the radiation.

We have shown, for example, that monochromatic light is always coherent. Hence, if we consider a monochromatic source radiation with a spatially varying amplitude and phase that may be described in a statistical sense,† nothing is learned by studying $\Gamma_{12}(\tau)$. Instead we would consider an ensemble-averaged coherence function to obtain meaningful results.

An ensemble approach, however, requires making many measurements, and it would be desirable to find $\Gamma_{12}^{E}(\tau)$ in a single measurement, by equating spatial and ensemble averages. To attempt to do this, we introduce the concept of a spatially averaged coherence function, $\Gamma_{1}^{s}(\tau, \alpha)$, defined as

$$\Gamma_{1}^{s}(\tau, \alpha) = \int_{\text{vol}} V(\mathbf{x}_1, t + \tau)\, V(\mathbf{x}_1 + \alpha, t)\, d\mathbf{x}_1 \tag{13–2}$$

where the characteristic dimension of the volume, d_c, over which the integration is taken must be small compared to distances over which the average properties of the field change. Further $\Gamma_{1}^{s}(\tau, \alpha)$ must $\rightarrow 0$ for $\alpha \ll d_c$. The source surface, too, must be large enough to define $\Gamma_{1s}^{s}(\tau, \alpha)$ over the surface. We note that by the definition we are implicitly assuming that the radiation field is locally stationary in a spatial sense.

The problem is to demonstrate an ergodic-type hypothesis that allows us to say that $\Gamma_{1}^{s}(\tau, \alpha)$ is equal to $\Gamma_{12}^{E}(\tau)$. This is a rather difficult problem since it is hard to determine d_c and in fact to prove it even exists; i.e., to prove that the spatial field is locally stationary over meaningful distances.

Little thorough analysis has been done with this type of averaging though this type of averaging may certainly become very important for the very narrow-band lasers that are now in existence.

---

†For example, radiation emerging from ground glass.

13.3 HIGHER-ORDER CORRELATION FUNCTIONS

We mentioned earlier that $\Gamma_{12}(\tau)$ did not completely characterize a statistical radiation field if the statistics of the field were not gaussian. Recently, some attention has been given to the problem of determining the fourth-order correlation function [see Beran and Parrent (1961)] in a case where the radiation statistics are clearly not gaussian. In this section, the equations governing the fourth-order and higher moments are presented and we shall consider the effect of source intensity fluctuations on the fourth-order moment. We conclude the section with a discussion of the equations governing the characteristic functional (the generalized Fourier transform of the probability distribution).

Equations governing higher-order correlation functions

Since Maxwell's equations are linear, we have shown that the second-order correlation function, the mutual coherence function $\Gamma_{12}(\tau)$, is determined by differential equations and boundary conditions that contain only $\Gamma_{12}(\tau)$. It may be similarly shown that this is true for any higher correlation function. For example, defining the time-averaged fourth-order correlation function $L_{1234}(\tau_2, \tau_3, \tau_4)$

$$L_{1234}(\tau_2, \tau_3, \tau_4) = \langle V_1(t)\, V_2(t+\tau_2)\, V_3(t+\tau_3)\, V_4(t+\tau_4)\rangle \tag{13–3}$$

(here V_i are real functions). We find

$$\begin{aligned} \nabla_i^2 L_{1234}(\tau_2, \tau_3, \tau_4) &= \frac{1}{c^2}\frac{\partial^2}{\partial \tau_i^2} L_{1234}(\tau_2, \tau_3, \tau_4) \qquad (i = 2, 3, 4) \\ \nabla_1^2 L_{1234}(\tau_2, \tau_3, \tau_4) &= \frac{1}{c^2}\left(\frac{\partial}{\partial \tau_2} + \frac{\partial}{\partial \tau_3} + \frac{\partial}{\partial \tau_4}\right)^2 L_{1234}(\tau_2, \tau_3, \tau_4) \end{aligned} \tag{13–4}$$

where the equations can be solved if $L_{1S,\,2S,\,3S,\,4S}(\tau_2, \tau_3, \tau_4)$ is known over some surface and the appropriate radiation condition is imposed.

For the ensemble-averaged coherence function, the procedure is even more direct. Defining $\Gamma^{nE}(\mathbf{x}_1, t_1, \ldots, \mathbf{x}_n, t_n)$ as

$$\Gamma^{nE}(\mathbf{x}_1, t_1, \ldots, \mathbf{x}_n, t_n) = \{V(\mathbf{x}_1, t_1) \ldots V(\mathbf{x}_n, t_n)\} \tag{13–5}$$

one finds immediately

$$\nabla_i^2 \Gamma^{nE}(\mathbf{x}_1, t_1, \ldots, \mathbf{x}_1, t_n) = \frac{1}{c^2}\frac{\partial^2}{\partial t_i^2}\Gamma^{nE}(\mathbf{x}_1, t_1, \ldots, \mathbf{x}_n, t_n) \qquad (i = 1, 2, \ldots, n) \tag{13–6}$$

The equations for the fourth-order vector case have been derived by Molyneux (1962). The equations for the *n*th-order vector case, including sources that are unaffected by the radiation, have also been derived by him. We will set down only the fourth-order vector equations when no sources are present. The equations are ($c = 1$)

$$\sum_{r=0}^{4} [(-1)^{4-r}]_4C_{4-r}\left[\nabla_\alpha^2, \frac{\partial^2}{\partial t_\beta^2}\right] L_{ijkl}^E = 0 \tag{13–7}$$

where $\qquad L_{ijkl}^E = \{E_i(\mathbf{x}_1, t_1)\, E_j(\mathbf{x}_2, t_2)\, E_k(\mathbf{x}_3, t_3)\, E_l(\mathbf{x}_4, t_4)\}$

${}_4C_{4-r}[\nabla_\alpha^2, \partial^2/\partial t_\beta^2]$ is to be read as the product combinations of the four ∇_α^2's ($\alpha = 1, 2, 3, 4$) taken $(4 - r)$ at a time multiplied by r products of $\partial^2/(\partial t_\beta^2)$ such that the numbers 1, 2, 3, and 4 appear only once in each product. That is,

$$[(-1)^{4-r}]_4C_{4-r}\left[\nabla_\alpha^2, \frac{\partial^2}{\partial t_\beta^2}\right] = \nabla_1^2\nabla_2^2\nabla_3^2\nabla_4^3 - \frac{\partial^2}{\partial t_1^2}\nabla_2^2\nabla_3^2\nabla_4^2 - \frac{\partial^2}{\partial t_2^2}\nabla_1^2\nabla_3^2\nabla_4^2 + \cdots$$

Fourth-order correlation functions and intensity source fluctuations

As discussed in the chapter on intensity interferometry, the contracted fourth-order moment $\langle V_1^2(t)\, V_2^2(t)\rangle$ can be measured and, under the assumption of gaussian statistics, has been related to $\Gamma_{12}(0)$. In this section, we briefly discuss a physical case where the assumption of gaussian statistics is not appropriate and where this fact is of potential use.†

The physical problem that we wish to consider is the intensity modulation of radiation by effects such as turbulent fluctuations.‡ To simplify the discussion, we consider here the effects of intensity modulation on radiation passing through a surface S rather than being emitted from a volume V. Since the latter problem can always be transformed into a surface problem, the problems are equivalent from a formal point of view and illustrate the same effects. In practice, the surface modulation is difficult to determine theoretically, but once given, it simplifies radiation calculations.

We first show that the statistics in such cases are not gaussian. Let us write $V_{1S}(t)$ and $V_{2S}(t)$ in the following manner ($1S$ and $2S$ are points on the surface through which the radiation is passing, and we take $V_i(t)$ to be real):

$$\begin{aligned} V_{1S}(t) &= A_1(t)\, U_1(t) \\ V_{2S}(t) &= A_2(t)\, U_2(t) \end{aligned} \tag{13–8}$$

†In considering intensity interferometry in the presence of a turbulent atmosphere, we have previously given an example of nongaussian statistics.

‡When we say here *intensity modulation*, we mean modulation of intensities that are determined by time averages long compared to characteristic radiation times but short compared to characteristic modulation times.

Here we suppose $A_1(t)$ and $A_2(t)$ represent an amplitude modulation on the basic radiation $U_1(t)$ and $U_2(t)$. Consider A_1 and A_2 to be uncorrelated to U_1 and U_2, and let U_1 and U_2 be uncorrelated unless $1S$ equals $2S$. The latter condition is just to make the example clearer. Mathematically, we then write

$$\begin{aligned} &\langle U_i(t)\, A_j(t)\rangle = 0 \qquad (i = 1, 2; j = 1, 2) \\ &\langle U_1(t)\, U_2(t)\rangle = 0 \end{aligned} \tag{13–9}$$

The correlation $\langle A_1(t)\, A_2(t)\rangle$ is assumed to be nonzero. The brackets $\langle\ \rangle$ indicate time averaging.

Then we have

$$\begin{aligned} \Gamma^{rr}_{1S,\,2S}(0) &= \langle V_{1S}(t)\, V_{2S}(t)\rangle \\ &= \langle A_1(t)\, U_1(t)\, A_2(t)\, U_2(t)\rangle \\ &= \langle A_1(t)\, A_2(t)\rangle\langle U_1(t)\, U_2(t)\rangle \\ &= 0 \text{ when } 1S \neq 2S \end{aligned} \tag{13–10}$$

On the other hand,

$$\begin{aligned} L^{rr}_{1S,\,1S,\,2S,\,2S}(0) &= \langle V^2_{1S}(t)\, V^2_{2S}(t)\rangle \\ &= \langle A^2_1(t)\, U^2_1(t)\, A^2_2(t)\, U^2_2(t)\rangle \\ &= \langle A^2_1(t)\, A^2_2(t)\rangle\langle U^2_1(t)\rangle\langle U^2_2(t)\rangle \end{aligned} \tag{13–11}$$

If the statistics of $V(t)$ had been gaussian, we should have

$$L^{Grr}_{1S,\,1S,\,2S,\,2S}(0) = 2[\Gamma^{rr}_{1S,\,2S}(0)]^2 + [\Gamma^{rr}_{1S,\,1S}(0)][\Gamma^{rr}_{2S,\,2S}(0)] \tag{13–12}$$

Using Eq. (13–8), this yields

$$L^{Grr}_{1S,\,1S,\,2S,\,2S}(0) = \langle A^2_1(t)\, U^2_1(t)\rangle\langle A^2_2(t)\, U^2_2(t)\rangle \tag{13–13}$$

since $\Gamma^{rr}_{1S,\,2S}(0)$ is zero.

Equation (13–12) further simplifies to

$$L^{Grr}_{1S,\,1S,\,2S,\,2S}(0) = \langle A^2_1(t)\rangle\langle A^2_2(t)\rangle\langle U^2_1(t)\rangle\langle U^2_2(t)\rangle \tag{13–14}$$

Since in general $\langle A^2_1(t)A^2_2(t)\rangle \neq \langle A^2_1(t)\rangle\, \langle A^2_2(t)\rangle$ the statistics are nongaussian.

If the statistics are nongaussian on the surface of the radiator, they will not be gaussian in the far field of the radiator. This may be seen by direct calculation of L_{1234} from $L_{1S,\,2S,\,3S,\,4S}$. The importance of this fact lies in the possibility it opens for determining $\langle A^2_1(t)A^2_2(t)\rangle$ on the surface of the radiator from comparison of the second- and fourth-order moments of the far-field radiation.

In principle, this comparison of second- and fourth-order moments gives us a way of studying large-scale intensity fluctuations in nonresolvable objects. In practice, the question arises as to whether or not the effect is measurable; the answer, of course, is that it depends upon the size and intensity of the fluctuations. The primary dependence, however, is reflected in the spatial extent of the fluctuations. The effect becomes important if the fluctuations are correlated over a significant fraction of the source diameter. It is also necessary that the frequency of the intensity fluctuations be small compared to the beat frequencies which are detected in the Hanbury Brown and Twiss experiment.

We present no calculations here as the problem is still being studied. Both the surface modulation and volume modulation problems are under study and the more general case of modulation of each frequency component of the radiation is being considered. If the reader desires he should have no difficulty in setting up the integrals relating the far-field moments to the surface moments since the fourth-order moment problem proceeds similarly to the second-order moment problem. The manipulation is merely more involved.

It should also be noted that the correlation of local intensity fluctuations of the radiation emitted from an optically thin turbulent gas may be used in laboratory studies of hot turbulent gases. Here, however, it is desirable to use two separate lens systems to delineate the regions from which the radiation arises. (Beran, 1963b).

Probability distribution and the characteristic functional

In Chapter 2, under "Ensemble of systems," we introduced the probability density distribution $P_s(V_1(\mathbf{x}_1, t_1), \ldots, V_s(\mathbf{x}_s, t_s))$. This function, as $s \to \infty$, contains all the information we possess about a scalar random field. All moments, like the second and fourth, are obtained by integration over P_s.

The difficulty in considering this function is that all the information is contained in P_s only in the limit $s \to \infty$. Thus $P_s(s \to \infty)$ becomes a functional $P\,(V(\mathbf{x}, t)) \equiv P(V)$, a function of the function $V(\mathbf{x}, t)$. The problem of determining the equations governing $P(V)$ is a problem in functional calculus and, within this framework Hopf (1952), has outlined a procedure appropriate for finding the equations governing the characteristic functional Φ (a generalized Fourier transform of $P(V)$). Unfortunately, no significant solutions of the functional equation have yet been found in electromagnetic theory, and the only practical method is still to work with the moment equations.

In spite of the difficulty of solving the functional equations, the equation governing Φ represents the solution to the total statistical problem and hence merits attention. We shall outline Hopf's formulation in order to indicate the manner of approach.

Hopf derived the equations for a turbulent velocity field. In turbulence theory, one usually considers moments like

$$R_{ij}(\mathbf{x}_1, \mathbf{x}_2, t) = \overline{u_i(\mathbf{x}_1, t)\, u_j(\mathbf{x}_2, t)} \tag{13–15}$$

where $u_i(\mathbf{x}_j, t)$ is the ith component of velocity at the point $\mathbf{x}_j$ and time t and the bar indicates ensemble averaging. t is the same for both components of velocity; one time, not two is used. For the electromagnetic field, a continuous time formulation was needed. A number of workers have independently considered the generalization that is a direct extension of Hopf's work, and we shall use a formulation that relies on Lewis and Kraichnan (1962) and Ho (1963).†

We cannot here give a detailed account of functional calculus and must refer the reader to Hopf's original paper or Volterra (1959). In a loose manner of speaking, however, all the operations of a functional calculus may be obtained from the finite variable case by letting the number of variables approach infinity and letting integrals replace sums. For example, if we desire the differential of $F(x_1, \ldots, x_n)$, we write

(13–16) $$dF = \sum_i \frac{\partial F}{\partial x_i}\, dx_i$$

Similarly for the functional $F(x(s))$, we write

(13–17) $$\delta F = \int_a^b F'(x(s), \epsilon)\, \delta y(\epsilon)\, d\epsilon$$

where ϵ is the continuous parameter replacing the discrete parameter i.

The Fourier transform of $F(x_1, \ldots, x_n)$ is

(13–18) $$F_t(y_1, \ldots, y_n) = \int_{-\infty}^{\infty} \cdots \int e^{i\sum x_n y_n} F(x_1, \ldots, x_n)\, dx_1, \ldots, dx_n$$

The Fourier transform of the functional $F(x(s))$ is

(13–19) $$F_t(y(s)) = \int_\Omega e^{i\int x(s)y(s)ds}\, F(dx)$$

where $F(dx)$ is symbolic generalization of $F(x_1, \ldots, x_n)\, dx_1 \ldots dx_n$ to infinitely many variables. Ω represents the region spanned by $x(s)$; it is the generalization of the n-dimensional volume.

Let us now represent the six components of the electromagnetic field $E_1, E_2, E_3, H_1, H_2, H_3$ by the single symbol F_α $(\alpha = 1, 2, \ldots, 6)$. The probability distribution functional P may then be represented by $P(F_\alpha(\mathbf{x}, t))$.

The Fourier transform $\phi(y_\alpha(\mathbf{x}, t))$, of $P(F_\alpha(\mathbf{x}, t))$ is defined as:

(13–20) $$\phi(y_\alpha(\mathbf{x}, t)) = \int_\Omega e^{i(y_\alpha, F_\alpha)} P(dF_\alpha(\mathbf{x}, t)) = \langle e^{i(y_\alpha, F_\alpha)} \rangle$$

†It may be of some interest to note that a theory of the electromagnetic tensor $\overline{E_i(\mathbf{x}_1, t)\, E_j(\mathbf{x}_2, t)}$ can be developed just as in the statistical theory of turbulence. Equations may be easily derived which govern this function [see Ho (1963)]. It is not of much use for anatenna-type problems but may be useful to follow the history of a radiation packet in infinite space.

where $$(y_\alpha, F_\alpha) = \int_R y_\alpha(\mathbf{x}, t)\, F_\alpha(\mathbf{x}, t)\, d\mathbf{x}\, dt$$

R is the region over which $\mathbf{x}$ and t are considered. Seeking an equation governing $\phi(y_\alpha(\mathbf{x}, t))$, we note that

(13–21) $$\frac{\delta\phi}{\delta y_\alpha} = \langle iF_\alpha e^{i(y_\beta, F_\beta)} \rangle$$

$(\delta\phi)/(\delta y_\alpha)$ is the functional derivative of ϕ and

(13–22) $$\frac{\partial}{\partial t}\frac{\delta\phi}{\delta y_\alpha} = \left\langle i\,\frac{\partial F_\alpha}{\partial t}\, e^{i(y_\beta, F_\beta)} \right\rangle$$

Now $(\partial F_\alpha)/(\partial t)$ is determined by the six Maxwell equations

(13–23) $$\begin{aligned} \frac{\partial F_1}{\partial t} &= \frac{\partial F_6}{\partial x_2} - \frac{\partial F_5}{\partial x_3} \\ &\vdots \\ \frac{\partial F_6}{\partial t} &= \frac{\partial F_1}{\partial x_2} - \frac{\partial F_2}{\partial x_1} \end{aligned}$$

Thus

(13–24) $$\frac{\partial}{\partial t}\frac{\delta\phi}{\delta y_1} = \left\langle i\left(\frac{\partial F_6}{\partial x_2} - \frac{\partial F_5}{\partial x_3}\right) e^{i(y_\alpha, F_\alpha)} \right\rangle$$
$$\vdots$$

and finally

(13–25) $$\frac{\partial}{\partial t}\frac{\delta\phi}{\delta y_1} = \frac{\partial}{\partial x_2}\frac{\delta\phi}{\partial y_6} - \frac{\partial}{\partial x_3}\frac{\delta\phi}{\partial y_5}$$
$$\vdots$$

Equation (13–25) is the functional equation governing ϕ that we sought. No solutions of any interest have yet been found. One immediate use of Eq. (13–25), however, is to derive the moment equations. If ϕ is assumed to possess a Taylor expression of the form

(13–26) $$\phi = \phi^{(0)} + \phi^{(1)} + \phi^{(2)} + \dots$$

it can be shown that

(13–27) $$\phi^{(s)} = \frac{i^s}{s!} \int_{R_1 \dots R_s} \overline{F_\alpha(\mathbf{x}_1, t_1) \dots F_\omega(\mathbf{x}_s, t_s)}\; y_\alpha(\mathbf{x}_1, t_1) \dots y_\omega(\mathbf{x}_s, t_s)\, d\mathbf{x}_1 \dots d\mathbf{x}_s\, dt_1 \dots dt_s$$

where $\overline{F_\alpha(\mathbf{x}_1, t_1) \dots F_\omega(\mathbf{x}_s, t_s)}$ is the s-order correlation function defined as

$$\overline{F_\alpha(\mathbf{x}_1, t_1) \ldots F_\omega(\mathbf{x}_s, t_s)} = \int_\Omega F_\alpha(\mathbf{x}_1, t_1) \ldots F_\omega(\mathbf{x}_s, t_s)\, P(dF_\beta(\mathbf{x}, t)) \tag{13–28}$$

Substituting Eq. (13–26) into Eq. (13–25) using (13–27), and comparing like powers of s yields the equations governing the correlation functions. For $s = 2$ we find, for example,

$$\frac{\partial}{\partial t_1} \overline{F_1(\mathbf{x}_1, t_1)\, F_1(\mathbf{x}_2, t_2)} = \frac{\partial}{\partial x_{12}} \overline{F_6(\mathbf{x}_1, t_1)\, F_1(\mathbf{x}_2, t_2)} - \frac{\partial}{\partial x_{13}} \overline{F_5(\mathbf{x}_1, t_1)\, F_1(\mathbf{x}_2, t_2)} \tag{13–29}$$

This equation is the same as one would derive from the equation,

$$\frac{\partial}{\partial t_1} E_1(\mathbf{x}_1, t_1) = \frac{\partial}{\partial x_{12}} H_3(\mathbf{x}_1, t_1) - \frac{\partial}{\partial x_{13}} H_2(\mathbf{x}_1, t_1) \tag{13–30}$$

upon multiplying both sides by $E_1(\mathbf{x}_2, t_2)$ and taking the ensemble average.

References

Adomian, G., (1963), *Rev. Mod. Phys.*, **35**, 185.

Arnulf, A., O. Dupuy and F. Flamant, (1953), *Rev. d'Optique*, **32**, 529.

Barakat, R., (1962), *J.O.S.A.*, **52**, 276.

———, (1963), *J.O.S.A.*, **53**, 317.

Batchelor, G. K., (1953), *The Theory of Homogenous Turbulence.* Cambridge: Cambridge University Press.

Bateman Manuscript Project, (1953) *Tables of Integral Transforms*, vol. 2, A. Erdelyi, ed., New York: McGraw-Hill, Inc.

Beran, M. (1960), *Statistical Methods of Radio Wave Propagation.* London: Pergamon Press, Ltd., p.93.

——— and G. B. Parrent, Jr., (1961), *J.O.S.A.*, **51**, 1474.
——— and ———, (1962), *Ibid.*, **52**, 98.
——— and ———, (1963a), *Nuovo Cimento*, **27**, 1049.
———, (1963b), *Bull. Amer. Phys. Soc.*, Ser. 11, **8**, 425.
Berek, M., (1926a), *Z. Phys.*, **36**, 675.
———, (1926b), *Ibid.*, **36**, 824.
———, (1926c), *Ibid.*, **37**, 287.
———, (1926d), *Ibid.*, **40**, 420.
Blanc-Lapierre, A., and P. Dumontet, (1955), *Rev. d'Optique*, **34**, 1.
Booker, H. G. and W. E. Gordon, (1950), *Proc. IRE*, **38**, 401.
Born, M. and E. Wolf, (1959), *Principles of Optics*. London: Pergamon Press, Ltd.
Bouche, E. and B. Thompson (1964). To be published.
Bourret, R. C., (1960), *Nuovo Cimento*, **18**, 347.
Bracewell, R. N. and J. A. Roberts, (1954), *Australian J. Phys.*, **7**, 615.
Brekhovskikh, L. M., (1960), *Waves in Layered Media*. New York: Academic Press, Inc.
Chernov, L. A., (1960), *Wave Propagation in a Random Medium*. New York: McGraw-Hill, Inc.
Cittert, P. H. van, (1934), *Physica*, **1**, 201.
———, (1939), *Ibid.*, **6**, 1129
Das Gupta, M., R. Jennison, and R. Hanbury Brown, (1952), *Nature* (London), **170**, 1061.
Davenport, W. B., Jr. and W. L. Root, (1958), *An Introduction to the Theory of Random Signals and Noise*. New York: McGraw-Hill, Inc.
De, M., (1955), *Proc. Roy. Soc.* (A), **233**, 91.
Dolph, C. D., (1946), *Proc. IRE.* **34**, 1946.
Drane, C., (1957), *Proceedings of the Symposium on Communication Theory and Antenna Design*, AFCRC–TR–57–105–ASTIA Doc. No. AD 117067
——— and G. B. Parrent, Jr. (1962), *Trans. IRE:* Antennas and Propagation, **AP-10**, No. 2 (March), 126.
Duffieux, P. M., (1946), *L'Intégrale de Fourier et ses Applications à l'Optique* (Rennec).
Dumontet, P. M., (1954), *C. R. Acad. Sci.* (Paris), **238**, 1109.
Edwards, S. and G. B. Parrent, Jr., (1959), *Opt. Acta*, **6**, 367.
Fellgate, P. B. and E. H. Linfoot, (1955), *Phil. Trans. Roy. Soc.* (A), **247**, 369.
Fukui, K., (1957), Unpublished Master's thesis, Boston University, Boston.
Gabor, D., (1946), J. Inst. Elec. Engrs. (London), **93**, 429.
Glauber, R., (1963a), *Physical Review*, **130**, 2529
———, (1963b), *Proceedings of the Third International Conference on Quantum Electronics, Paris, France.*
Hanbury Brown, R., R. Jennsion, and M. Das Gupta, (1952), *Nature* (London), **170**, 1061.
——— and R. Q. Twiss, (1954), *Phil. Mag.*, **45**, 663.
——— and ———, (1956a), *Nature*, (London), **177**, 27.
——— and ———, (1956b), *Ibid.*, **178**, 1046.
——— and ———, (1956c), *Ibid.*, **178**, 1956.
——— and ———, (1957a), *Proc. Roy. Soc.* (A). **242**, 300.

——— and ———, (1957b), *Ibid.*, **243**, 291.
Ho, T. L. (1963), Private communication.
Hopf, E., (1952), *Rational Mechanics* Anal. **1**, 87.
Hopkins, H. H., (1951), *Proc. Roy. Soc.* (A), **208**, 263.
———, (1955), *Ibid.* **231**. 91.
———, (1956), *Proc. Phys. Soc.* (B), **69**, Pt. 5, 562.
———, (1957), *J.O.S.A.*, **47**, 508.
Jennison, R. and M. Das Gupta, (1956), *Phil. Mag.* (8), **1**, 55.
Lakeman, C. and J. Th. Groosmuller, (1928), *Physica* (Gravenhage), **8**, 193 and 199.
Laue, M. von., (1907), *Ann. Phys.* (Leipzig), **23**, 1.
Lewis, R. and R. Kraichnan, (1962), *Communications of Pure and Applied Mathematics*, **15**, 397.
Mandel, L., (1958), *Proc. Phys. Soc.*, **72**, 1037.
——— (1961), *J.O.S.A.*, **51**, 797.
——— and E. Wolf, (1961), *Phys. Rev.*, **124**, 1696.
Maréchal, A. and P. Croce, (1953), C. R. Acad. Sci. (Paris), **237**, 607.
Markovic, B., (1957), *J.O.S.A.*, **47**, 1074.
Michelson, A. A., (1890), *Phil. Mag.* (5), **30**, 1.
——— and F. G. Pease, (1921), *Astrophys.*, **53**, 249.
Middleton, David, (1960), *Introduction to Statistical Communication Theory.* New York: McGraw-Hill, Inc.
Molyneux, J., (1962), Private communication.
O'Neill, E. L., (1956a), *J.O.S.A.*, **46**, 285.
———, (1956b), *Selected Topics in Opics and Communication Theory.* Boston: Boston Univ. Publication.
———, (1956c), *IRE Trans.*: Information Theory, IT-2, No. 2, 56.
———, (1963), *Introduction to Statistical Optics.* Reading, Mass: Addison-Wesley.
Parrent, G. B., Jr., (1955), Unpublished Master's thesis, Boston University, Boston.
——— and C. Drane, (1956), *Opt. Acta*, **3**, 195.
———, (1959a), *Proceedings of the Radio Wave Propagation Symposium.* New York: Academic Press, Inc.
———, (1959b), *J.O.S.A.*, **49**, 787.
———, (1959c), *Optica Acta*, **6**, 285.
———, R. Shore, and T. Skinner, (1962), *J. Math. Phys.*, **3**, 178.
——— and P. Roman, (1960), *Nuovo Cimento*, **15**, 370.
———, (1961a), *J.O.S.A.*, **51**, 143.
——— and T. Skinner, (1961b), *Opt. Acta*, **8**, 93.
Rojak, F., (1961), Unpublished Master's thesis, Lowell Techonological Institute, Lowell, Mass.
Roman, P. and E. Wolf, (1960a), *Nuovo Cimento*, **17**, 462.
——— and ———, (1960b), *Ibid.*, **17**, 477.
———, (1961a), *Ibid.*, **20**, 759.
———, (1961b), *Ibid.*, **22**, 1005.
Sarfatt, J., (1963), *Ibid.*, **27**, 1119.
Schade, O. H., (1953), *J.O.S.A.*, **43**, 704.
Skinner, T. (1961a), *Ibid.*, **51**, 1246.
———, (1961b), *Ibid.*, **51**, 909.

———, Doctoral disseration, Boston University, Boston (to appear 1964).
Steel, W. H., (1953), *Rev. Opt.*, **32**, 4, 143, 269.
———, (1957), *J.O.S.A.*, **47**, 405.
Tatarski, V. I., (1961), *Wave Propagation in a Turbulent Medium.* New York: McGraw-Hill, Inc.
Thompson, B. and E. Wolf, (1957), *J.O.S.A.*, **47**, 895
———, (1958), *J.O.S.A.*, **48**, 95
Titchmarsh, E. C., (1948), *Introduction to the Theory of Fourier Integrals*, 2nd ed. Oxford: Clarendon Press.
Verdet, E., (1869), Leçons d'Optique Physique (Paris: L'imprimerie Impériale), I, 106.
Volterra, V., (1959), *Theory of Functionals and of Integro-Differential Equations.* New York: Dover Publications, Inc.
Wolf, E., (1954), *Nuovo Cimento*, **12**, 884.
———, (1955), *Proc. Roy. Soc.* (A), **230**. 246.
———, (1958), *Math. Rev.*, **19**, 802.
———, (1959), *Nuovo Cimento*, **13**, 1165.
Woodward, P. M., (1953), *Probability and Information Theory with Applications to Radar*. London: Pergamon Press, Ltd.
Zernike, F., (1938), *Physica*, **5**, 785.
Zucker, F. J., (1957), *Proceedings of Symposium on Communication Theory and Antenna Design*, AFCRC–TR–57–105–ASTIA Doc. No. AD 117067.

Index